BASIC ENGINEERING SCIENCES AND STRUCTURAL ENGINEERING FOR ENGINEER-IN-TRAINING EXAMINATIONS

H. JACK APFELBAUM & WALTER O. OTTESEN

Uniquely comprehensive and well balanced in its coverage of the concepts and techniques fundamental to the practice of engineering, the first volume in the *Hayden Professional Engineering Examination Series* is designed to provide the most thorough preparation for the preliminary examinations given by the individual states.

The book presents an all-encompassing review of material that the reader is likely to encounter in Engineer-in-Training examinations by means of illustrated representative problems carefully chosen by the authors from recent, actual examinations.

These typical problems, clearly arranged by subject area, are dealt with in self-contained chapter units covering three broad areas: background material in mathematics, physics, and chemistry; the basic engineering sciences: statics, dynamics, fluid mechanics, thermodynamics, electricity, and engineering economy: and seven chapters detailing topics in structural engineering. Each of these three major areas, together with its sub-topics, receives equally detailed, concisely worded coverage.

Preceding each area and its worked-out solutions to problems, introductory sections provide essential background in the concepts, principles, and terminology peculiar to that specific topic. The step-by-step solutions to problems are augmented by fully illustrated diagrams to insure a complete grasp of problem-solving techniques.

This volume's clear separation of the subject matter into principal areas of concern will prove a great time-saver to recent graduates and practicing engineers preparing for professional licensure. The thoroughness with which the authors approach all facets of theory and practice will insure its continuing value as a working reference.

BASIC
ENGINEERING
SCIENCES
AND STRUCTURAL
ENGINEERING
FOR
ENGINEER-
IN-TRAINING
EXAMINATIONS

hayden professional engineering examination series

LAWRENCE J. HOLLANDER
editor-in-chief

Professional Engineer
New York State

BASIC ENGINEERING SCIENCES AND STRUCTURAL ENGINEERING
FOR ENGINEER-IN-TRAINING EXAMINATIONS
H. Apfelbaum and W. Ottesen
CIVIL ENGINEERING AND ECONOMICS AND ETHICS
FOR PROFESSIONAL ENGINEERING EXAMINATIONS
M. Sanders and S. Dublin
ELECTRICAL ENGINEERING AND ECONOMICS AND ETHICS
FOR PROFESSIONAL ENGINEERING EXAMINATIONS
J. Lyons and S. Dublin
MECHANICAL ENGINEERING AND ECONOMICS AND ETHICS
FOR PROFESSIONAL ENGINEERING EXAMINATIONS
E. Stamper and S. Dublin

BASIC ENGINEERING SCIENCES AND STRUCTURAL ENGINEERING FOR ENGINEER-IN-TRAINING EXAMINATIONS

H. JACK APFELBAUM, P.E.

*Department of Mechanical Engineering
Lowell Technological Institute*

AND

WALTER O. OTTESEN, P.E.

Patent Specialist

HAYDEN BOOK COMPANY, INC.
Rochelle Park, New Jersey

5   6   7   8   9   PRINTING

77 78   YEAR

FOREWORD

In the 1970's the number of licensed professional engineers in the United States and its territories will surpass 500,000, and by the end of the decade may approach three quarters of a million. Licensure will be required in an ever-increasing array of new activities; registered engineers will be active in consumer protection, air pollution control, water pollution control, urban planning and renewal, not to mention the traditional projects of designing bridges, dams, office buildings, computers, power systems, etc. No discipline of engineering is exempted, for laws that regulate licensure in engineering are primarily for the protection of the public.

The Hayden series of preparatory books for engineering licensure is designed for both study and reference. These books present problems that occur over and over again on the preliminary and professional examinations for licensure in engineering. As the examinations among the states change in style and content over a span of years, the basic fundamentals of engineering found in these books will remain as important keystones in bridging the gap from student to licensed professional engineer.

The first volume in the series is devoted to the preliminary examinations (Engineer-in-Training). The remaining volumes, identified by major engineering disciplines (electrical, mechanical, civil, etc.), are designed for preparing the reader for the professional examinations, sometimes referred to as the second-day or final examinations. An important feature of these books is the terse development of each subject, beginning with an easily understood explanation and concluding with one or more sample problems with complete solutions. The engineering student will find himself completely at ease with these books, since the authors have acted on the premise that the reader is versed in engineering, that he has handled engineering problems, and that he is approaching the time when his State Board of Examiners will consider him qualified for taking the examinations.

The authors have been most careful not only in selecting the problems for inclusion in the books, but also in the preparation of the solutions to these problems; at all times the authors have considered the needs of the candidate who is preparing for the preliminary and professional examinations in engineering.

Although the problems and solutions in these books have been checked and rechecked for accuracy many times, candidates should understand that problems in engineering often are open to different interpretations or their solutions are affected by different municipal or national codes and other requirements. In all cases it is the State Board of Examiners of Professional Engineers in each state that determines what is acceptable to it.

LAWRENCE J. HOLLANDER

PREFACE

This book has been written to assist practicing engineers as well as engineering students in preparing for the preliminary examinations given by the individual states. From the following, it will be seen that the book contains features that also make it useful as a reference.

The book is a comprehensive review of the material covered by the Engineer-in-Training examination and is presented in the form of illustrated examples. The problems used in the examples are virtually all taken from actual examinations and are representative of the types of problems one may encounter on future examinations. These problems are arranged broadly by subject matter into chapters and chapter subdivisions. These chapters, each a self-contained unit, cover three broad areas: background material in mathematics, physics, and chemistry; the basic engineering sciences: statics, dynamics, fluid mechanics, thermodynamics, electricity, and engineering economy; and seven chapters dealing with topics in structural engineering. Although the subdivisions are devoted primarily to worked out problems, they include prefatory material reviewing the theory and equations used in the solutions of the illustrated examples. The prefatory material and the illustrated examples together provide the reader with a background sufficient to handle any problem relating to the particular section.

Terminology gleaned from the many examination problems studied in preparing the manuscript have been woven into the material of the book. The terminology is defined and illustrated so that otherwise straightforward examination problems will not be difficult because of unfamiliar technical expressions.

The examinations given by the various states are all based on the same understanding—namely, that to practice engineering, a clear and concise knowledge of the fundamental physical sciences is necessary. And this knowledge must be available in such a form as to allow immediate application to a variety of practical applications.

The method adopted in this book is to first detail the concepts and principles involved and then apply these to specific problems. The reader should study the theoretical portion thoroughly before looking at the problems.

In all cases, whether the reader is trying his hand at the problems in this book or on the actual examination or for that matter in practice, the steps to be followed are the same.

1. Read the instructions carefully. Determine the number of problems to be chosen in each group and the time available for solving them. Budget time accordingly.

2. Read and clearly understand the question or problems to be solved. Determine what information is available from the problem—supplement this by knowledge you have built up during your years of study and practice—then determine what is to be found out.

3. Devise a technique of converting the given information to the desired end results. Often alternate methods can be used.

4. If the problem statement allows, guess at the numerical solution to get a feeling of magnitude.

5. Proceed to write down assumptions, if any, which have to be made.

6. Clearly draw all necessary illustrations. For a large number of problems in engineering, the mere act of illustrating the problem is often the greatest help in solving it. Simple line figures are invariably sufficient.

7. Write down the required equations. If unusual symbols are used, provide a key for these.

8. Work out the mathematics by substituting the appropriate numbers in the equations.

9. A highly satisfactory guide for checking the correctness of the work is to check and double check the units such as pounds, feet, etc., which are being used.

10. Complete the solution and clearly indicate the answer by underlining it. Always state the applicable units.

11. Complete all the necessary problems first, then if time allows (and time should be budgeted so it is available), review your entire work.

Although the book is self-contained and should enable the reader to prepare for the preliminary examinations without consulting other texts, it is suggested that the American Institute of Steel Construction Handbook be used in connection with the work on steel beams and columns. It would also be helpful for the reader to familiarize himself with the pertinent pages of the American Concrete Institute Handbook.

The authors express their thanks and appreciation to the many state examining boards and state chapters of the National Society of Professional Engineers for their assistance in providing the sample problems and related material. Thanks are extended to Dr. S.F. Borg of Stevens Institute of Technology and Mr. O.A. Ondroczky of Grumman Aircraft and Engineering Company for their helpful discussions and suggestions; Mr. E. Lindberg and former Dean G. Marston of Western New England College; and of course our editor Lawrence J. Hollander for his persistence.

H. JACK APFELBAUM
WALTER O. OTTESEN

CONTENTS

PROBLEMS

Dynamics

Mechanics of Incompressible Fluids

Thermodynamics

Heat Transfer

Electricity and Electronics

Chemistry

chapter 1
REVIEW OF MATHEMATICS

Most engineering problems involve basic mathematical theory, definitions, and values. The illustrative problems in the following sections were chosen to reflect the range of topics usually dealt with in examinations.

1-1 COORDINATE SYSTEMS AND ANALYTIC GEOMETRY

Two systems commonly used are the right-handed rectangular (Cartesian) coordinate system and the right-handed polar coordinate system. The system is right-handed when a right-handed screw located with its centerline on the Z-axis will move in the positive Z-direction when it is turned 90° from +X to +Y. (See Fig. 1-1.) A point in the rectangular system is located by three mutually perpendicular distances or vectors laid off parallel to the X-, Y-, and Z-axes. A point is identified by its X-, Y-, Z-coordinates, as shown in Fig. 1-1.

In a plane rectangular coordinate system, the Z-coordinate is 0. (See Fig. 1-2.) In plane polar coordinates, a point $P(R,\theta)$ in the XY-plane is located by a vector R drawn from the origin and the angle θ that the vector makes with the X-axis, as shown in Fig. 1-3.

Spacial polar coordinate systems in common engineering use are the cylindrical and the spherical systems. In the cylindrical system, a point is defined as in the plane polar system by R and θ. In addition, its Z-coordinate is required, as seen in Fig. 1-4. Note that R is the projection of vector ρ into the XY-plane. Also,

$$\rho = \sqrt{R^2 + (-Z)^2}$$

The spherical coordinates are ρ, θ, ϕ. (See Fig. 1-5.) Table 1-1 shows equations of the coordinate systems while Table 1-2 shows equations of the straight line.

The slope m of a straight line is the value of the tan θ, where θ is the angle between the line and the X-axis. (See Fig. 1-6.)

1

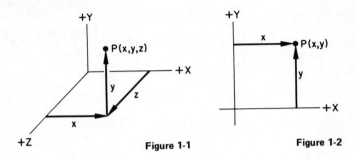

Figure 1-1

Figure 1-2

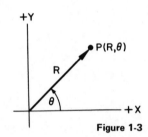

Figure 1-3

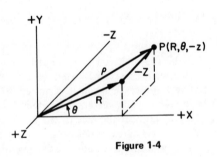

Figure 1-4

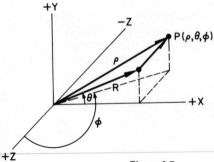

Figure 1-5

$$\tan \theta = \frac{y_2 - y_1}{x_2 - x_1}$$

The angle α is the angle between two lines having slopes m_1 and m_2, as shown in Fig. 1-7. Line AB has slope m_1, and CD has slope m_2.

$$\alpha = \tan^{-1} \frac{m_1 + m_2}{1 - m_1 m_2}$$

Table 1-1   Relation Among Coordinate Systems

Plane	Cylindrical	Spherical
$x = R \cos \theta$	$x = R \cos \theta$	$\rho = \sqrt{x^2 + y^2 + z^2}$
$y = R \sin \theta$	$y = R \sin \theta$	$\theta = \tan^{-1} y/x$
$\theta = \tan^{-1} y/x$	$\theta = \tan^{-1} y/x$	
$R = \sqrt{x^2 + y^2}$	$R = \sqrt{x^2 + y^2}$	$\phi = \cos^{-1}\left(\dfrac{z}{\rho \cos\theta}\right)$
	$Z = Z$	
	$\rho = \sqrt{R^2 + Z^2}$	

Distance between points P_1 (x_1, y_1, z_1) and P_2 (x_2, y_2, z_2)

$$D = \sqrt{(x_2 - x_1)^2 + (y_2 - y_1)^2 + (z_2 - z_1)^2}$$

For plane systems, $z_2 = z_1 = 0$.

Table 1-2   Equations of the Straight Line

Known Information	Suitable Form of Equation
A point (x_1, y_1) on the line and its slope m	$y - y_1 = m(x - x_1)$
The y intercept, b, and its slope *Note:* y = b when x = 0	$y = mx + b$
Two points (x_1, y_1) and (x_2, y_2) on the line	$\dfrac{y - y_1}{x - x_1} = \dfrac{y_2 - y_1}{x_2 - x_1}$
The intersection of the line with the X-axis at a and the Y-axis at b	$\dfrac{x}{a} + \dfrac{y}{b} = 1$

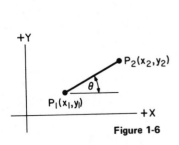

Figure 1-6

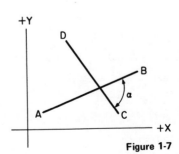

Figure 1-7

Problem 1-1 Line equation determined from slope and intercept
A straight line has a slope of ¾ and passes through the point (2,5). Write the equation of the line.

Solution:

$$y = mx + b$$

Substitute the known values of y_1, m_1, and x.

$$5 = (3/4)(2) + b$$
$$b = 5 - 3/2 = 7/2$$
$$y = (3/4)x + 7/2 \qquad Answer$$

Problem 1-2 Three-dimensional space trigonometry
Point A is located at (4,0,0), point B at (0,3,2), and point C at (0,0,6). Find (a) the length AB and (b) the angle between lines AC and CB, i.e., angle ACB.

Solution:
(a) To find distance AB, first determine lengths AD and DB; see Fig. 1-8. In plane XY,

$$AD^2 = OA^2 + OD^2$$
$$= 4^2 + 3^2$$
$$AD = 5$$

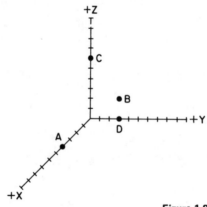

Figure 1-8

In plane YZ, DB = 2. In right triangle ADB,

$$AB^2 = AD^2 + DB^2$$
$$= 5^2 + 2^2$$
$$AB = \sqrt{29} = 5.38 \qquad Answer$$

(b) In triangle ACB,

$$AC = \sqrt{4^2 + 6^2} = 7.21 \qquad and \qquad CB = \sqrt{4^2 + 3^2} = 5$$

Using Law of Cosines,

$$AB^2 = AC^2 + BC^2 - 2(AC)(BC) \cos \angle ACB$$

$$\cos \angle ACB = \frac{AC^2 + BC^2 - AB^2}{2\ AC\ BC} = \frac{52 + 25 - 29}{2 \times 7.21 \times 5} = 0.665$$

$$\angle ACB = 48.3° \qquad Answer$$

Problem 1-3 Area of sector of circle

A sector of a circle of radius 8 in. has an angle of 75°. Find the area formed by a chord stretched between the radii forming the sector and the perimeter of the sector.

Solution:

Area of sector equals 75/360 parts of a circle, as shown in Fig. 1-9.

$$A_{sector} = \frac{75}{360}\pi 8^2 = 41.8 \text{ sq in.}$$

$$A \text{ of triangle } BCO = \frac{BC \times OA}{2}$$

$$BC = 2\ OB \sin 37.5°$$

$$OA = OB \cos 37.5°$$

Area of triangle $BCO = OB^2 \sin 37.5° \cos 37.5°$

$$= 8^2(0.61)(0.794) = 31 \text{ sq in.}$$

$$\text{Area } A = 41.8 - 31 = 10.8 \text{ sq in.} \qquad Answer$$

Table 1-3 shows equations of the circle in the X-Y plane.

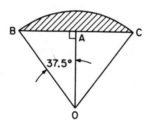

Figure 1-9

Table 1-3   Equations of Circles in the X-Y Plane

Location of Center	Equation
Origin	$x^2 + y^2 = r^2$
h,k	$(x - h)^2 + (y - k)^2 = r^2$ (Fig. 1-10)

All points on the circle lie at a distance r from the center.

Equations of the parabola. Any point of the parabola is at an equal distance from the directrix and the focus, as seen in Fig. 1-11. See Table 1-4 for equations of the parabola.

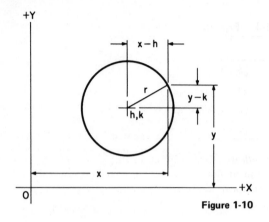

Figure 1-10

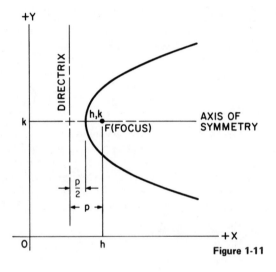

Figure 1-11

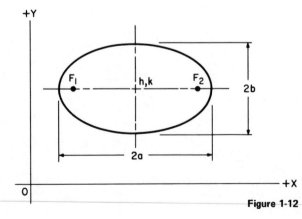

Figure 1-12

Table 1-4   Equations of Parabolas in the X-Y Plane

Location of Vertex	Equation	Axis of Symmetry	Focus
Origin	$y^2 = 2px$	X-axis	½p, 0
Origin	$x^2 = 2py$	Y-axis	0, ½p
h,k	$(y - k)^2 = 2p(x - h)$	$y = k$	(h + p/2), k
h,k	$(x - h)^2 = 2p(y - k)$	$x = h$	h, (k − p/2)

Equations of the ellipse. Any point of an ellipse is so located with reference to the foci that the sum of the distances to the foci is a constant and equals 2a. The foci are two points located on the major axis; see Fig. 1-12. Table 1-5 shows equations of the ellipse.

Table 1-5   Equations of Ellipses in the X-Y Plane

Major Axis	Minor Axis	Location of Center	Equation
2a	2b	h,k	$\dfrac{(x - h)^2}{a^2} + \dfrac{(y - k)^2}{b^2} = 1$
2a	2b	Origin	$\left(\dfrac{x}{a}\right)^2 + \left(\dfrac{y}{b}\right)^2 = 1$

Equations of the hyperbola. Any point of a hyperbola is so located that the difference of its distance from the foci is constant and equals 2a. The hyperbola is symmetric with respect to two perpendicular axes. Standard form of the equation with its foci on the X-axis and its center at the origin, as seen in Fig. 1-13, is $x^2/a^2 - y^2/b^2 = 1$. For an equilateral hyperbola with its center at the origin and with the X-Y axes as asymptotes the equation is $xy = \pm\, a^2/2$. (See Fig. 1-14.)

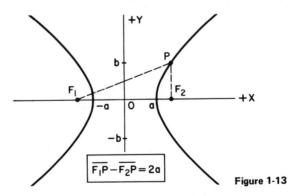

$$\overline{F_1P} - \overline{F_2P} = 2a$$

Figure 1-13

1-2   ALGEBRAIC OPERATIONS

Summation: $(-a) + (-2a) - 3b = -3a - 3b$.
Multiplication: $(a^2 + b)(c - d) = a^2c + bc - a^2d - bd$.
Division: Arrange polynomials in descending order of a common symbol. Divide the first term of the dividend by the first term of the divisor. The result

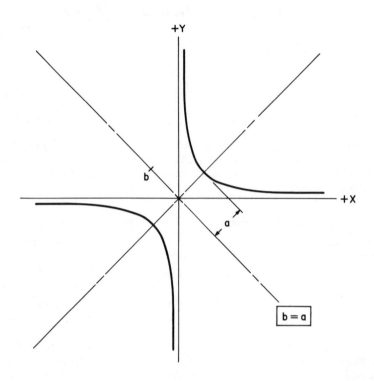

Figure 1-14

is the first term of the quotient. Multiply all terms of the divisor by the first term of the quotient just obtained and subtract the result from the dividend. Repeat the operation until a remainder results that is either zero or of lower order than the divisor. For example, divide $(3x^3 + 2x^2 - 4)$ by $x - 8$.

$$
\begin{array}{r}
3x^2 + 26x + 208 \\
x - 8 \overline{)\ 3x^3 + \ 2x^2 + \ \ \ 0x - 4} \\
\underline{3x^3 - 24x^2} \\
26x^2 + \ \ \ 0x \\
\underline{26x^2 - 208x} \\
+ 208x - 4 \\
\underline{208x - 1664} \\
+ 1660
\end{array}
$$

$$\frac{3x^3 + 2x^2 - 4}{x - 8} = 3x^2 + 26x + 208 + \frac{1660}{x - 8} \qquad Answer$$

Problem 1-4 Roots of third-order equation

Find the roots of the following cubic equation:

$$x^3 + 3x^2 - 13x - 15 = 0$$

Solution:

By inspection, one root is $x = -1$.

Factor:

$$
\begin{array}{r}
x^2 + 2x - 15 \\
x + 1 \overline{\smash{\big)}\ x^3 + 3x^2 - 13x - 15} \\
\underline{x^3 + \ x^2} \\
2x^2 - 13x \\
\underline{2x^2 + \ 2x} \\
-15x - 15 \\
\underline{-15x - 15} \\
0 \qquad 0
\end{array}
$$

Reduced equation: $x^2 + 2x - 15 = 0$
Factor: $(x + 5)(x - 3) = 0$
Roots: $x = -5$, $x = +3$; $x = -1$ *Answers*

    Many polynomials can be simplified by factoring, referring to the standard forms in Table 1-6.

    Solutions of equations involve finding values for the unknowns that satisfy the initial or boundary conditions for which the equation has been set up. Graphing, i.e., plotting the possible values of the unknowns and connecting them by a suitable straight line or curve, often assists in solving equations. Any linear equation in one unknown has at most one solution, or one root. Any quadratic equation in one unknown has at most two roots. These may readily be found by (a) factoring, (b) completing the square, or (c) the use of the quadratic formula.

    To factor a quadratic equation, write it so that all terms are equated to zero, then factor by inspection and comparison to products with known factors. For example, $4x^2 - 3x - 10 = 0$ is identical to form III in Table 1-6 if it is rearranged thus:

$$x^2 - \frac{3}{4}x - \frac{10}{4} = 0$$

$$\left(x + \frac{5}{4}\right)(x - 2) = 0$$

$$x = -\frac{5}{4}, +2$$

    To solve a quadratic equation by completing the square the following example sequence is useful:

Solve: $4x^2 - 3x - 10 = 0$.

Divide the equation by the coefficient of x^2

$$x^2 - \frac{3}{4}x - \frac{10}{4} = 0$$

Separate the terms so that the unknown appears on the left side of the equation only.

$$x^2 - \frac{3}{4}x = \frac{10}{4}$$

Table 1-6

Factors	Product or Polynomial
I $a(x \pm y) =$	$ax \pm ay$
II $(x \pm y)^2 =$	$x^2 \pm 2xy + y^2$
III $(x + a)(x + b) =$	$x^2 + x(a + b) + ab$
IV $(x + y)(x - y) =$	$x^2 - y^2$
V $(x + y + z)^2 =$	$x^2 + y^2 + z^2 + 2xy + 2xz + 2yz$
VI $(x \pm y)^3 =$	$x^3 \pm 3x^2y + 3xy^2 \pm y^3$
VII $(x + y)(x^2 - xy + y^2) =$	$x^3 + y^3$
VIII $(x - y)(x^2 + xy + y^2) =$	$x^3 - y^3$

Add the square of one half the coefficient of x to both sides.

$$x^2 - \frac{3}{4}x + \left(\frac{1}{2} \times \frac{3}{4}\right)^2 = \frac{10}{4} + \left(\frac{1}{2} \times \frac{3}{4}\right)^2$$

The left side of the equation is now a perfect square that can be factored into form II, Table 1-6.

$$\left(x - \frac{3}{8}\right)^2 = \frac{10}{4} + \frac{9}{64}$$

$$\left(x - \frac{3}{8}\right)^2 = \frac{160}{64} + \frac{9}{64} = \frac{169}{64}$$

$$x = \pm\sqrt{\frac{169}{64}} + \frac{3}{8} = \pm\frac{13}{8} + \frac{3}{8} = 2, \ -\frac{5}{4}$$

To solve the quadratic equation by the quadratic formula,

$$x = \frac{-b \pm \sqrt{b^2 - 4ac}}{2a}$$

Write the equation in standard form $ax^2 + bx + c = 0$ and substitute the coefficient into the formula, observing all signs carefully.

Determinants are square arrays of 4, 9, 16, or n^2 numbers or symbols. A second-order determinant has 2^2 numbers, thus

$$\begin{vmatrix} a_1 & b_1 \\ a_2 & b_2 \end{vmatrix}$$

which is identical in meaning to $a_1 b_2 - a_2 b_1$. Determinants are useful in solving systems of linear equations. For example:

$$x + 4y = 3$$
$$3x - 8y = 4$$

$$x = \frac{\begin{vmatrix} 3 + 4 \\ 4 - 8 \end{vmatrix}}{\begin{vmatrix} 1 + 4 \\ 3 - 8 \end{vmatrix}} = \frac{3(-8) - 4(4)}{1(-8) - 3(4)} = \frac{-24 - 16}{-8 - 12} = 2$$

$$y = \frac{\begin{vmatrix} 1+3 \\ 3+4 \end{vmatrix}}{\begin{vmatrix} 1+4 \\ 3-8 \end{vmatrix}} = \frac{1(4) - 3(3)}{1(-8) - 3(4)} = \frac{4-9}{-8-12} = \frac{1}{4}$$

Third-order determinants have 3^2 numbers arranged that can be expanded in the following manner:

$$\begin{vmatrix} a_1 & b_1 & c_1 \\ a_2 & b_2 & c_2 \\ a_3 & b_3 & c_3 \end{vmatrix} = a_1 \begin{vmatrix} b_2 & c_2 \\ b_3 & c_3 \end{vmatrix} - b_1 \begin{vmatrix} a_2 & c_2 \\ a_3 & c_3 \end{vmatrix} + c_1 \begin{vmatrix} a_2 & b_2 \\ a_3 & b_3 \end{vmatrix}$$

$$= a_1(b_2 c_3 - b_3 c_2) - b_1(a_2 c_3 - a_3 c_2) + c_1(a_2 b_3 - a_3 b_2)$$

Imaginary numbers are real numbers multiplied by the square root of -1. For example: $9\sqrt{-1}$. The symbol i or j is used to represent $\sqrt{-1}$. Therefore, $9\sqrt{-1} \equiv 9j$. The symbol j is used like other algebraic symbols with the following restrictions:

$$j^1 = j = \sqrt{-1}$$
$$j^2 = (\sqrt{-1})^2 = -1$$
$$j^3 = (\sqrt{-1})^3 = (\sqrt{-1})^2 \sqrt{-1} = -j, \text{ etc.}$$

Complex numbers are numbers that have a real part and an imaginary part, for example, a + bj or 3 + 4j.

Complex or argand plane is a plane on which complex as well as real numbers may be represented as points. Positive real parts of complex numbers are plotted to the right of the Y-axis; positive imaginary parts are plotted above the X-axis. (See Fig. 1-15.)

Problem 1-5 Simultaneous quadratic equations

Find the values of x and y that will satisfy the following two quadratic equations:

$$2x^2 - 3xy + y^2 = 15$$
$$x^2 - 2xy + y^2 = 9$$

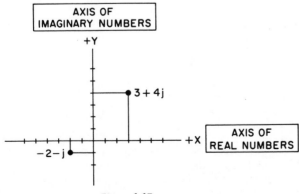

Figure 1-15

Solution:

The solution is obtained by "eliminating the constant."

$$6x^2 - 9xy + 3y^2 = 45$$
$$5x^2 - 10xy + 5y^2 = 45$$
$$\overline{x^2 + xy - 2y^2 = 0}$$

Factor: $(x + 2y)(x - y) = 0$

$$x + 2y = 0 \qquad \therefore x = -2y$$
$$x - y = 0 \qquad \therefore x = y$$

Substitute $x = -2y$ in initial equation:

$$8y^2 + 6y^2 + y^2 = 15$$
$$y = \pm 1 \qquad Answer$$
$$x = \mp 2 \qquad Answer$$

Check: $(-2)^2 - 2(-2)(1) + 1^2 = 9$
$$9 = 9$$

Problem 1-6 Simultaneous equations with third-order unknowns

Find the corresponding values of x and y to satisfy Eq. (a) and Eq. (b).

(a) $x^3 + y^3 = 56$
(b) $x + y = 2$

Solution:

Find x in terms of y from Eq. (b) and substitute in Eq. (a). Solve Eq. (a).

$$x = 2 - y$$

Use Table 1-6.

$$x^3 = 8 + 3(2^2)(-y) + 3(2)(-y)^2 + (-y)^3$$
$$= 8 - 12y + 6y^2 - y^3$$

Substitute in Eq. (a).

$$8 - 12y + 6y^2 - y^3 + y^3 = 56$$
$$6y^2 - 12y - 48 = 0$$
$$y^2 - 2y - 8 = 0$$
$$y = +4, -2 \qquad Answers$$

From Eq. (b)
$$x = -2, +4 \qquad Answers$$

Problem 1-7 Distance-speed simultaneous equations

A jet plane flying east makes the trip between two cities in 4 hr with the aid of a 50-mph tailwind. The return trip takes 5 hr against a 30-mph headwind. Find the distance between cities.

Solution:

Set up two simultaneous equations relating time, speed, and distance for both directions.

Let x = rate of jet plane in still air in mph
  D = distance between cities in miles

1. $(x - 30)5 = D$
2. $(x + 50)4 = D$

$$5x - 150 = D$$
$$\underline{4x + 200 = D}$$
$$x - 350 = 0$$
$$x = 350 \text{ mph}$$

$D = (350 + 50)4 = 1600$ miles   *Answer*

Check the answer using Eq. 1. $D = (350 - 30)5 = 1600$ miles.

Problem 1-8 Rate-time simultaneous equations

A tank may be filled with water by using pipes A, B, and C singly or in combination. Pipes A and B fill the tank in 15 hr, B and C in 10 hr, and A and C in 12 hr. How long would it take to fill the tank using pipe A only?

Solution:

Let T = quantity of water required to fill tank
Q_A, Q_B, and Q_C = flow rate of water through pipes A, B, and C, respectively
  x = length of time required to fill the tank using pipe A only

Three simultaneous equations can be written. Set these up with coefficients for each quantity.

$$15Q_A + 15Q_B + 0Q_C = 1(T)$$
$$0Q_A + 10Q_B + 10Q_C = 1(T)$$
$$12Q_A + 0Q_B + 12Q_C = 1(T)$$

$$Q_A = \frac{\begin{vmatrix} 1(T) & 15 & 0 \\ 1(T) & 10 & 10 \\ 1(T) & 0 & 12 \end{vmatrix}}{\begin{vmatrix} 15 & 15 & 0 \\ 0 & 10 & 10 \\ 12 & 0 & 12 \end{vmatrix}} = \frac{1(T)(120 - 0) - 15(12T - 10T) + 0}{15(120 - 0) - 15(0 - 120) - 0}$$

$$= \frac{120T}{3600} - \frac{30T}{3600} = \frac{90T}{3600}$$

$$xQ_A = x\,\frac{90}{3600}T = T \qquad x = 40 \text{ hr} \qquad \textit{Answer}$$

Problem 1-9 Sides of rectangle determined from diagonal and area

The diagonal of a rectangle is 13 ft, the area of the rectangle is 60 sq ft. Find the sides of the rectangle.

Solution:

Let a and b represent the sides and c the diagonal of the rectangle.

$$a \times b = 60$$
$$b = 60/a$$
$$a^2 + b^2 = c^2 = 13^2$$
$$a^2 + (60/a)^2 = 13^2$$
$$a^2 + 3600/a^2 = 169$$
$$a^4 + 3600 = 169a^2$$

Let $x = a^2$, $x^2 = a^4$. Substitute:

$$x^2 - 169x + 3600 = 0$$
$$x = 144, 25$$
$$a = \pm 12, \pm 5$$

The negative numbers are not applicable in this problem. Thus,

a = 12 ft, 5 ft   *Answer*

b = 5 ft, 12 ft   *Answer*

Problem 1-10 Equation of line intersecting curve

Write the equation of a line that intersects the curve $x^2 + y^2 = 169$ at $x = +5, -12$.

Solution:

When x = +5,

$$y = \sqrt{169 - 25}$$
$$y = \pm 12$$

When x = −12,

$$y = \sqrt{169 - 144}$$
$$y = \pm 5$$

Four combinations of points are possible. Selecting one of these combinations, x = +5, y = +12, x = −12, y = −5, and, using the two-point equation for the straight line, we get

$$\frac{y_2 - y_1}{x_2 - x_1} = \frac{y_2 - y}{x_2 - x}$$

$$\frac{-5 - 12}{-12 - 5} = \frac{-5 - y}{-12 - x}$$

$$\frac{-17}{-17} = 1 = \frac{-5 - y}{-12 - x}$$

$$-12 - x = -5 - y$$

$$12 + x = 5 + y$$

$$x = y - 7 \qquad Answer$$

Problem 1-11 Algebraic trigonometric equation

Find the first positive value of x that would satisfy the equation $\sin x = -\frac{1}{6}x$.

Solution:

Equations containing a mixture of both algebraic and logarithmic or algebraic and trigonometric terms are best solved by either graphical methods, approximate methods, or a combination of these. Using a combination approach here, first prepare a table of x, sin x, y_1, y_2; then neatly plot, as seen in Fig. 1-16, the following two equations:

$$y_1 = \sin x \quad \text{and} \quad y_2 = -\frac{1}{6}x$$

x	sin x	y_1	y_2
0	0	0	0
$\frac{1}{4}\pi$	0.707	0.707	$-(\frac{1}{6})(\frac{1}{4})\pi = 0.13$
$\frac{1}{2}\pi$	1.000	1.000	$-(\frac{1}{6})(\frac{1}{2})\pi = -0.26$
$\frac{3}{2}\pi$	−1.000	−1.000	$-(\frac{1}{6})(\frac{3}{2})\pi = -0.78$
2π	0	0	$-(\frac{1}{6})2\pi = -1.04$

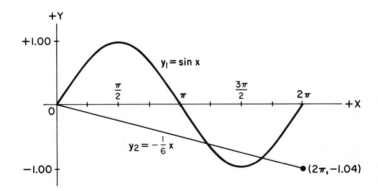

Figure 1-16

The points of intersection of the straight line and the sine curve (Fig. 1-16) are the desired roots. The first root, x = 0 rad (or 0 degrees), is obtained by inspection. A second root is between x = 3.40 and x = 4.00 rad. A more exact answer may be obtained through the use of linear interpolation. Let $y = \frac{1}{6}x + \sin x$. Whenever the right-hand side of the equation is 0, the corresponding value of x is a root.

x (rad)	3.400	3.600	3.800	4.000
$\frac{1}{6}x$	0.568	0.600	0.632	0.668
sin x	−0.260	−0.438	−0.602	−0.744
y	+0.308	+0.162	+0.030	−0.076

Now by similar triangles, as seen in Fig. 1-17, i.e., by linear interpolation

$$\frac{\Delta y}{\Delta x} = \frac{0.03}{-x} = \frac{y_1 - y_2}{x_1 - x_2} = \frac{0.106}{-0.200} \qquad x = \frac{(0.03)(0.200)}{0.106} = 0.057$$

The first positive root is, therefore,

$$3.800 + 0.057 = 3.857 \text{ rad} \qquad \textit{Answer}$$

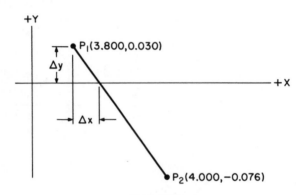

Figure 1-17

Problem 1-12 Distance-speed trigonometric equations

A ship proceeding at a speed of 20 mph due west is 10 miles north, and 25 miles east of a coastguard station when it radios a distress signal. A coastguard cutter is immediately sent to help the ship. If the cutter proceeds at 30 mph, what heading shall it take? How long will it take to reach the ship?

Solution:

A sketch will clarify the problem. In Fig. 1-18, the ship is shown in its initial position (1) and its final position (2). Assume the origin of the X-Y coordinate system to be at the coastguard station. During the time t required to reach the ship, the ship travels west −20t, the cutter travels north 10 miles and travels east or west (+x or −x) a distance equal to the difference of 25 miles and the distance traveled by the ship, i.e., −20t.

In the N-direction,

$$10 = 30t \sin \theta$$

$$t = \frac{1}{3 \sin \theta}$$

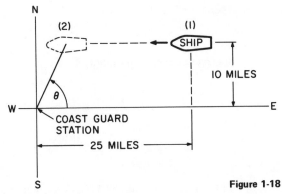

Figure 1-18

In the E-direction,

$$25 - 20t = 30t \cos \theta$$

$$25 - \frac{20}{3 \sin \theta} = \frac{30}{3}\left(\frac{\cos \theta}{\sin \theta}\right)$$

$$2.5 \sin \theta - \cos \theta = 0.667$$

This is best solved by trial and error as shown below:

θ	$\sin \theta$	$2.5 \sin \theta$	$\cos \theta$	$2.5 \sin \theta - \cos \theta$
0	0	0	1	−1.000
30	0.500	1.250	0.866	+0.384
45	0.707	1.770	0.707	+1.063
35	0.572	1.430	0.816	+0.614
40	0.640	1.600	0.765	+0.835

$$\theta = 36° \qquad Answer$$

Exponents

The symbol 2^3 indicates that 2 is a factor three times, $2^3 = 2 \times 2 \times 2 = 8$. 2 is called the base; 3, the exponent. $3^3 \times 3^2$ indicates 3 is a factor five times. $3^3 \times 3^2 = 3^{3+2} = (3 \times 3 \times 3) \times (3 \times 3) = 243$.

Rules for Exponents.

(a) In multiplying, exponents of identical bases are added:

$$a^3 \times a^5 = a^{3+5} = a^8$$

$$x^{1.4} x^{2.0} x^{2.5} = x^{5.9}$$

$$x^{0.8} \times x^{0.7} \times y^{2.4} = x^{1.5} \times y^{2.4}$$

(b) In dividing, exponents of identical bases are subtracted:

$$2^5/2^3 = 2^{5-3} = 2^2 = 4.$$

$$a^4/a^6 = a^{4-6} = a^{-2} = 1/a^2$$

(c) Any base with an exponent of zero is equal to 1:

$$2^2/2^2 = 2^{2-2} = 2^0 = 1 \qquad a^0 = e^0 = 1000^0 = 1$$

(d) The denominator of a fractional exponent indicates a root:

$$4^{\frac{1}{2}} = \sqrt{4} = \pm 2$$
$$10^{\frac{3}{4}} = \sqrt[4]{10^3}$$

Logarithms

In the process of multiplying or dividing numbers, raising a number to a power (i.e., $281^{3.6}$) or finding the root of a number, logarithms are often used because of their convenience and accuracy. The logarithm of a number is the exponent to which a second number called the base must be raised to produce the original number. Two bases are in common use; the number 10, which forms the base of the "common" or Briggsian logarithm, and the number 2.718 . . ., which is the base of the natural or Napierian logarithm system. The letter "e" is usually used to designate the natural base. The common logarithm of 100 is 2 or 2.000 because $10^2 = 100$; similarly the natural logarithm of 100 is 4.60517 because $(2.718 . . .)^{4.60517} = 100$ or $e^{4.60517} = 100$.

The operations indicated as multiplication, division, obtaining powers or roots of numbers are obtained by first finding the logarithms of the numbers involved, then carrying out the operations by following the laws of exponents, and finally finding the number corresponding to the new logarithm, i.e., obtaining the antilogarithm.

Common Logarithms. The logarithm of the number 180.5 is 2.25648 because $10^{2.25648} = 180.5$. The logarithm consists of two parts, the number(s) before the decimal point, called the "characteristic," and the number(s) after the decimal point, called the "mantissa."

The characteristic indicates the location of the decimal point, i.e., the characteristic 2 indicates the number lies between 100. and 1000. because $10^{2.00000} = 100.$ and $10^{3.00000} = 1000.$ $\bar{2}$ indicates a number between 0.01 and 0.001 because $10^{-2} = 1/10^2 = 0.01$ and $10^{-3} = 1/10^3 = 0.001$.

The mantissa specifies the actual value of the number but does not locate its decimal point. The relation between a given number and its mantissa or vice versa is given in the tables of common logarithms found in most engineering handbooks.

Following are examples using common logarithms.

Example
Find the logarithm of 180.50.

Solution:
(a) Determine the characteristic. By inspection = 2
(b) Look up the mantissa for 1805 = 0.25648
(c) log 180.50 = 2.25648   *Answer*

Example
Find the logarithm of 0.01805.

Solution:
(a) The characteristic is $\bar{2}$
(b) The mantissa (as above) = 0.25648
(c) log 0.01805 = $\bar{2}$.25648   *Answer*

Interpolation is the process of finding the value of an intermediate term in a series of terms for which values are given. Linear interpolation is used in connection with logarithms as shown by the following example.

Example
Find the logarithm of 62.34 in a table in which the mantissa for 623 and 624 are given.

Solution:
log 62.40 = 1.7952 (from table)

log 62.34 = 1.79xx

log 62.30 = 1.7945 (from table)

By proportion,

$$\frac{4}{10} = \frac{xx}{07}$$

$$xx = (07)\,\frac{4}{10} = 028 = 03$$

Therefore, log 62.34 = 1.7945 + 0.0003 = 1.7948   *Answer*

Antilogarithms are the numbers that correspond to given logarithms. Finding the antilog is the reverse of finding the log; thus the antilog of 2 is 100, i.e., 100 is the number whose log is 2.

Natural logarithm tables commonly give the natural logs for numbers ranging from 1 to 10. For numbers greater than ten, the rules of exponents are applied to find the natural log.

Problem 1-13 Natural logarithms
Find the natural log of 65.

Solution:

$$\ln 65 = n$$

$$\ln (6.5 \times 10) = \ln 6.5 + \ln 10.0$$

$$\ln 6.5 = 1.8718 \qquad \text{and} \qquad \ln 10.0 = 2.3026$$

$$\ln 6.5 + \ln 10.0 = 4.1744$$

Therefore, $\ln 65 = 4.1744$ *Answer*

Problem 1-14 Natural logarithms

Find the natural log of 650.

Solution:

$$\ln 650 = \ln (6.5 \times 10^2) = \ln 6.5 + 2 \ln 10$$
$$= 1.8718 + 4.6052$$
$$\ln 650 = 6.4770 \qquad Answer$$

Relation Between Common and Natural Logarithms

$e^{2.3026} = 10$; therefore, $\ln 10 = 2.3026$

$10^{0.4343} = e$; therefore, $\log e = 0.4343$

$$\frac{1}{0.4343} = 2.3026$$

Let $N = 10^x$; then $\log N = x$.

$$\ln N = \ln 10^x = x \ln 10$$
$$x = \frac{\ln N}{\ln 10} = \log N$$

Thus $\ln N = \ln 10 \log N = 2.3026 \log N$ or

$$\log N = \frac{\ln N}{\ln 10} = 0.4343 \ln N$$

Problem 1-15 Common logarithms

Determine the value of x if $\log_{10}(6x - 2) = 2$.

Solution:

$\log (100) = 2$. Therefore, $(6x - 2) = 100$.

$$x = 102/6 = 17.0 \qquad Answer$$

Problem 1-16 Common logarithm algebraic equation

Find the value of x if $\log_4 (x + 1) - \log_4 (x - 1) = 0.5$.

Solution:

$$\log_4 \frac{(x + 1)}{(x - 1)} = 0.5$$
$$\frac{(x + 1)}{(x - 1)} = (4)^{0.5}$$
$$(x + 1) = (x - 1)\sqrt{4} = (x - 1)(\pm 2)$$

Using +2,

$$x + 1 = 2x - 2$$
$$x = 3 \qquad Answer$$

Using -2,

$$x + 1 = -2x + 2$$

$$x = \frac{1}{3} \qquad Answer$$

Problem 1-17 Common logarithms
(a) Using common logarithms find the value of $\sqrt{0.401^3 \times 0.206}$.
(b) Find the value of $\log_{12} 4$.

Solution:

(a) $\log \sqrt{0.401^3 \times 0.206} = \frac{1}{2}(3 \log 0.401 + \log 0.206)$

$$\log 0.401 = 9.6031 - 10$$
$$3 \log 0.401 = 28.8093 - 30$$
$$\log 0.206 = 9.3139 - 10$$
$$3 \log 0.401 + \log 0.206 = 38.1232 - 40$$

$$\frac{1}{2}(3 \log 0.401 + \log 0.206) = 19.0616 - 20$$

$$\text{antilog}(19.0616 - 20) = \sqrt{0.401^3 \times 0.206} = 0.115 \qquad Answer$$

(b) $\log_{12} 4 = x$

$$12^x = 4$$

Take logarithms of both sides:

$$x \log 12 = \log 4$$
$$x = \log 4/\log 12 = 0.602/1.079 = 0.558 \qquad Answer$$

Calculus

Differential calculus refers to the mathematics involved in determining the instantaneous rate of change of related variables, or the amount of change that occurs in a dependent variable with a unit change in the independent variable. The relation between the dependent and independent variable must, of course, be stated either explicitly or implicitly. The dependent variable is often designated y or f(x), the independent variable is designated x.

The increment Δx of a variable x is the algebraic difference between x, and x_0. For example, if $x_0 = 3$ and $x_1 = 5$, then $\Delta x = 5 - 3 = 2$. The increment Δy is similarly $y_1 - y_0$.

The average rate of change of a function $y = f(x)$ with respect to x is

$$\frac{\Delta y}{\Delta x} = \frac{y_1 - y_0}{x_1 - x_0}$$

A List of Basic Derivatives. In these derivatives assume c is a constant, x is the independent variable, u and v are dependent variables.

1. $\dfrac{d}{dx}(c) = 0$ or $\dfrac{d}{dx}\dfrac{(1)}{(c)} = 0$

2. $\dfrac{d}{dx}(x) = 1$ or $\dfrac{d}{dx}(cx) = c$

3. $\dfrac{d}{dx}(u + v + \cdots)$ $=$ $\dfrac{d}{dx}(u) + \dfrac{d}{dx}(v) + \cdots$

4. $\dfrac{d}{dx}(cu)$ $=$ $c\dfrac{d}{dx}(u)$

5. $\dfrac{d}{dx}(uv)$ $=$ $u\dfrac{d}{dx}(v) + v\dfrac{d}{dx}(u)$

6. $\dfrac{d}{dx}(x^n)$ $=$ nx^{n-1}

7. $\dfrac{d}{dx}(u^n)$ $=$ $nu^{n-1}\dfrac{d}{dx}(u)$

8. $\dfrac{d}{dx}(e^u)$ $=$ $e^u\dfrac{d}{dx}(u)$

9. $\dfrac{d}{dx}(a^u)$ $=$ $a^u \ln a\dfrac{d}{dx}(u)$

10. $\dfrac{d}{dx}(\log_k u)$ $=$ $\dfrac{1}{u}\log_k e\dfrac{du}{dx}$

11. $\dfrac{d}{dx}(\ln u)$ $=$ $\dfrac{1}{u}\dfrac{d}{dx}(u)$

Slope of a Tangent. If the relation y = f(x) is plotted as a curve, then the value of the derivative dy/dx at any point P (x,y) on the curve is equal to the slope of the tangent to the curve at that point. For example, obtain the slope of the tangent to the curve $y = x^2 + 4$ at x = 3, y = 13.

$dy/dx = y' = 2x = 2(3) = 6$

Slope of the tangent = $\tan \alpha = 6$

Maximum and minimum values of a function y = f(x) are those values of the function for which immediately preceding and succeeding values are both either less or more, respectively. These values are usually approximately obtainable by plotting the function on rectangular coordinates. Mathematically, maxima and minima may be found by:

1. Finding the first derivative of the function y'.
2. Finding the critical values of x for which $y' = 0$ or becomes infinite.
3. Testing to see whether a maximum or minimum value has actually been found by determining if $y' = f'(x)$ undergoes a change of sign by assuming values of x slightly less and then slightly more than the critical values found in 2. above and noting if $f'(x)$ changes sign.

   a. If $f'(x)$ changes sign from + to − as x is made slightly less and more than its critical value, then f(x) is a maximum.
   b. If $f'(x)$ changes sign from − to + for the same test, then f(x) is a minimum.
   c. If $f'(x)$ does not change sign, neither a maximum nor minimum value has been found.

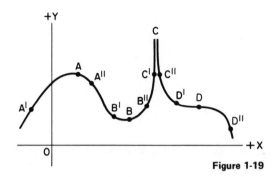

Figure 1-19

For example, see Fig. 1-19.

$f'(x) = 0$ at A; $f'(x) = +$ at A^1, $-$ at A^{11} $f(x)$ reaches a maximum value at A

$f'(x) = 0$ at B; $f'(x) = -$ at B^1, $+$ at B^{11} $f(x)$ reaches a minimum value at B

$f.(x) \to \infty$ at C; $f'(x) = + C^1$, $-$ at C^{11} $\therefore$ C is another maximum value of $f(x)$

$f'(x) = 0$ at D; $f'(x) = -$ at D^1, $-$ at D^{11} $\therefore$ $f(x)$ is neither a maximum nor minimum value at D

Applied problems involving maximum and minimum values are expressed as word statements for the relation between variables. Included in these statements there will be a phrase calling for the largest (most farthest) or the least (nearest smallest) value of the function. The word statements must be resolved into algebraic equations, arranged, if possible, so that one side represents the function whose maximum or minimum value is to be found.

Problem 1-18 Differentiation

Differentiate the following expressions:

(a) $y = \sqrt{x^3 + 2x}$

(b) $y = 3x^2 \sqrt{4 - x^2}$

Solution:

(a) $y = \sqrt{x^3 + 2x} = (x^3 + 2x)^{\frac{1}{2}}$

$$\frac{dy}{dx} = \frac{1}{2}(x^3 + 2x)^{-\frac{1}{2}} \frac{d}{dx}(x^3 + 2x)$$

$$= \frac{1}{2}(x^3 + 2x)^{-\frac{1}{2}}(3x^2 + 2)$$

$$= \frac{3x^2 + 2}{2(x^3 + 2x)^{\frac{1}{2}}} \qquad Answer$$

(b) $y = 3x^2 \sqrt{4 - x^2} = 3x^2 (4 - x^2)^{\frac{1}{2}}$

$$\frac{dy}{dx} = \frac{d(u \times v)}{dx} = \frac{ud(v)}{dx} + \frac{vd(u)}{dx}$$

Let $u = 3x^2$, $v = (4 - x^2)^{\frac{1}{2}}$

$$\frac{d(y)}{dx} = 3x^2 \frac{d(4 - x^2)^{\frac{1}{2}}}{dx} + (4 - x^2)^{\frac{1}{2}} \frac{d(3x^2)}{dx}$$

$$= 3x^2 \frac{(4 - x^2)^{-\frac{1}{2}}}{2} \frac{d(4 - x^2)}{dx} + (4 - x^2)^{\frac{1}{2}} 6x \frac{d(x)}{dx}$$

$$= \frac{3x^2}{2}(4 - x^2)^{-\frac{1}{2}}(-2x) + (4 - x^2)^{\frac{1}{2}} 6x$$

$$= -3x^3 (4 - x^2)^{-\frac{1}{2}} + 6x(4 - x^2)^{\frac{1}{2}} \qquad Answer$$

Problem 1-19 Slope by differentiation

The equation of the curve described by a cable, supporting a uniform load is

$$y = -\frac{3}{4}x + \frac{1}{1280}x^2$$

(a) Determine the coordinates of point B if the slope at B is $+\frac{1}{2}$. (b) Calculate the coordinates of the low point. (c) Calculate the slope at the origin.

Solution:

(a) The slope at B is defined by

$$dy/dx = -\tfrac{3}{4} + (2/1280)x$$

$$\tfrac{1}{2} = -\tfrac{3}{4} + (1/640)x$$

$$x = (640)(\tfrac{5}{4}) = 800 \qquad Answer$$

$$y = -(\tfrac{3}{4})800 + (1/1280)800^2$$

$$= -100 \qquad Answer$$

The coordinates of B are $(800, -100)$.

(b) At the lowest point the slope of the curve is zero.

$$0 = -\tfrac{3}{4} + (1/640)x$$

$$x = 480$$

$$y = -180 \qquad Answer$$

(c) $dy/dx = -\tfrac{3}{4} + (1/640)x$. At $x = 0$

$$dy/dx = -\tfrac{3}{4} \qquad Answer$$

Problem 1-20 Slope and tangent to curve

Given the function $y = 0.6x + x^{0.6}$,

(a) calculate the value of y when $x = 3$;

(b) find the slope of the tangent to the curve when $x = 0$ and when $x = 4$.

Solution:
(a) Using the LL3 and LL2 scales of the slide rule, $3^{0.6} = 1.93$. A convenient way of recalling the slide rule operation is to use a known example. Thus, $2^{0.5} = 2^{\frac{1}{2}} = \sqrt[2]{2} = 1.414$. Using common logarithms, let

$$N = 3^{0.6}$$

$$\log N = (0.6) \log 3 = (0.6)(0.477) = 0.286$$

$$N = 1.93$$

Therefore, $y = 1.80 + 1.93 = 3.73$ *Answer*

(b) Slope of tangent $= dy/dx = 0.6 + 0.6x^{0.6-1}$
$$= 0.6 + 0.6/x^{0.4}$$

If $x = 0$, $dy/dx = \infty$

If $x = 4$, $dy/dx = 0.6 + 0.6/4^{0.4} = 0.6 + 0.6/1.74 = 0.945$ *Answer*

Problem 1-21 Container dimensioned for least surface area
A rectangular metal container open at the top is to have a capacity of 45 cu in. The ratio of the length to the width of the base is 3:2. Find the dimensions of the length, width, and height so that the least area of metal is used.

Solution:
The volume of the container is $V = wLh$. The area of metal used consists of four sides and the bottom, thus: $A = wL + 2wh + 2Lh$. Since the least area is desired, express the area in terms of one of the variables and carry out the differentiation. A convenient variable is w.

$$L/w = 3/2$$
$$L = \tfrac{3}{2} w$$
$$V = w(\tfrac{3}{2} w) h = \tfrac{3}{2} w^2 h$$
$$45 = \tfrac{3}{2} w^2 h$$
$$h = 30/w^2$$
$$A = 1.5w^2 + 60/w + 2\tfrac{3}{2} w (30/w^2)$$
$$= 1.5w^2 + 150/w$$
$$\frac{dA}{dw} = 3w - \frac{150}{w^2} = \frac{3(w^3 - 50)}{w^2}$$

Minimum area occurs where $dA/dw = 0$

$$3(w^3 - 50)/w^2 = 0$$

Since w cannot equal 0, therefore,

$$w^3 - 50 = 0$$

$w = 3.68$ in. $L = 5.52$ in. $h = 2.22$ in.   *Answer*

Problem 1-22 Maxima by first derivative

A manufacturer of binoculars can earn a net profit of $20 per binocular if he sells 100 binoculars or less each month. For every binocular over 100, his profit per binocular is reduced $0.10. For maximum profit how many should he sell?

Solution:

Let P = net profit

n = the number of binoculars sold per month

$$P = n[20.00 - (n - 100)0.10]$$
$$= 20.00n - 0.10n^2 + 10n$$
$$= 30n - 0.10n^2$$

As the profit varies with number sold, take the derivative dP/dn and set it equal to zero.

$$dP/dn = 30 - 0.20n = 0$$
$$n = 150 \quad \textit{Answer}$$

Problem 1-23 Rate of change of parameter by first derivative

A rectangular pool with vertical sides and ends has an inclined floor. The pool is 50 ft long and 20 ft wide, 12 ft deep at one end, 2 ft at the other end. See Fig. 1-20. If the water fills the pool at 200 cu ft/min, how fast is the water level rising when the water is 3 ft high at the deep end?

Solution:

Sketch the problem.

$$\text{volume} = \frac{h \times 20 \times L}{2} = 10hL$$

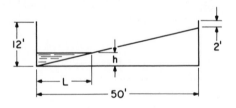

Figure 1-20

Relating all variables to the height h,

$$\frac{L}{h} = \frac{50}{12 - 2} \quad (0 \leqslant h \leqslant 10)$$

$$L = 50h/10 = 5h$$

$$\text{volume} = 50h^2$$

$$\frac{dV}{dt} = 200\frac{\text{ft}^3}{\text{min}} = 100h\frac{dh}{dt}$$

When h = 3

$$\frac{dh}{dt} = \frac{200}{100 \times 3} = \frac{2}{3} \text{ ft/min} \quad \textit{Answer}$$

Problem 1-24 Rate of increase of surface area of sphere as a function of rate of increase of radius

A spherical balloon lying in the sun is increasing in volume at the rate 2.0 cu in./min when its radius is 5 in. At what rate is the surface area increasing?

Solution:

$dV/dt = 2.00$ in.^{3}/min

$$V = \frac{4}{3}\pi r^3 \qquad A = 4\pi r^2 \qquad r = 5 \text{ in.}$$

$$\frac{dV}{dt} = \frac{4}{3}\pi 3r^2 \frac{dr}{dt} = 2.00$$

$$\frac{dr}{dt} = \frac{2.00 \text{ in.}^3/\text{min}}{4\pi 5^2 \text{ in.}^2} = \frac{0.02}{\pi} \text{ in./min}$$

$$\frac{dA}{dt} = 8\pi r \frac{dr}{dt} = 8\pi r \frac{0.02}{\pi} = 0.8 \text{ in.}^2/\text{min} \qquad Answer$$

Approximation of a small change Δy in the dependent variable, y, can be determined if the independent variable x changes by an increment Δx.

Problem 1-25 Area of ring by differentials

Find the approximate area of a ring or annulus having an inside diameter of 8 in. and a radial width of 0.02 in.

Solution:

Let A = area of the circle

   dA = the approximate area of the ring

   x = diameter of the circle

The area of a circle = $A = \frac{1}{4}\pi x^2$.

$$dA/dx = \frac{1}{2}\pi x$$

If $dA = A_{ring}$,

$$A_{ring} = \frac{1}{2}\pi x \, \Delta x$$

$$= \frac{1}{2}\pi(8)(0.04) = 0.502 \text{ sq in.} \qquad Answer$$

Note: The exact area $= \frac{1}{4}\pi(8 + 0.04)^2 - \frac{1}{4}\pi 8^2$

$$= \frac{1}{4}\pi[8^2 + 2(0.04)(8) + (0.04)^2 - 8^2]$$

$$= 0.503 \text{ sq in.}$$

Differentials can also be used to determine errors. The relation dx/x defines relative error and 100(dx/x) defines percentage error. This concept is illustrated in the next problem.

Problem 1-26 Determination of error by differentials

Find the relative error and percentage error in the volume of spheres manufactured to the following dimension: 6.00 ± 0.02 in. A standard sphere has a 6.00-in. diameter.

Solution:

Volume = $V = \frac{4}{3}\pi r^3$

To determine dx/x or dV/V, find the natural logarithm of both sides of the above equation and differentiate with respect to r.

$$\ln V = \ln(4\pi/3) + 3 \ln r$$

$$\frac{1}{V}\frac{dV}{dr} = \frac{3}{r}$$

$$\frac{dV}{V} = \frac{3dr}{r}$$

$$dr = 0.01 \text{ in.} \qquad r = 3 \text{ in.}$$

$$\frac{dV}{V} = \frac{3(0.01)}{3} = 0.01$$

Therefore, the relative error = ± 0.01 *Answer*
The percentage error = $\pm 1.0\%$ *Answer*

Integral calculus is formally defined as the process of finding a function f(x) whose derivative dy/dx = f'(x) has been given. In a more physical sense integration is said to be the process of summation, of adding together all the differential (i.e., minutely small) parts that together make up the whole.

Integration provides a means for finding the areas of surfaces, the volumes or weights of solids, the total work done during a process, etc. For simple integrands the integral may be found by either determining what function when differentiated would give the integrand or resorting to integration tables. A short integration table of common integrands and their integrals is given below:

1. $\int a \, du = a \int du = au + C$

2. $\int u^n \, du = \frac{u^{n+1}}{n+1} + C \qquad (\text{if } n \neq -1)$

3. $\int au \, dv = a \int u \, dv = a(uv - \int v \, du)$

4. $\int du/u = \ln u + C \qquad (\text{if } u > 0)$

5. $\int a^u \, du = \frac{a^u}{\ln a} + C \qquad (\text{if } a > 0)$

6. $\int \frac{1}{a^2 + u^2} \, du = \frac{1}{a} \tan^{-1}\frac{u}{a} + C$

7. $\int \frac{1}{a^2 - u^2} \, du = \frac{1}{2a} \ln \frac{a+u}{a-u} + C$

8. $\int \dfrac{1}{\sqrt{a^2 - u^2}} \, du = \sin^{-1} \dfrac{u}{a} + C$

9. $\int \dfrac{1}{\sqrt{u^2 \pm a^2}} \, du = \ln (u + \sqrt{u^2 \pm a^2}) + C$

10. $\int \sin u \, du = -\cos u + C$

11. $\int \cos u \, du = \sin u + C$

12. $\int \tan u \, du = \ln \sec u + C$

13. $\int \cot u \, du = \ln \sin u + C$

14. $\int \sec u \, du = \ln (\sec u + \tan u) + C$

15. $\int \csc u \, du = \ln (\csc u - \cot u) + C$

16. $\int \sec^2 u \, du = \tan u + C$

17. $\int \csc^2 u \, du = -\cot u + C$

For complicated integrands a number of procedures are available including: (1) integration by parts, (2) substitution of a new variable, (3) conversion into partial fractions, (4) graphical integration, and (5) numerical integration. For integration by parts formula 3. is used.

Example

Find $\int x \sin x \, dx$ using $\int u \, dv = uv - \int v \, du$.

Solution:

Let $u = x$

$dv = \sin x \, dx$

$du = dx$

$v = -\cos x$

$\int x(\sin x \, dx) = -x \cos x - \int -\cos x \, dx$

$\qquad\qquad\qquad = -x \cos x + \sin x + C$

Note: (a) The expression for dv must contain dx; (b) it must be possible to integrate dv.

Integration by substitution is exemplified by trigonometric substitutions. A three-step solution is necessary when the integrand contains the variable u in one of the radicals shown below. (1) Substitute the trigonometric function of θ for the variable u in the radical. (2) Integrate using the substitute variable. (3) Reverse the procedure to fit the original variable back into the solution.

Use the Trigonometric Relation	In the Radical	Which Yields
$u = a \tan \theta$ (Fig. 1-21)	$\sqrt{a^2 + u^2}$	$a\sqrt{1 + \tan^2 \theta} = a \sec \theta$
$u = a \sin \theta$ (Fig. 1-22)	$\sqrt{a^2 - u^2}$	$a\sqrt{1 - \sin^2 \theta} = a \cos \theta$
$u = a \sec \theta$ (Fig. 1-23)	$\sqrt{u^2 - a^2}$	$a\sqrt{\sec^2 \theta - 1} = a \tan \theta$

If the integrand is a fraction in which the degree of the denominator is greater than that of the numerator and the exponents of the variable are neither fractions nor negative, then integration can be readily effected by resolving the integrand into partial fractions.

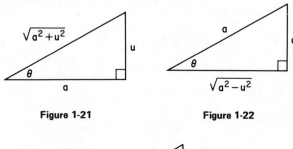

Figure 1-21   Figure 1-22

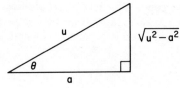

Figure 1-23

Problem 1-27 Integration by substitution of variable

Find the value of $\displaystyle\int \frac{dx}{\sqrt{4x^2 + 9}}$

Solution:
Represent
$$\sqrt{4x^2 + 9} = \sqrt{u^2 + a^2}$$
$$u = 2x \qquad a = 3$$
Then
$$x = u/2$$
$$dx = du/2$$

$$\int \frac{dx}{\sqrt{4x^2 + 9}} = \frac{1}{2} \int \frac{du}{\sqrt{u^2 + a^2}}$$

Let $u = a \tan \theta$ and $du = a \sec^2 \theta \, d\theta$.

$$\sqrt{u^2 + a^2} = \sqrt{a^2 \tan^2\theta + a^2} = a \sec\theta$$

$$\frac{1}{2}\int \frac{du}{\sqrt{u^2 + a^2}} = \frac{1}{2}\int \frac{a\sec^2\theta\,d\theta}{a\sec\theta} = \frac{1}{2}\int \sec\theta\,d\theta$$

$$= \tfrac{1}{2}\ln(\sec\theta + \tan\theta) + C$$

Referring to Fig. 1-21,

$$\sec\theta = \sqrt{(a^2 + u^2)}/a \qquad \tan\theta = u/a$$

$$\int \frac{dx}{\sqrt{4x^2 + 9}} = \tfrac{1}{2}\ln(\sqrt{(4x^2 + 9)}/3 + 2x/3) + C \qquad \textit{Answer}$$

Problem 1-28 Integration by partial fractions

Find $\displaystyle\int \frac{(x + 2)\,dx}{x^3 + 5x^2 + 6x}$

Solution:
Factor denominator:

$$\int \frac{(x + 2)\,dx}{x(x + 5x + 6)} = \int \frac{(x + 2)\,dx}{x(x + 2)(x + 3)}$$

Resolve the fraction into partial fractions:

$$\frac{x + 2}{x(x + 2)(x + 3)} = \frac{A}{x} + \frac{B}{x + 2} + \frac{C}{x + 3}$$

Clear fractions:

$$x + 2 = A(x + 2)(x + 3) + B(x)(x + 3) + C(x)(x + 2)$$
$$= Ax^2 + 5Ax + 6A + Bx^2 + 3Bx + Cx^2 + 2Cx$$
$$= (A + B + C)x^2 + (5A + 3B + 2C)x + 6A$$

Equate coefficients of like powers:

$$A + B + C = 0$$
$$5A + 3B + 2C = 1$$
$$6A = 2$$

$$A = \tfrac{1}{3} \qquad B = 0 \qquad C = -\tfrac{1}{3}$$

$$\int \frac{(x + 2)\,dx}{x(x^2 + 5x + 6)} = +\frac{1}{3}\ln x - \frac{\ln(x + 3)}{3} \qquad \textit{Answer}$$

In addition to the formal mathematical approach to integral calculus, the physical concept of integration as being a process of summation is useful.

Example

Find the work U done by the force of gas on a piston if the piston moves 6 in.

Solution:

The force-displacement diagram is recorded in Fig. 1-24; the work done is the area between the force curve, the X-axis, and the x = 6 ordinate.

$$U = A_1 + A_2 + A_3$$

These three areas can be approximated very closely by three rectangular areas, as shown in Fig. 1-25. If, however, a suitable equation can be found that defines F vs. x, as, for example, $F = 1.5x^2$, then formal integration would be used to determine it. Thus,

$$U = \int_0^6 F\ dx = \int_0^6 1.5x^2\ dx = \frac{1.5}{3} x^3 \Big|_0^6 = 0.5(216 - 0) = 108 \qquad Answer$$

Double and triple integration is often more convenient when the area or volume to be evaluated lies between two curves or surfaces. For example, find the area between the curves $y = x^2$ and $y = \frac{1}{4}x^3$ in the first quadrant. By inspection, the curves intersect at x = 0,4.

$$\text{Area} = \int_0^4 \int_{y=\frac{1}{4}x^3}^{y=x^2} dy\ dx = \int_0^4 y \Big|_{\frac{1}{4}x^3}^{x^2} dx$$

$$= \int_0^4 (x^2 - \frac{1}{4}x^3)\ dx = \left[\frac{x^3}{3} - \frac{x^4}{16} \right]_0^4 = 5\frac{1}{3}$$

Problem 1-29 Area of curve by integration

The equation of a curve is $y = 15x - 2x^2$. Find the area bounded by the curve, the X-axis, and the line x = 5.

Solution:

See Fig. 1-26.

$$\text{Area} = \int_0^5 y\ dx = \int_0^5 (15x - 2x^2)\ dx$$

$$= 15x^2/2 - 2x^3/3 \Big|_0^5 = 104.2 \text{ sq units} \qquad Answer$$

Problem 1-30 Volumetric increase by integration

In a chemical reaction the volume of a substance increases at a rate proportional to itself. Predict the volume of this substance at t = 24 min if the initial volume (at t = 0) is 20 cc and at t = 10 the volume is 36 cc.

Solution:

Let V = volume. The change of volume with respect to time = dv/dt.

$$dv/dt = kV$$

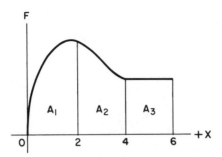

Figure 1-24

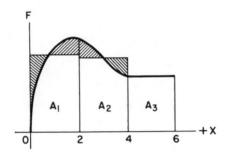

Figure 1-25

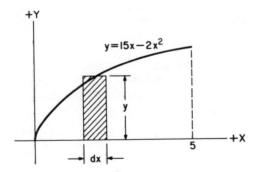

Figure 1-26

$$\int dv/V = \int k\ dt + C'$$
$$\ln V = kt + \ln C$$

Changing to exponential form, $V = Ce^{kt}$. Using the given boundary conditions, when $t = 0$, $V = 20$; therefore, $C = 20$.

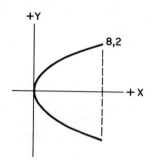

Figure 1-27

$$V = 20e^{kt}$$

When t = 10, V = 36.

$$36 = 20e^{10k}$$

$$1.8 = e^{10k}$$

$$k = 0.059$$

When t = 24,

$$V = 20e^{24(0.059)}$$

$$= 82.4 \text{ cc} \qquad Answer$$

Problem 1-31 Volume of paraboloid of revolution

A parabola having the dimensions shown in Fig. 1-27 is *revolved* about its axis of symmetry. Determine by integration the volume of the paraboloid of revolution.

Solution:

The equation of a parabola must first be determined to find the relation between x and y. For a parabola symmetric about the X-axis and passing through the origin, the equation is $y^2 = ax$. From the dimensions $2^2 = a(8)$. Therefore, $a = 4/8 = 1/2$.

For this case,

$$y^2 = \tfrac{1}{2} x$$

When the parabola is revolved about the X-axis, each point on it will describe a circle. A circle multiplied by a small distance dx will form a cylinder. The summation of the volumes of all cylinders so formed will be the required volume.

$$\int dV = \int_0^8 \pi y^2 \, dx = \pi \int_0^8 x/2 \, dx$$

$$V = \tfrac{1}{4} \pi x^2 \Big|_0^8 = 16\pi = 50.4 \text{ cu units} \qquad Answer$$

chapter 2
STATICS

Statics is the subdivision of engineering mechanics that deals with the equilibrium of bodies at rest and the application of external forces upon them. Elastic deformations and stresses induced in the structural members by the application of such forces are not considered in this chapter. The subject is within the scope of strength of materials and is treated in Chaps. 11 through 17.

2-1 FORCES AND THEIR COMPONENTS

A force applied to an object by an abutting object is represented by a vector that is movable along its line of action. The external reactions produced by the force are independent of its point of application along this line. For example, in the simple truss of Fig. 2-1, the force F will produce the same reactions at points A and B irrespective of its point of application to the truss along line of action n-n. The direction and magnitude of the reaction forces produced at points A and B establish static equilibrium.

A force vector may be replaced by component vectors having direction and magnitude different from the original vector. Consider the force F applied by the cable AB to the platform CD in Fig. 2-2. By adding a set of rectangular coordinates, the vector components in the X- and Y-directions are determined by calculating the product of F and the appropriate angle function. The rectangular components take the sign required by the particular quadrant wherein the force vector is located.

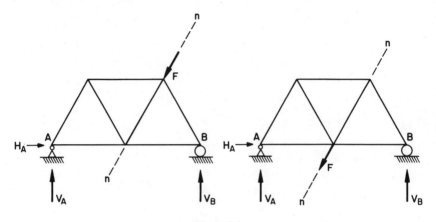

Figure 2-1

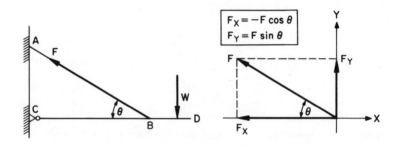

Figure 2-2

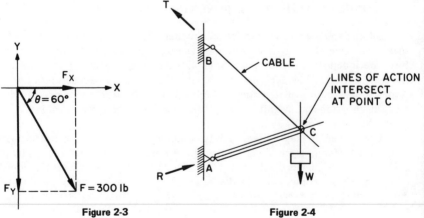

Figure 2-3

Figure 2-4

Problem 2-1 Force vector

Determine the rectangular coordinates of the 300-lb force shown in Fig. 2-3.

Solution:

Determine the rectangular coordinates:

$$F_X = F \cos \theta = 300 \cos 60° = 150 \, \text{lb}$$

$$F_Y = -F \sin \theta = -300 \sin 60° = -260 \, \text{lb}$$

Answer

2-2 RESULTANT OF CONCURRENT FORCES

Forces are concurrent if their lines of action intersect at a common point. Figure 2-4 shows a boom supported by a cable at end C and connected to a hinge at end A. The reaction R, cable tension T, and weight W all have lines of action that intersect at point C.

Problem 2-2 Resultant of a concurrent force system

Three forces of 1050 lb, 700 lb, and 500 lb are acting upon a small boat on a lake. The first force acts due south, the second force acts due west, and the third acts 60 degrees west of south. Determine: (a) the magnitude of the resultant force on the boat, and (b) the direction of the resultant force on the boat.

Solution:

A vector diagram is first drawn that describes the force system, as shown in Fig. 2-5. Then a set of coordinate XY-axes is superimposed upon the vector diagram, as shown in Fig. 2-6. The vector diagram represents a concurrent force system because the lines of action of all the forces intersect at a single point, i.e., the origin of the coordinate axes. Judicious positioning of the coordinate axes minimizes computations. Here, by making the X-axis coincide with the 700-lb force, only the 500-lb force requires resolution into its X- and Y-component vectors; this resolution is shown in Fig. 2-7.

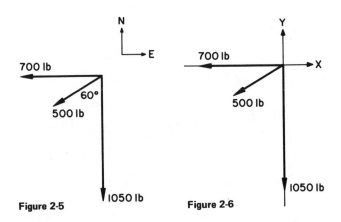

Figure 2-5   **Figure 2-6**

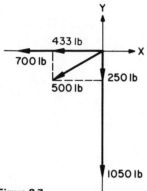
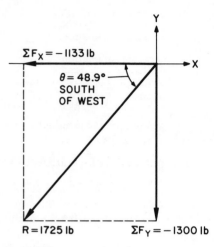

Figure 2-7

Figure 2-8

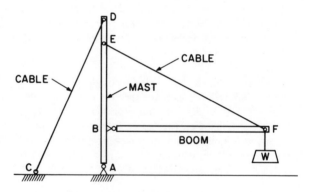

Figure 2-9

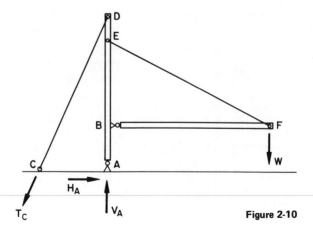

Figure 2-10

The coordinate summations are made:

X-coordinate summation: $\Sigma F_X = -700 - 500 \cos 30° = -1133$ lb

Y-coordinate summation: $\Sigma F_Y = -1050 - 500 \sin 30° = -1300$ lb

$R = \sqrt{(\Sigma F_X)^2 + (\Sigma F_Y)^2} = \sqrt{(1133)^2 + (1300)^2}$

$\quad = 1725$ lb *Answer*, part (a)

The position of the resultant with respect to the X-axis is determined below and shown in Fig. 2-8.

$\theta = \arctan \Sigma F_Y / \Sigma F_X = \arctan 1300/1133$

$\quad = 48.9°$ south of west *Answer*, part (b)

2-3 FREE-BODY DIAGRAM AND TYPES OF SUPPORT

The analysis of a force system is greatly facilitated by first drawing a free-body diagram. This diagram shows only the external forces that act upon the structure under consideration. Figure 2-9 shows a crane for which a free-body diagram is drawn in Fig. 2-10. The external forces acting on the crane consist of the pull force T_C, which assumes a position along the cable CD; the force of weight W applied to the boom at point F; and the reaction components H_A and V_A applied to the mast at pin connection A.

The free-body concept may be extended to individual members and joints of the structure. Figure 2-11 shows a free-body diagram of the boom wherein the reaction R_B is the force applied to the boom by the mast. Reaction R_B is not shown in Fig. 2-10 because there it is an internal force of the structure; this is also true for the force T_F applied to end F of the boom by cable EF. Reaction R_B, force T_F, and weight W are all forces that are external to and act upon the boom.

A free-body diagram of joint F is shown in Fig. 2-12 where reaction R_F is the force exerted by the boom on the joint. The force W exerted by the weight

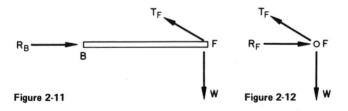

Figure 2-11　　　　　**Figure 2-12**

appears in each free-body diagram because in each case it is a force acting upon and external to the particular structure, member, or joint considered.

It is now appropriate to look at the possible types of support and the nature of the attendant reactions. The beam shown in Fig. 2-13 is roller supported at point A and supported by a hinge or pin connection at point B. The roller support at point A constrains movement only in the vertical downward direction. The pin connection at point B is constrained to remain stationary irrespective of the direction of the forces applied to the beam; this connection does permit rotation

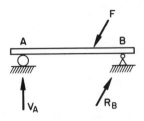

Figure 2-13

of the beam-end section. The reaction at point B may assume any direction depending upon the external forces applied to the beam and is, of course, replaceable by its vertical and horizontal components.

Problem 2-3 Evaluation of a concurrent force system

In Fig. 2-14 a loaded concrete transfer bucket weighing 4500 lb is transported by an overhead cable and a single-wheel trolley. The cable suspension points are 575 ft apart horizontally and the cable length is 600 ft. What is the tension in the cable when the bucket has been pulled to within 100 ft horizontally of a suspension point by a horizontal drag line fastened to the trolley? What is the pull on the drag line? Neglect the weight of the cable.

Solution:

This is a concurrent force system with the lines of action intersecting at point B. Point B is a roller connection and, for any particular point in the excursion of the bucket, the cable constrains movement of the bucket in only the vertical

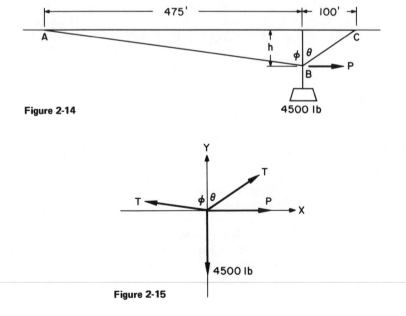

Figure 2-14

Figure 2-15

direction. Therefore, the tensile force in length AB is the same as in length BC and the vector diagram is drawn in Fig. 2-15.

The angles ϕ and θ, which establish the directions of T, must be determined.

$$\sin \phi = 475/L_{AB} \tag{2-1}$$
$$\sin \theta = 100/L_{BC} \tag{2-2}$$

Calculate L_{AB} and L_{BC}. From the statement of the problem

$$L_{AB} + L_{BC} = 600 \tag{2-3}$$

A second equation relating L_{AB} and L_{BC} is established using right-triangle properties.

$$h^2 + 475^2 = L_{AB}^2$$
$$h^2 + 100^2 = L_{BC}^2$$

Equate h^2,

$$L_{AB}^2 - 475^2 = L_{BC}^2 - 100^2$$
$$L_{AB}^2 - L_{BC}^2 = 216,000 \tag{2-4}$$

Solving Eqs. (2-3) and (2-4) simultaneously,

$$L_{AB} = 480 \text{ ft} \qquad L_{BC} = 120 \text{ ft}$$

and

$$\phi = \arcsin 475/L_{AB} = \arcsin 475/480 = 81.5^\circ$$
$$\theta = \arcsin 100/L_{BC} = \arcsin 100/120 = 56.5^\circ$$

The force system is concurrent and two equations of static equilibrium are available to solve for the two unknowns T and P. (Equilibrium in a coplanar concurrent force system is achieved when the sum of all the forces in the X-direction is zero and the sum of all the forces in the Y-direction is zero; thus, $\Sigma F_X = 0$ and $\Sigma F_Y = 0$. Also, the sum of all the moments taken about any point, whether or not on the body, is zero; thus $\Sigma M = 0$.)

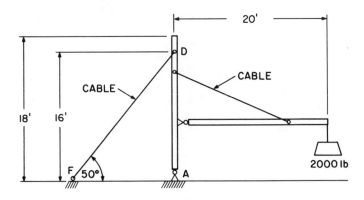

Figure 2-16

$$\Sigma F_Y = 0 \qquad T(\cos\theta) + T(\cos\phi) - 4500 = 0$$
$$T(\cos 56.5°) + T(\cos 81.5°) - 4500 = 0$$
$$T = 6430\ lb \qquad Answer$$

$$\Sigma F_X = 0 \qquad T(\sin\theta) - T(\sin\phi) + P = 0$$
$$T(\sin 56.5°) - T(\sin 81.5°) + P = 0$$
$$P = 997\ lb \qquad Answer$$

Problem 2-4 Evaluation of a nonconcurrent force system

In Fig. 2-16 the boom and mast of the crane weigh 50 lb/linear ft. Neglect the weights of the other members. A is a pin connection. Solve for the reactions at F and A.

Solution:

A free-body diagram is drawn in Fig. 2-17 in accordance with Sec. 2-3. Point A is a pin connection and the reaction may be replaced by its horizontal and vertical components as shown. The weight of the boom and mast are simulated by point loads applied at their respective centers of gravity. These weights are treated as external forces and are so depicted in the free-body diagram.

By drawing in the lines of action and examining their configuration, it is evident that the force system acting on the crane is nonconcurrent and non-parallel. Therefore, three equations of static equilibrium are available to solve for the three unknown reactions T_F, H_A, and V_A.

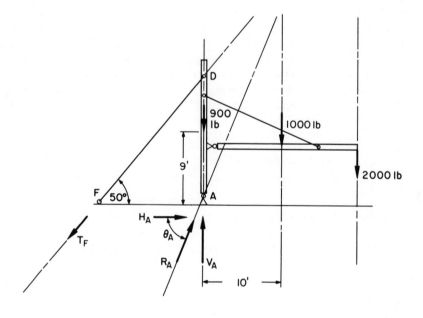

Figure 2-17

$$\pmb{\zeta} + \Sigma M_D = 0 \qquad 1000(10) + 2000(20) - H_A(16) = 0$$
$$H_A = 3120 \text{ lb}$$
$$\Sigma F_X = 0 \qquad H_A - T_F(\cos 50^\circ) = 3120 - T_F(\cos 50^\circ)$$
$$T_F = 4860 \text{ lb} \qquad Answer$$
$$\Sigma F_Y = 0 \qquad V_A - T_F(\sin 50^\circ) - 900 - 1000 - 2000 = 0$$
$$V_A = 7620 \text{ lb}$$

In applying $\Sigma M_D = 0$, point D was selected as a moment center because it eliminated unknowns T_F and V_A from the moment equation.

The calculations resulted in positive values that indicate that the positions assumed in the free-body diagram are correct. The magnitude and direction of the reaction at A are determined from the components H_A and V_A.

$$R_A = \sqrt{H_A{}^2 + V_A{}^2} = \sqrt{(3120)^2 + (7620)^2}$$

$$= 8230 \text{ lb} \qquad Answer$$

$$\theta_A = \arctan V_A/H_A = \arctan 7620/3120$$

$$= 67.8^\circ \qquad Answer$$

2-4 TRUSSES

Trusses are comprised of bars that are pin connected at their ends to form a succession of triangles. These end connections are called joints or panel points. All loads applied to the truss are assumed to act at the panel points causing the bars to be stressed in axial tension or compression without associated lateral loading between joints. The direction of the force that a bar exerts on the panel point to which it is connected is therefore defined by the bar position. A roof truss is shown in Fig. 2-18 to familiarize the reader with necessary nomenclature.

Snow loads are sometimes given as pounds per horizontal square foot of roof, in which event the area used to compute the roof loading is defined by the projection of the roof area in a horizontal plane. The snow load is transmitted by the purlins to the upper panel points where it is applied to the truss as vertical point loads. Wind loads are assumed to act normal to the roof surface.

The forces in a truss may be analytically determined using either the method of joints or the method of sections. The following problems will illustrate each method.

Problem 2-5 Analysis of a truss using the method of joints

The Fink-type truss shown in Fig. 2-19 is subjected to a snow load of 40 lb/ft² of horizontal projection. If the bay length is 15 ft and the purlins are at panel points only, calculate the stresses in all the members due to full snow load. Indicate the magnitude and type of stress directly on a sketch of the truss.

Solution:

It will be assumed that the truss is roller supported at L_3. If this assumption is not made, the support reactions would have horizontal components induced by the

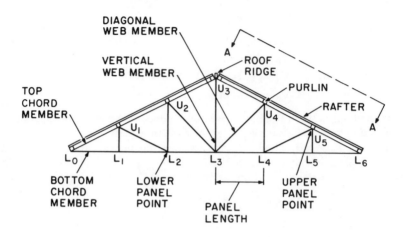

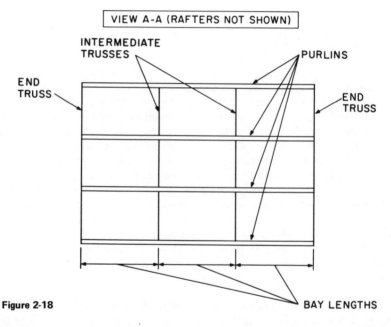

Figure 2-18

BAY LENGTHS

bending action of the truss in response to the applied load. Each end reaction would comprise two unknown components; this would render their solution by the equations of static equilibrium impossible.

Assume that the truss in question is an intermediate truss. Consequently, it will support the snow load between it and the two adjacent trusses equally. The effective area of snow loading is defined by the projection of the roof area in a horizontal plane and is $(15)(40) = 600$ sq ft. The total snow load is therefore 24,000 lb. The 24,000-lb load is transmitted to the upper panel points by the

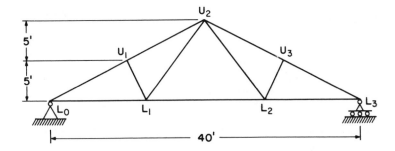

Figure 2-19

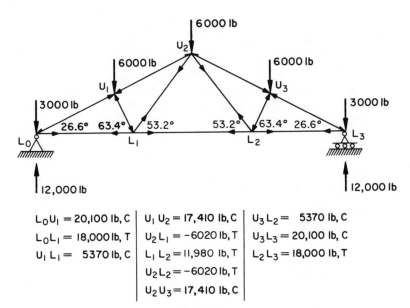

$L_0U_1 = 20,100$ lb, C	$U_1U_2 = 17,410$ lb, C	$U_3L_2 = 5370$ lb, C
$L_0L_1 = 18,000$ lb, T	$U_2L_1 = -6020$ lb, T	$U_3L_3 = 20,100$ lb, C
$U_1L_1 = 5370$ lb, C	$L_1L_2 = 11,980$ lb, T	$L_2L_3 = 18,000$ lb, T
	$U_2L_2 = -6020$ lb, T	
	$U_2U_3 = 17,410$ lb, C	

Figure 2-20

purlins, as shown in Fig. 2-20. Since the load is symmetrical, each reaction supports one half the load.

The method of joints is applied by considering each joint separately and determining the unknown forces acting upon it. Since the forces acting on a joint are concurrent, only two unknowns may be determined at each joint. It is therefore essential that the computations originate at either L_0 or L_3. Begin at L_0 and refer to Fig. 2-21.

$$\Sigma F_Y = 0 \qquad -3000 - L_0U_1 \sin 26.6° + 12,000 = 0$$
$$L_0U_1 = 20,100 \text{ lb, C} \qquad \textit{Answer}$$
$$\Sigma F_H = 0 \qquad -L_0U_1 \cos 26.6° + L_0L_1 = 0$$
$$L_0L_1 = 18,000 \text{ lb, T} \qquad \textit{Answer}$$

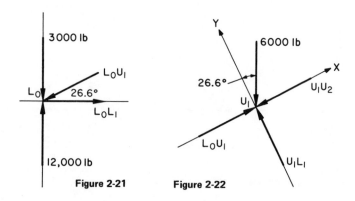

Figure 2-21   Figure 2-22

$L_0 U_1$ was assumed to be in compression and is shown pushing against L_0. $L_0 L_1$ was assumed to be in tension and is shown pulling at L_0. The correctness of these assumptions is confirmed by the calculated positive force values.

Joint U_1 is considered next, as seen in Fig. 2-22, since only two of the forces, $U_1 U_2$ and $U_1 L_1$, acting there are unknown. The force in member $L_0 U_1$ was determined as compressive; it is therefore shown as pushing against joint U_1. Computations are made less tedious by positioning the coordinate axes so that an unknown force member lies on an axis.

Considering joint U_1:

$\Sigma F_X = 0$ $20,100 - 6000 \sin 26.6° - U_1 U_2 = 0$

$\qquad\qquad U_1 U_2 = 17,410$ lb, C   *Answer*

$\Sigma F_Y = 0$ $U_1 L_1 - 6000 \cos 26.6° = 0$

$\qquad\qquad U_1 L_1 = 5370$ lb, C   *Answer*

Consider next joint L_1:

$\Sigma F_V = 0$ $-5370 \sin 63.4° - U_2 L_1 \sin 53.2° = 0$

$\qquad\qquad U_2 L_1 = -6020$ lb, T   *Answer*

$\Sigma F_H = 0$ $L_1 L_2 - L_0 L_1 + U_1 L_1 \cos 63.4° - U_2 L_1 \cos 53.2° = 0$

$\qquad\qquad L_1 L_2 - 18,000 + 5370 \cos 63.4° - (-6020) \cos 53.2° = 0$

$\qquad\qquad L_1 L_2 = 11,980$ lb, T   *Answer*

Here a negative value is calculated for member $U_2 L_1$. This indicates that the member was assumed incorrectly to be in compression in Fig. 2-23. Member $U_2 L_1$ is actually in tension and is shown pulling at its connecting joints in Fig. 2-20.

The bar configuration and loading are symmetrical about the truss center. It is therefore unnecessary to make further computations. The force in member $L_0 U_1$ is the same as the force in member $U_3 L_3$, etc. The correct force magnitude and type, either compressive or tensile, for each member is shown in Fig. 2-20.

For an unsymmetrical loading the computations can be continued by considering in turn the remaining joints. If joint L_3 is evaluated last, a vertical and horizontal summation there will total zero provided that the preceding calculations have determined accurately the force in members $U_3 L_3$ and $L_2 L_3$.

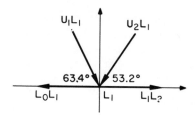

Figure 2-23

Problem 2-6 Analysis of a truss using the method of sections

Determine the magnitude and kind of stress in each of the three members BH, BC, and GD of the pin-connected truss shown in Fig. 2-24.

Solution:

The method of sections is applied by passing a plane through the truss at a location that includes the member or members requiring solution. The two truss sections are separated and their equilibrium is sustained by applying axial forces to the cut members; these axial forces may be assumed to be either tensile or compressive. An incorrect assumption will result in a correct numerical value prefixed with a minus sign. Since the equations of equilibrium can be used to determine no more than three unknowns, the plane must be passed so that is separates the truss into two sections without cutting more than three members. The truss section requiring the fewer computations is made the subject of evaluation; this section is usually subjected to fewer external loads.

It is first necessary to determine the reactions. The truss is assumed to be roller supported at joint E for the same reasons stated in Problem 2-5. Since all loads are vertical, there is no horizontal reaction component at joint A.

$$\circlearrowleft + \Sigma M_E = 0 \qquad R_L(40) - 300(30) - 400(20) = 0$$
$$R_L = 425 \text{ lb}$$
$$\circlearrowleft + \Sigma M_A = 0 \qquad -R_R(40) + 400(20) + 300(10) = 0$$
$$R_R = 275 \text{ lb}$$

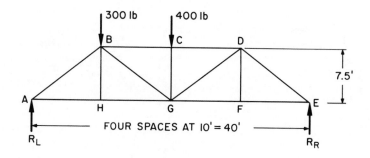

Figure 2-24

(a) *Member GD:*

Pass plane gd through the truss and separate the truss sections, as shown in Fig. 2-25. Apply an axial tensile force to each cut member to sustain the equilibrium of the two truss sections. The right-hand truss section is evaluated and T_{GD} resolved into its vertical and horizontal components. Apply the equilibrium condition: $\Sigma F_V = 0$, thereby eliminating the other unknowns T_{CD} and T_{GF}.

$$275 - T_{GD} \sin 36.8° = 0$$

$$T_{GD} = 458 \text{ lb, T} \qquad Answer$$

(b) *Member BC:*

Pass plane bc through the truss and separate the truss sections, as shown in Fig. 2-26. The equilibrium-sustaining forces are applied and the left-hand truss section is evaluated. Extend the lines of action of forces T_{BG} and T_{HG} until they intersect; this intersection forms a convenient moment center that eliminates these forces from the equilibrium equation. Apply the equilibrium equation:

$$\mathcal{C}+ \Sigma M_G' = 0 \qquad 425(20) - 300(10) + T_{BC}(7.5) = 0$$

$$T_{BC} = 733 \text{ lb, C} \qquad Answer$$

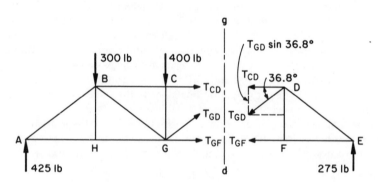

Figure 2-25

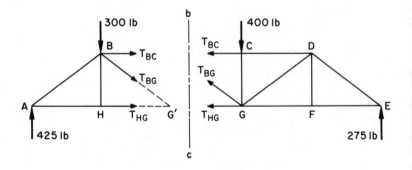

Figure 2-26

(c) *Member BH:*

Pass plane bh through the truss and separate the truss sections as shown in Fig. 2-27. A moment summation about point A will show that member BH experiences no load.

This result could have been ascertained quickly by considering joint H separately. Since there are no vertical components of other forces at joint H, a vertical summation must yield zero force in member BH.   *Answer*

It is usually desirable to use the method of joints where the force in each truss member is required. If the force in only selected members requires solution, it is more convenient to use the method of sections. It is occasionally expeditious to apply both methods to the same problem, as indicated in the solution of member BH in Problem 2-6.

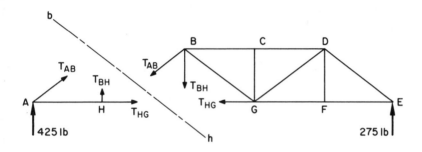

Figure 2-27

2-5   THREE-FORCE MEMBERS

In Sec. 2-4 reaction forces acting at pin connections within the truss structure were determined by evaluating free-body diagrams of individual joints as in the Method of Joints or by passing a cutting plane through the truss and evaluating the free-body diagram of the truss section on one side of the cutting plane as in the Method of Sections. These methods are based on the supposition that the lines of action of the reaction forces acting at opposite ends of an individual member are coincident with its longitudinal axis.

However, it is often necessary to know the reaction forces at the connecting pins of laterally loaded individual members within a structure, e.g., it could be required to determine the reactions acting on member BC of Fig. 2-28(A). The member is acted upon by lateral load P between joints. Consequently, the reaction forces do *not* assume lines of action coincident with the longitudinal axis, as indicated by Fig. 2-28(B). Such a member is known as a three-force member and the methods of Sec. 2-4 are therefore not applicable. Another means for evaluation must be used.

The reactions in Fig. 2-28(B) are shown represented by their vertical and horizontal components. Horizontal components appear at both ends because of the restraint imposed on longitudinal movement by the pinned end connections.

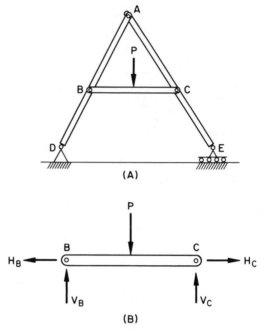

(A)

(B)

Figure 2-28

Although the member by itself is statically indeterminate (there are more unknowns than equations of static equilibrium), a solution is obtained by drawing a free-body diagram for each of the other members comprising the structure. By writing the equilibrium equations for each member, a number of equations equal to the number of unknowns is obtained. The solution can usually be facilitated by drawing a free-body diagram of the composite structure and calculating the external reactions. The procedure will be applied in the following problem.

Problem 2-7 Structure comprising three-force members

A pipe weighing 20 lb/ft is supported every 30 ft by a small frame, as shown in Fig. 2-29. (a) Determine the components of the reactions and the components of the force exerted at B on member AB. (b) Prove the forces at A, D, and B concurrent.

Solution:

(a) A free-body diagram of the frame considered as an entity is drawn in Fig. 2-30. The reactions at A and C are equal because the load distribution is symmetrical. The vertical reaction components acting at A and C are determined.

$$\Sigma F_Y = 0 \qquad 2V_A - 600 = 0$$
$$V_A = V_C = 300 \text{ lb} \uparrow \qquad Answer$$

The reaction at B and the horizontal reaction components at A and C are found by evaluating the force systems of the individual elements of the frame.

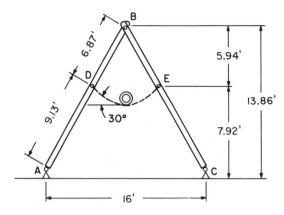

Figure 2-29

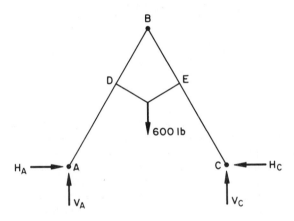

Figure 2-30

A free-body diagram is drawn in Fig. 2-31 for each member together with a third free-body diagram comprising the pipe support chain and its load.

The connection at point B is a pinned connection and the force exerted on member AB by member BC is represented by components V_B and H_B. Since member AB exerts the same force on member BC, the components applied to the latter are the same but act in the opposite direction.

The pipe and chain form a roller connection.

$$\Sigma F_Y = 0 \qquad T \sin 30° + T \sin 30° - 600 = 0$$
$$T = 600 \text{ lb}$$

A moment summation is taken about point B of member AB to determine the horizontal reaction component H_A. Because of symmetry, the horizontal reaction component H_C at C is equal in magnitude but opposite in direction to H_A.

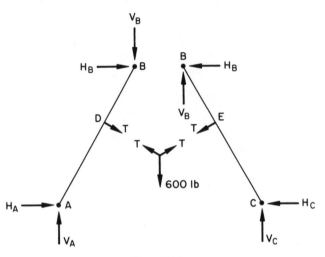

Figure 2-31

$$\circlearrowleft + \Sigma M_B = 0 \quad V_A(8) - H_A(13.86) - T(6.87) = 0$$
$$H_A = -124.1 \text{ lb}$$

The minus sign indicates that the direction of H_A is opposite to that assumed in the free-body diagram.

$$H_A = 124.1 \text{ lb} \leftarrow \qquad Answer$$
$$H_C = 124.1 \text{ lb} \rightarrow \qquad Answer$$

Again considering member AB and applying the conditions of equilibrium, $\Sigma F_X = 0$ and $\Sigma F_Y = 0$.

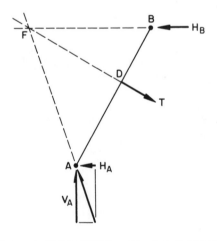

Figure 2-32

$$\Sigma F_X = 0 \qquad H_A + T \cos 30° + H_B = 0$$
$$-124.1 + 600(0.866) + H_B = 0$$
$$H_B = -395 \text{ lb}$$
$$= 395 \text{ lb} \leftarrow \qquad Answer$$

Observe that the value of H_A used in this equation is the same as that found for its initially assumed direction.

$$\Sigma F_Y = 0 \qquad V_A - T \sin 30° - V_B = 0$$
$$300 - 600(0.500) - V_B = 0$$
$$V_B = 0 \qquad Answer$$

(b) The forces applied to member AB at A, D, and B are concurrent if their lines of action intersect at a common point. Consider Fig. 2-32 wherein the forces are shown acting in the directions determined above. When the lines of action are extended, they all intersect at point F.

2-6 PROPERTIES OF AN AREA

Of special importance are the moment of an area, the moment of inertia of an area, and the radius of gyration. In many of the examples in this section and in subsequent chapters, reference will be made to the American Institute of Steel Construction (AISC) Manual, which contains data concerning the properties of most steel members and common geometric sections.

Moment of an Area

The moment of an area about a particular reference axis is given by the product of the area and the perpendicular distance between the area centroid and the reference axis. In Fig. 2-33 $M_X = Ay_c$ is the expression for the moment of area A with respect to the X-axis, and $M_Y = Ax_c$ is the expression for the moment of area A with respect to the Y-axis.

The centroid of an area is the point at which the total area acts and is analogous to the center of gravity of a solid body. Often it is required to determine the

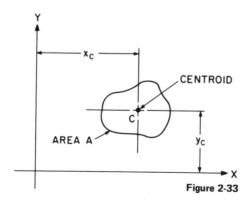

Figure 2-33

centroid of a composite area comprising several defined areas. The area moment of the composite area is equal to the algebraic sum of the area moments of the several defined areas. This is expressed by

$$Ax_c = \sum_{n=1}^{n=p} a_n x_{cn} \tag{2-5}$$

$$Ay_c = \sum_{n=1}^{n=p} a_n y_{cn} \tag{2-6}$$

where   A = total area

x_c = X-coordinate of centroid of composite area

y_c = Y-coordinate of centroid of composite area

x_{cn} = X-coordinate of centroid of an individual area

y_{cn} = Y-coordinate of centroid of an individual area

a_n = area of an individual area

In applying these equations, care must be taken to associate the proper sign with the centroid coordinates as required by the centroid location with respect to the reference axes.

Problem 2-8 Centroid of a composite area

With reference to the coordinate axes X and Y, locate the centroid of the area of the plane figure shown in Fig. 2-34.

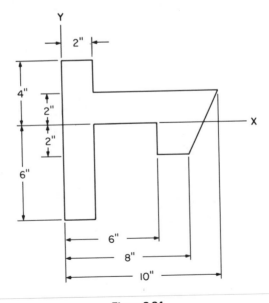

Figure 2-34

Solution:

The area may be divided into the three rectangles and a triangle shown in Fig. 2-35. The individual area centroids and their distances from the coordinate axes are also shown.

$$Ax_c = \sum_{n=1}^{n=p} a_n x_{cn} \tag{2-5}$$

$$(a_1 + a_2 + a_3 + a_4)x_c = a_1 x_{c1} + a_2 x_{c2} + a_3 x_{c3} + a_4 x_{c4}$$

$$(20 + 8 + 8 + 4)x_c = (20)(1) + (8)(4) + (8)(7) + (4)(8\tfrac{2}{3})$$

$$x_c = 3.57 \text{ in.} \qquad \textit{Answer}$$

$$Ay_c = \sum_{n=1}^{n=p} a_n y_{cn} \tag{2-6}$$

$$(20 + 8 + 8 + 4)y_c = (20)(-1) + (8)(1) + (8)(0) + (4)(\tfrac{2}{3})$$

$$y_c = -0.233 \text{ in.} \qquad \textit{Answer}$$

Problem 2-9 Centroidal axis of a composite section

The area shown in Fig. 2-36 is the cross section of a machine part that is subjected to flexural stresses. Find the location of the centroidal axis OX above the base.

Solution:

The centroidal axis passes through the centroid of the composite section. The determination of the y_c-coordinate for the composite section therefore locates the centroidal axis OX. The cross section is divided into three rectangles as shown

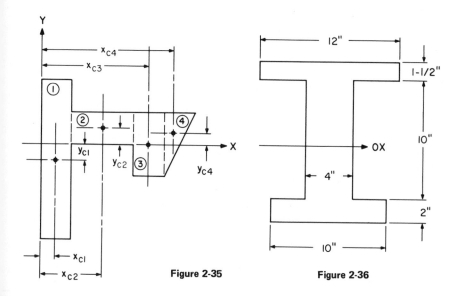

Figure 2-35   **Figure 2-36**

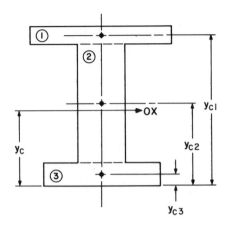

Figure 2-37

in Fig. 2-37 and Eq. (2-6) is applied with the base axis X taken as the area moment reference.

$$Ay_c = \sum_{n=1}^{n=p} a_n y_{cn} \qquad (2\text{-}6)$$

$$(a_1 + a_2 + a_3)y_c = a_1 y_{c1} + a_2 y_{c2} + a_3 y_{c3}$$
$$(18 + 40 + 20)y_c = (18)(12.75) + (40)(7) + (20)(1)$$
$$y_c = 6.78 \text{ in.} \quad \textit{Answer}$$

Problem 2-10 Centroid of a built-up section

A steel column is composed of the elements shown in Fig. 2-38. Locate the centroid of the composite section.

Solution:

Reference axes X and Y are positioned as shown in Fig. 2-39. Since the section is symmetrical about the Y-axis, the x_c-coordinate of the centroid is located on

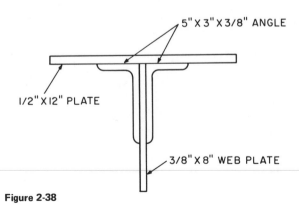

5" X 3" X 3/8" ANGLE

1/2" X 12" PLATE

3/8" X 8" WEB PLATE

Figure 2-38

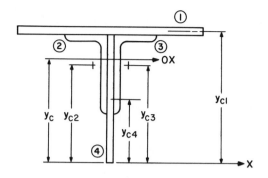

Figure 2-39

this axis. The y_c-coordinate is not ascertainable by inspection and must be calculated. The centroid and area data for the angles are found in the AISC Manual.

$$Ay_c = \sum_{n=1}^{n=p} a_n y_{cn} \qquad (2\text{-}6)$$

$$(a_1 + a_2 + a_3 + a_4)y_c = a_1 y_{c1} + a_2 y_{c2} + a_3 y_{c3} + a_4 y_{c4}$$
$$(6 + 2.86 + 2.86 + 3)y_c = (6)(8.25) + (2.86)(6.3) + (2.86)(6.3) + (3)(4)$$
$$y_c = 6.61 \text{ in.} \qquad Answer$$

Moment of Inertia of an Area

The moment of inertia of an area about the X-axis is given by: $I_{OX} + Ay_c^2$; this is the sum of the moment of inertia of the area about its own centroidal axis OX plus the product of its area and the square of the perpendicular distance between the OX- and X-axes. The moment of inertia thus expressed is shown in Fig. 2-40 together with the moment of inertia of the area about the Y-axis.

The moment of inertia about the X- and Y-axes of a composite area comprising several defined areas is given by

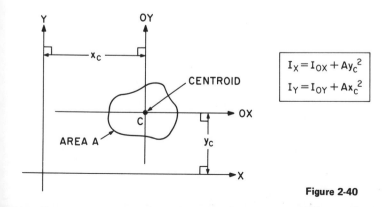

$$I_X = I_{OX} + Ay_c^2$$
$$I_Y = I_{OY} + Ax_c^2$$

Figure 2-40

$$I_X = \sum_{n=1}^{n=p} I_{OXn} + \sum_{n=1}^{n=p} a_n y_{cn}^2 \tag{2-7}$$

$$I_Y = \sum_{n=1}^{n=p} I_{OYn} + \sum_{n=1}^{n=p} a_n x_{cn}^2 \tag{2-8}$$

where I_{OXn} = moment of inertia of individual area n about its centroidal axis parallel to X-axis

I_{OYn} = moment of inertia of individual area n about its centroidal axis parallel to Y-axis

a_n = area of individual area n

x_{cn} = X-coordinate of centroid of individual area n

y_{cn} = Y-coordinate of centroid of individual area n

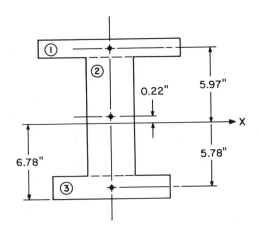

Figure 2-41

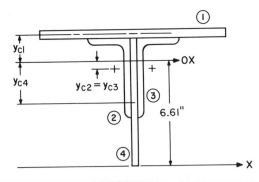

Figure 2-42

Problem 2-11 Moment of inertia of a composite area

For the cross section of Problem 2-9, find the moment of inertia with respect to the axis OX.

Solution:

In Problem 2-9 the centroidal axis OX of the composite cross section was found to be 6.78 in. above the base axis X. See Fig. 2-41. The moment of inertia with respect to axis OX is found by applying Eq. (2-7). The expression for the moment of inertia of an individual rectangular area is given in the AISC Manual.

$$I_X = \sum_{n=1}^{n=p} I_{OXn} + \sum_{n=1}^{n=p} a_n y_{cn}^2 \qquad (2\text{-}7)$$

$$I_{OX} = \sum_{n=1}^{n=3} I_{OXn} + \sum_{n=1}^{n=3} a_n y_{cn}^2$$

$$= I_{OX1} + I_{OX2} + I_{OX3} + a_1 y_{c1}^2 + a_2 y_{c2}^2 + a_3 y_{c3}^2$$

$$= \frac{12(1.5)^3}{12} + \frac{4(10)^3}{12} + \frac{10(2)^3}{12} + (18)(5.97)^2 + (40)(0.22)^2$$

$$+ (20)(-5.78)^2$$

$$= 1656 \text{ in.}^4 \qquad Answer$$

Problem 2-12 Moment of inertia of a built-up section

Find the moment of inertia about the centroidal axis OX for the built-up tee section of Problem 2-10.

Solution:

In Problem 2-10 the centroidal axis OX of the composite built-up section was found to be 6.61 in. above the X-axis. See Fig. 2-42. The moment of inertia with respect to axis OX is found by applying Eq. (2-7). The moment of inertia of the 5 X 3 X 3/8 in. angle about its centroidal axis is given in the AISC Manual.

$$I_X = \sum_{n=1}^{n=p} I_{OXn} + \sum_{n=1}^{n=p} a_n y_{cn}^2 \qquad (2\text{-}7)$$

$$I_{OX} = \sum_{n=1}^{n=4} I_{OXn} + \sum_{n=1}^{n=4} a_n y_{cn}^2$$

$$= I_{OX1} + I_{OX2} + I_{OX3} + I_{OX4} + a_1 y_{c1}^2 + a_2 y_{c2}^2 + a_3 y_{c3}^2 + a_4 y_{c4}^2$$

$$= \frac{(12)(0.5)^3}{12} + 7.4 + 7.4 + \frac{(3/8)(8)^3}{12} + (6)(1.64)^2 + (2.86)(-0.31)^2$$

$$+ (2.86)(-0.31)^2 + (3)(-2.61)^2$$

$$= 68 \text{ in.}^4 \qquad Answer$$

Radius of Gyration

The radius of gyration of an area is a concept related to the moment of inertia. The area A in Fig. 2-43 has a moment of inertia I_X about the X-axis. Now assume that the area A is distributed along a horizontal line of infinite extent. The line is parallel to the X-axis and positioned so that the moment of inertia of the distributed area A about the X-axis is also equal to I_X. The perpendicular distance r_X between the line of infinite extent and the X-axis is the radius of gyration of the area A with respect to the X-axis and is given by

$$r_X = \sqrt{I_X/A} \tag{2-9}$$

The selection of the distance r_X is quite arbitrary and is done for the specific purpose of establishing a relation that expresses the moment of inertia of an area about a given axis in terms of its area A.

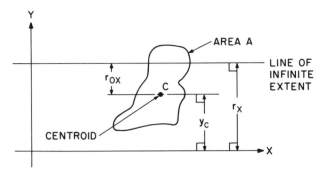

Figure 2-43

Most often and especially in column work, the radius of gyration required is that taken with respect to the centroidal axis of the transverse cross-sectional area of a column. For the area of Fig. 2-43, the radius of gyration of the area A with respect to its own centroidal axis OX is given by

$$r_{OX} = \sqrt{I_{OX}/A} \tag{2-10}$$

chapter 3
DYNAMICS

3-1 FRICTION

Friction is a force that resists the relative motion between two bodies in contact. The direction of the force is always opposite to the direction of relative motion, or impending relative motion. It always acts perpendicular to the normal forces at the surface of contact.

The coefficient of friction μ is the ratio of the frictional force F to the normal force N at the point of contact.

$\mu = F/N$

The value of μ is determined experimentally and depends on the materials in contact. If relative motion is merely impending, one speaks of the coefficient of static friction. Values are usually given or determined from handbooks. For bodies in motion μ is the coefficient of kinetic friction. The latter value is normally much smaller than the former.

The reaction R of one body to another is the vector sum of the normal and frictional forces, as seen in Fig. 3-1,

$$\mathbf{R} = \mathbf{F} + \mathbf{N} \qquad R = \sqrt{F^2 + N^2} \qquad \tan a = F/N = \mu$$

For static equilibrium, the sum of all the forces W, N, μN, and F must be zero.

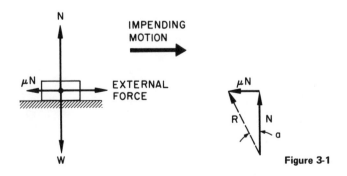

Figure 3-1

Angle a, shown in Fig. 3-1, is called the angle of friction. It is the angle between the reaction and the normal force.

The angle of repose b is the maximum angle to which a plane with an object thereon may be raised relative to a horizontal plane before the object starts sliding. It is equal to the angle of friction a; see Fig. 3-2.

Problem 3-1 Friction force of block on inclined plane

Determine the magnitude of the horizontal force P, as shown in Fig. 3-3, which will just prevent the block from sliding down the inclined plane. The coefficient of friction is 0.15. The block weighs 10 lb.

Solution:

Sketch the block as a free body, as shown in Fig. 3-4; assume all forces to act through its center of gravity. The only unknown forces are N and P. The equilibrium equations in the horizontal and vertical direction are used to determine the unknowns.

$\Sigma F_X = 0$ $P + 0.15N \cos 20° - N \sin 20° = 0$

$\Sigma F_Y = 0$ $0.15N \sin 20° + N \cos 20° - 10 = 0$

Solving simultaneously,

$P = 2.03$ lb   *Answer*

The closed vector polygon, as seen in Fig. 3-5, may also be drawn to find the answer graphically or as a check on the above solution.

Problem 3-2 Friction force of block with uniform velocity on inclined plane

Find the coefficient of sliding friction if the 13-lb weight pulls the 20-lb block up the inclined plane with a uniform velocity. Assume the pulley is frictionless. (See Fig. 3-6.)

Solution:

This problem is similar to the previous problem because a body in uniform motion is essentially in static equilibrium since it experiences no acceleration.

Draw a free-body diagram of the block indicating all forces, as shown in Fig. 3-7. Note the alignment of the X- and Y-axes. The tension T in the cable is equal to the weight W, i.e., 13 lb.

$\Sigma F_X = 0$ $13 - \mu N - 20 \sin 30° = 0$

$\Sigma F_Y = 0$ $N - 20 \cos 30° = 0$

$N = 17.32$ lb   and $\mu = 0.174$ *Answer*

Another problem of a similar nature concerns the raising or lowering of loads by means of a screw. The problem is essentially that of an inclined plane. The force is applied horizontally. Typically the problem involves a question of efficiency, i.e., the ratio of output to input. The pitch of a screw is the height through which a load is raised (or lowered) during one revolution of the screw.

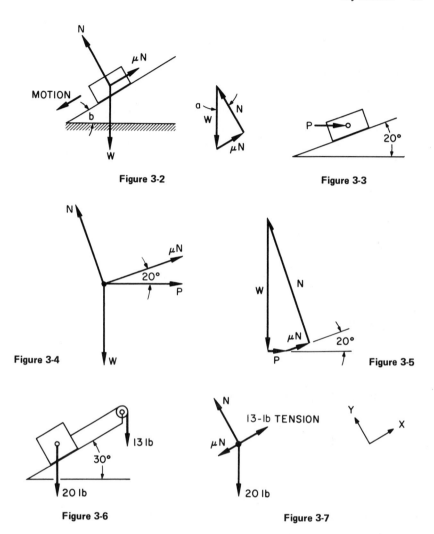

Figure 3-2

Figure 3-3

Figure 3-4

Figure 3-5

Figure 3-6

Figure 3-7

Problem 3-3 Jack screw efficiency and coefficient of friction

A square-threaded jack screw is used to raise a 2800-lb load. 4 hp is required to raise the load at 30 ft/min. The thread has a 1-in. pitch and a 1.5-in. pitch diameter. Determine the efficiency of the thread and the coefficient of friction.

Solution:

The efficiency can be determined either as the ratio of the output horsepower (2800)(30)/33,000 to the input horsepower or as a ratio of output energy to input energy.

Efficiency = (2800)(30)/(33,000)(4) = 0.635 = 63.5%

With an efficiency of 63.5%, the horizontal force F required to raise the load 1 in. is determined; see Fig. 3-8. Here 1.5π represents the pitch circumference.

$$0.635 = (2800)(1)/F(1.5\pi)$$
$$F = 936 \text{ lb}$$

To solve for the coefficient of friction, the equilibrium conditions are set up similar to those in Problem 3-2; see Fig. 3-9.

$$\cos a = (1.5\pi)/\sqrt{(1.5\pi)^2 + 1^2} = 0.976$$
$$\sin a = 1/\sqrt{(1.5\pi)^2 + 1^2} = 0.207$$
$$\Sigma F_H = 0 \qquad F - N\sin a - \mu N \cos a = 0$$
$$\Sigma F_V = 0 \qquad N\cos a - W - \mu N \sin a = 0$$

where W = 2800 lb and F = 936 lb.

Solving simultaneously,

$$\mu = 0.114 \qquad Answer$$

Note: When lowering the load, the direction of the friction force μN is reversed. The direction of the horizontal force F may or may not need reversal depending on whether or not the screw is overhauling. The screw will overhaul if μ is less than tan a.

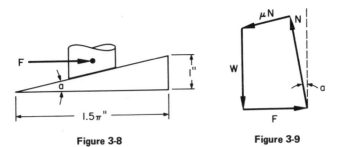

Figure 3-8   Figure 3-9

3-2   KINEMATICS

Kinematics is merely the study of motion without regard to the causes of the motion. Of particular interest are the position, displacement, velocity, acceleration, or pulse of a particle or a body. A particle is undergoing *plane motion* if its position at any time can be fully described in a two-dimensional coordinate system, as the rectangular coordinate system (X,Y) or the polar system (R,θ). A rigid body is in plane motion if all its particles are likewise in plane motion.

The *displacement* of a particle is the vector difference between its second and first position. The *velocity* of a particle is the ratio of its displacement s to the time interval during which displacement occurred.

$$v_{avg} = \Delta s/\Delta t \qquad \text{and} \qquad v_{inst} = \lim_{\Delta t \to 0} \Delta s/\Delta t = ds/dt$$

Acceleration and *pulse* are similarly defined, thus:

$$a_{avg} = \Delta v/\Delta t \qquad a_{inst} = dv/dt = d^2s/dt^2$$
$$P_{avg} = \Delta a/\Delta t \qquad P_{inst} = da/dt = d^3s/dt^3$$

For constant acceleration, $da/dt = 0$; therefore pulse = 0. This is exemplified by the constant acceleration of a freely falling body near the earth's surface. Constant acceleration indicates that the ratio of velocity change to time is constant as given by

$$dv/dt = a \qquad \therefore v = \int a \, dt = at + c_1$$

where c_1 = first constant of integration.

The relation between displacement and time for constant acceleration is given by

$$s = \int v \, dt = \int (at + c_1) \, dt = at^2/2 + c_1 t + c_2$$

For an initial displacement s_0 and an initial velocity v_0, the following formulas may be derived:

$$s = s_0 + v_0 t + at^2/2 = s_0 + (v + v_0)t/2$$
$$v = v_0 + at \qquad v^2 = v_0^2 + 2as$$

where s and v represent displacement and velocity at time t. The acceleration a will have any value given in a problem. In the earth's gravitational field, it is usually taken as 32.2 ft/sec^2.

3-3   MOTION OF A PROJECTILE

In determining the motion of a projectile, it is customary to assume motion unaffected by friction (but note if statements for other assumptions are made). The easiest method for solving these problems is to resolve the motion into horizontal (X) and vertical components (Y). For free flight $a_X = 0$, $a_Y = -g$ if the upward direction is assumed positive.

Problem 3-4 Motion of a projectile

A ball is thrown upward at an angle of $40°$ with the horizontal and a velocity of 80 ft/sec. How far from its initial position will it be after 2 sec? At what time will it reach its highest position?

Solution:

The initial velocity is given, and the initial distance is 0. $a_X = 0$, $a_Y = -32.2 \text{ ft/} sec^2$. Resolving the motion into X- and Y-components:

$$s_X = s_{OX} + v_{OX} t + a_X t^2/2 = v_{OX} t$$
$$v_{OX} = 80 \cos 40° = 61.4 \text{ ft/sec}$$
$$s_Y = s_{OY} + v_{OY} t + a_Y t^2/2$$
$$v_{OY} = 80 \sin 40° = 51.5 \text{ ft/sec}$$
$$s_Y = 51.5t - 16.1t^2$$

At the end of 2 sec,

$$s_X = (61.4)2 = 122.8 \text{ ft}$$
$$s_Y = (51.5)2 - (16.1)2^2 = 38.6 \text{ ft}$$
$$s = \sqrt{s_X^2 + s_Y^2} = 128.8 \text{ ft} \qquad Answer$$

At the highest elevation, $v_Y = 0$ or $ds_Y/dt = 0$

$$ds_Y/dt = 51.5 - 32.2t = 0$$
$$t = 51.5/32.2 = 1.6 \text{ sec} \qquad Answer$$

3-4   CIRCULAR AND SIMPLE HARMONIC MOTION

The formulas for circular (angular) motion are similar to those for straight-line motion. For example, the basic formulas for constant angular acceleration α are

$$d\omega/dt = \alpha \qquad \therefore \omega = \int \alpha \, dt = \alpha t + c_1$$
$$\theta = \int \omega \, dt = \alpha t^2/2 + c_1 t + c_2$$

where ω = angular velocity, rad/sec, and θ = angular displacement, rad.

In determining the instantaneous linear motion for a body moving in a circular (or curved) path, it must be remembered that if a change in either direction or magnitude of the velocity vector occurs there must be an accompanying acceleration. Thus a body moving with constant angular velocity still experiences a change in direction and the centripetal or inward-directed acceleration.

Peripheral or tangential velocity: $v = \omega r$

Centripetal acceleration: $a_n = \omega^2 r = v^2/r$

Tangential acceleration: $a_T = \alpha r$ if $\alpha \neq 0$

Total acceleration of a body moving along a curved path with angular acceleration
$$= \sqrt{a_T^2 + a_n^2}$$

In simple harmonic motion (S.H.M.) a body moves with a prescribed periodic motion along a straight line so that its acceleration a is always negatively proportional to its displacement x from its equilibrium position: $a = d^2x/dt^2 = -cx$

In Fig. 3-10 point P moves with constant angular velocity ω in a circle of radius r. The reflection of this motion onto diameter AB constitutes S.H.M. This is also the component of motion in the X-direction. If $t = 0$ when $\theta = 0$, then

$$x = r \cos \omega t = \text{displacement along AB}$$
$$dx/dt = -\omega r \sin \omega t = \text{velocity along AB}$$
$$d^2x/dt^2 = -\omega^2 r \cos \omega t = -\omega^2 x = \text{acceleration along AB}$$

Note that the displacement and acceleration reach maximum values at A and B where the velocity = 0. Conversely the velocity is maximum at the origin. The amplitude of the motion equals the radius of the circle r. The frequency of the periodic motion is often given in cycles per second n, so that $\omega = 2\pi n$ and $x = r \cos 2\pi n t$. The period T of a S.H.M. is given by $T = 2\pi/\omega$. Vibration problems depend for their analysis on an understanding of S.H.M.

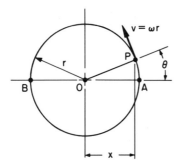

Figure 3-10

3-5 RELATIVE MOTION

When two particles A and B move independently but simultaneously with respect to a fixed reference system, they have relative motion with respect to each other. Usually the fixed system is assumed to be the earth G. Thus the relative velocity of B with respect to A is given by $V_{B/A} = V_{B/G} - V_{A/G}$. (See Fig. 3-11). $V_{B/G}$ and $V_{A/G}$ represent the velocity of B and A with respect to the fixed system, respectively. Since velocities are vector quantities, it is often convenient to resolve these into rectangular components. For plane motion,

$$(V_{B/A})_X = (V_{B/G})_X - (V_{A/G})_X$$
$$(V_{B/A})_Y = (V_{B/G})_Y - (V_{A/G})_Y$$

Relative displacement, acceleration, and pulse are treated similarly.

Problem 3-5 Relative motion of four-bar linkage

In a four-bar linkage, driver AB rotates about fixed center A, driving follower CD through connecting rod BD, as shown in Fig. 3-12. AB is vertical at the instant shown, and CD makes an angle of 60° with the horizontal as shown. If AB turns at 6 rpm, determine the speed in rpm of link CD. AB = 2 in.; CD = 4 in.; AC = 3 in.

Solution:

The geometry of the problem must be obtained first, as shown in Fig. 3-13.

$$BC = \sqrt{2^2 + 3^2} = 3.6 \text{ in.}$$

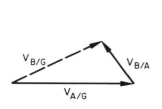

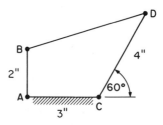

Figure 3-11   **Figure 3-12**

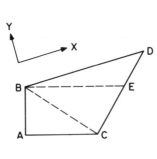

Figure 3-13

Angle BCA = $\tan^{-1} 2/3 = 33.7°$

Angle BCD = $180 - 60 - 33.7 = 86.3°$

By the law of cosines: BD = $\sqrt{BC^2 + CD^2 - 2\,(BC)(CD)\cos 86.3} = 5.21$ in.

By the law of sines: $\sin \angle DBC = (0.996/5.21)4 = 0.765$

Angle DBC = $50.0°$

Hence angle DBE = $50.0° - 33.7° = 16.3°$

The absolute velocities of B and D must be at right angles to cranks AB and CD, respectively, as shown. Assume a coordinate system parallel to BD. Then $(V_{D/G})_X = (V_{B/G})_X + (V_{B/D})_X$. But there can be no relative motion between points B and D in the X-direction, since relative motion of two points on a rigid link in the direction of the two points is impossible; hence $(V_{B/D})_X = 0$. Therefore,

$$(V_{D/G})_X = (V_{B/G})_X = V_B \cos \angle DBE = 2(6)(2\pi)0.960 = 72.4 \text{ in./min}$$
$$V_{D/G} = (V_{D/G})_X / \cos\theta = (V_{D/G})_X / \cos(16.3° + 30°) = 104.5 \text{ in./min}$$
$$\omega_{CD} = V_{D/G}/4 = 26.1 \text{ rad/min}$$
angular velocity = $26.1/2\pi = 4.15$ rpm   *Answer*

3-6   WORK AND ENERGY CONCEPTS

Work U is defined as the product of the component of a force parallel to the path F cos θ and the length of the path.

$$U = \int_{S1}^{S2} F \cos\theta \, ds$$

For a constant force pushing along a straight $U = Fs \cos\theta$. Work is a scalar quantity. The units usually used are ft-lb or joules (1 joule = 0.7378 ft-lb.) Work done in rotation is the product of the unbalanced moment M and the angular displacement θ expressed in radians.

$$U = \int_{\theta_1}^{\theta_2} M \, d\theta \qquad \text{or} \qquad U = M\theta$$

for a constant moment M acting through angle θ.

Energy is the ability of a body or system to do work due to its position or state. Potential energy is measured and expressed as the difference of energy between datum levels. For example, the increase in potential energy of a body is equal to the work required to raise the body from one level to another, provided there is no friction. Kinetic energy K.E. is the energy a particle possesses due to its motion.

$$\text{K.E.} = \tfrac{1}{2} mv^2 + \tfrac{1}{2} I_0 \omega^2$$

where m = mass, v = velocity, I_0 = mass moment of inertia, and ω = angular velocity. Energy units are identical to work units. Both energy and work are scalar units.

An increase or decrease in the kinetic energy of a body is equal to the work done in accelerating or decelerating the body. Ideally kinetic energy is totally convertible to potential energy and vice versa. Practically, some work always must be done to overcome friction.

The Law of the Conservation of Energy summarizes this thus:

The sum of the kinetic and potential energies of a body remains constant if the body is acted upon by a conservative force system.

Problem 3-6 Friction of and energy absorbed by brake shoes

A grab bucket weighing 400 lb is operated by a single cable that unwinds from a 1.5-in diameter hoist drum. The grab bucket is lowered at a uniform speed of 50 ft/min. Two radial brake shoes act against a brake drum 1 ft in diameter that is fastened to the hoist drum. The coefficient of friction between the shoes and the drum is 0.20. Determine (a) the force exerted by each shoe and (b) the energy absorbed by the brakes in Btu during a 40-ft descent of bucket.

Solution:

Since the speed is uniform, there is no acceleration and the downward force due to gravitational attraction must be just balanced by the restraining torque T exerted by the brakes.

(a) $T = 400 \times 1.5/2 = 300 \text{ lb/ft}$

$2N\mu \times 1.0/2 = 300 \text{ ft-lb}$

$N = 300/1.0(0.20) = 1500 \text{ lb} \qquad Answer$

(b) The energy absorbed by the brakes is equal to the loss of potential energy of the bucket.

Energy absorbed $= 400 \text{ lb} \times 40 \text{ ft}$

$= 16,000 \text{ ft-lb of energy}$

$$= \frac{16,000 \text{ ft-lb}}{778 \text{ ft-lb/Btu}} = 20.58 \text{ Btu} \qquad Answer$$

3-7   MOMENTUM

The product of the mass m of a body and its linear velocity **V** is known as the momentum **G**. Momentum is a vector quantity, $G = mV$. Newton's Second Law of Dynamics, often given as $F = ma$, is better expressed as: $F = dG/dt$. The rate of change of momentum of a body with respect to time is proportional to the unbalanced force acting on the body. Note that the direction of the change in momentum is parallel to direction of the force. For a body of constant mass

$$F = m \, dV/dt = ma$$

Problem 3-7 Forces on weight suspended from moving plane

In an aerial acrobatic performance, a 160-lb man is suspended by means of a 15-ft flexible cable from a plane. The plane is flying horizontally and accelerating at 20 ft/sec^2. Find (a) the angle between the cable and a vertical line and (b) the tension in the cable.

Solution:

After equilibrium has been reached, the man and the plane accelerate at the same rate. If the angle between the vertical and the cable is θ, then the force causing acceleration is $T \sin \theta$, where T is the tension in the cable, as seen in Fig. 3-14.

$$T \sin \theta = ma = (160)(20)/32.2 = 99.5 \text{ lb}$$

$$T \cos \theta = W = 160 \text{ lb}$$

$$\frac{T \sin \theta}{T \cos \theta} = \tan \theta = 99.5/160 \qquad \therefore \theta = 31.8° \qquad Answer, \text{ part (a)}$$

$$T = 160/\cos 31.8° = 188 \text{ lb} \qquad Answer, \text{ part (b)}$$

Problem 3-8 Deceleration forces of truck climbing grade

A truck pulls a trailer unit up a 5% grade for a distance of 2000 ft starting at 50 mph and ending at 20 mph. Deceleration is constant. The truck weighs 2 tons; the trailer unit 6 tons. The frictional resistance to rolling is 120 lb/ton. From these data, determine (a) the drawbar pull of the truck, (b) the deceleration of the truck, and (c) the horsepower exerted by the engine at the end of the 2000-ft distance.

Solution:

To solve for the drawbar pull using the equation $F = ma$, the deceleration must be solved for first: $V^2 = V_0{}^2 + 2as$. Since 30 mph = 44 ft/sec, then 50 mph = 73.4 ft/sec; 20 mph = 29.3 ft/sec, $29.3^2 = 73.4^2 + 2a$ (2000).

$$a = -1.13 \text{ ft/sec}^2 \qquad Answer, \text{ part (b)}$$

To determine the drawbar pull P, the forces acting on the trailer must be determined. Resolve the weight W into components normal and parallel to the road. Then the forces and accelerations acting parallel to the road are

$$-F - W \sin \alpha + P = (W/g)a$$

where $F = 6 \times 120 = 720$ lb, the frictional resistance of the trailer.

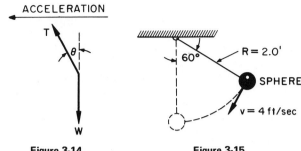

Figure 3-14   **Figure 3-15**

$$\sin \alpha \cong \tan \alpha = 5/100 = 0.05$$
$$-720 - 6(2000)(0.05) + P = (12{,}000/32.2)(-1.13)$$
$$P = 720 + 600 - 421 = 899 \text{ lb} \qquad \textit{Answer,}$$
$$\text{part (a)}$$

Note: The positive direction for acceleration and forces is taken upward. The pull required by the engine for the truck alone is (2/6)899. Thus the total pull is 899 lb + (2/6)899 = 1198 lb.

$$\text{hp} = FV/550 = (1198)(29.3)/550 = 63.7 \qquad \textit{Answer, part (c)}$$

Problem 3-9 Energy and forces of weight on cord
At the instant shown, the tension in the cord is 10 lb and the velocity of the sphere is 4 ft/sec in the direction shown; see Fig. 3-15. Determine (a) the weight of the sphere and (b) the total height through which the sphere drops from release to its lowest point.

Solution:
(a) The tension in the cord is due to the sum of the component of the weight parallel to the cord and the centrifugal force.

$$10 \text{ lb} = W \cos 60° + (W/g)V^2/r$$
$$10 \text{ lb} = W (0.500) + \left(\frac{W}{32.2 \text{ ft/sec}^2}\right)\left(\frac{16 \text{ ft}^2/\text{sec}^2}{2 \text{ ft}}\right)$$
$$10 \text{ lb} = 0.500 \, W + 0.248 \, W = 0.748 W$$
$$W = 10 \text{ lb}/0.748 = 13.38 \text{ lb} \qquad \textit{Answer}$$

(b) The kinetic energy at the instant shown must equal the loss of potential energy due to dropping.

$$\tfrac{1}{2}(W/g)V^2 = Wh$$
$$h = \frac{V^2}{2g} = \frac{16 \text{ ft}^2/\text{sec}^2}{64.4 \text{ ft/sec}^2}$$
$$= 0.248 \text{ ft}$$

Total height dropped = 0.248 ft + (2.0 − 1.0)
$$= 1.248 \text{ ft} \qquad \textit{Answer}$$

Problem 3-10 Friction force of weight on inclined plane

A 2500-lb skid is pulled up a $20°$ inclined plane by a variable force $F = (2000 + t)$ lb that acts parallel to the inclined plane. The coefficient of sliding friction is 0.15. If the skid is initially at rest, determine the distance the skid has traveled by the end of the fifth second ($t = 5$).

Solution:

Normal force between skid and plane = $2500 \cos 20°$

$$= 2350 \text{ lb}$$

Component of weight parallel to plane = $2500 \sin 20° = 855$ lb

Friction force = $2350 \times 0.15 = 352$ lb

Net force on skid parallel to plane $F = (2000 + t) - 855 - 352 = 2000 + t - 1207$

$$F = ma = (W/g)a = (2500/32.2)a$$

$$a = d^2s/dt^2 = d/dt \, (ds/dt) = Fg/W$$

$$d/dt \, (ds/dt) = [(2000 + t) - 1207] g/W$$

$$ds/dt = \int_0^5 [(2000 + t) - 1207] 32.2/2500 \times dt$$

$$ds/dt = (32.2/2500)(793t + t^2/2)|_0^5$$

$$= (32.2/2500)(3965 + 25/2) = 51.2 \text{ ft/sec}$$

$$S = \int_0^5 51.2 \, dt = 256.0 \text{ ft} \qquad \textit{Answer}$$

Problem 3-11 Velocity and height attained by rocket

A 10-ton rocket is being propelled upward at an angle of $15°$ with the vertical. Forty percent of the total rocket weight is fuel and oxygen. The fuel is ejected as a gas at a constant rate of 200 lb/sec and 7000 ft/sec. Neglecting air resistance and the decrease of rocket weight determine (a) maximum velocity of the rocket and (b) height attained by the rocket at the end of fuel consumption

Solution:

First determine the force exerted on the rocket by the escaping gas.

(a) From the momentum equation:

$$F = dG/dt = \frac{VdM}{dt} = \frac{Vdw}{gdt} = \left(7000 \, \frac{ft}{sec}\right) \left(\frac{200 \text{ lb/sec}}{32.2 \text{ ft/sec}^2}\right)$$

$$= 43,500 \text{ lb}$$

Initial fuel weight = $(0.40)(10)(2000) = 8000$ lb

Fuel consumption time = $8000 \text{ lb}/200 \text{ lb/sec} = 40$ sec

Unbalanced force in vertical direction = $43,500 \cos 15° - (10)(2000) = 22,000$ lb

(Total vertical impulse) = (Momentum of rocket at vertical end of impulse)

Vertical components:

$$F_Y (t) = (W_{rocket}/g)(V_Y)_{rocket}$$

$$22,000(t) = (20,000/32.2)V_Y$$

$$V_Y = \frac{22,000}{20,000} t(32.2) = 35.40t$$

Therefore, maximum vertical component of velocity = (35.40)(40) = 1416 ft/sec
Force in horizontal direction = 43,500 sin 15° = 11,250 lb
(Total horizontal impulse) = (Momentum of rocket at horizontal end of impulse)
Horizontal components:

$$F_X(t) = [W_{rocket}/g](V_X)_{rocket}$$
$$11,250(t) = (20,000/32.2)V_X$$
$$V_X = \frac{11,250}{20,000}t(32.2) = 17.30t$$

Therefore, maximum horizontal component of velocity = (17.30)(40) = 692 ft/sec
Maximum velocity of rocket = $\sqrt{(1416)^2 + (692)^2}$ = 1575 ft/sec   *Answer*

(b) Height = S = $\int_0^{40} V_Y(t)\,dt = 35.40t^2/2\,\Big|_0^{40}$ = 28,400 ft   *Answer*

Problem 3-12 Friction force of weights sliding down inclined plane

Determine the initial acceleration of block A, as seen in Fig. 3-16, if the two blocks A and B are sliding at the instant shown. Block A weighs 40 lb, block B 60 lb. The coefficient of sliding friction is 0.20. The pulley is frictionless.

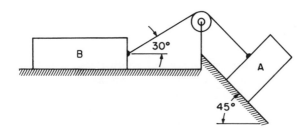

Figure 3-16

Solution:

Since the pulley is frictionless, the tension T in the rope is the same at A and B. The direction of the frictional forces is opposite to the direction of sliding. All forces are assumed to act through the center of mass of each block.

For block A use the forces parallel to the guideway. The net force F_A = 40 cos 45° − T − 40(sin 45°)0.20. Net force on block B is F_B = T cos 30° − (60 − T sin 30°)0.20.

Note that T sin 30° is the upward force on block B exerted by the rope. Assuming the cable to be inelastic, the acceleration of both ends must be the same. Therefore

$$a_B = a_A \cos 30°$$
$$a_A = F_A g/W_A \quad \text{and} \quad a_B = F_B g/W_B$$

Therefore,

$$F_B g/W_B = (F_A g/W_A) \cos 30°$$

Substituting the values for F_A and F_B in terms of T and solving for T,

$$[T \cos 30° - (60 - T \sin 30°)0.20]/60 = [40 \cos 45° - T - 40(\sin 45°)(0.20)]$$
$$\times (\cos 30°)/40$$

$$T = 18.3 \text{ lb}$$
$$F_A = 4.4 \text{ lb}$$
$$a_A = 3.54 \text{ ft/sec}^2 \qquad \textit{Answer}$$

Conservation of Momentum

A restatement of Newton's Second Law leads to the Principle of Conservation of Momentum:

The total momentum of a body does not change *provided no unbalanced external forces are acting on the body.*

An additional restatement of Newton's Second Law leads to the concept of impulse. *Impulse* is defined as the product of a force **F** which acts on a body for a time $dt = t_2 - t_1$. It is a vector quantity. Linear impulse = **F** dt. The change in momentum of a body is equal to the linear impulse acting on it: **F** dt = m d**V**.

Angular units corresponding to the linear units developed above are summarized in Table 3-1.

3-8   IMPACT

The collision of one moving body with another body that may be either moving or stationary is defined as impact. Because no external forces are acting during impact, the momentum of a system of bodies before impact must equal the system's momentum after impact, $m_1 U_1 + m_2 U_2 = m_1 V_1 + m_2 V_2$, where m_1, m_2 = masses of bodies 1 and 2, U_1, U_2 = velocities before impact of bodies 1 and 2, and V_1, V_2 = velocities after impact of bodies 1 and 2.

Direct Impact

The velocities of the colliding bodies are perpendicular to the surfaces of contact. Direct central impact occurs if the normals to the contact surfaces pass through the center of gravity of the two bodies.

Coefficient of Restitution or Impact Coefficient

The ratio of the difference of velocities during separation to the difference of velocities in approach is defined as the coefficient of restitution e.

$$e = (V_2 - V_1)/(U_1 - U_2)$$

The velocity components normal to the contacting surfaces are used to determine e. For a perfectly elastic body, e = 1. For totally inelastic bodies, e = 0.

If both colliding bodies are perfectly elastic, then no energy will be lost during collision and both the conservation of momentum and the conservation of

Table 3-1 Summary of Dynamics Relations

Name of Quantity	Linear System	Angular System
Work	$\int_{S_1}^{S_2} F\, dS$	$\int_{\theta_1}^{\theta_2} m\, d\theta$
Kinetic energy	$\frac{1}{2}mV^2$	$\frac{1}{2}I_0\omega^2$
Potential energy	$(Wh)^*$ or $(\frac{1}{2}kS^2)^{**}$	
Momentum	mV	$I_0\omega$
Impulse	$\int_{t_1}^{t_2} F\, dt$	$\int_{t_1}^{t_2} m_0\, dt$
Newton's Second Law	$F = \dfrac{d(mV)}{dt} = \dfrac{dG}{dt}$	$m_0 = \dfrac{d(I_0\omega)}{dt}$
	or, if m is constant	If I_0 is constant
	$F = \dfrac{mdV}{dt} = ma$	$m_0 = I_0\alpha$
Impulse-momentum relation	$F\, dt = m\, dV$	$m_0\, dt = I_0\, d\omega$

*Wh is the potential energy of weight W raised through vertical distance h.

**$\frac{1}{2}kS^2$ is the potential energy stored in a spring that has a constant spring rate k and is stretched a distance S from the no-load condition.

energy relationships can be used to solve problems. If e is less than 1, then the energy lost to heat or internal strain cannot normally be obtained and the conservation of energy relationship cannot be used.

Problem 3-13 Velocity change of horizontal conveyor affected by falling weight

A 60-lb bag is dropped through a height of 10 ft onto a rolling conveyor trolley. The trolley weighs 20 lb. If the trolley was rolling along a horizontal track with no friction at 16 ft/sec, determine its velocity after impact.

Solution:

The 60-lb bag falling in the Y-direction has momentum only in that direction and causes an impulse in the Y-direction, which is lost as impact energy. From the conservation of linear momentum in the horizontal (X) direction,

$$m_t(U_t)_X = (m_b + m_t)V_X$$
$$(20/32.2)(16) = [(60 + 20)/32.2]V_X$$
$$V_X = (20/80)(16) = 4 \text{ ft/sec} \qquad Answer$$

3-9 SPRINGS

Most spring problems are concerned with either the storage of mechanical energy or the rate of vibration. A number of terms associated with springs are reviewed here.

Spring rate or spring constant k is the ratio of the force F applied to the spring to cause a deflection S: $k = dF/dS$. Most springs have a constant spring rate so that $k = F/S$. k is usually expressed in lb/in.

Work done to compress a spring $= \int_{S_1}^{S_2} F dS = \int_{S_1}^{S_2} kS \, dS$

For a constant-rate spring, work $= \frac{1}{2} k(S_2{}^2 - S_1{}^2)$

Free length = the uncompressed length of a spring

Compressed height or length = the length of a spring under a given load

Problem 3-14 Spring compression by moving weight

A 200-lb block moving on a smooth horizontal plane with a velocity of 4 ft/sec strikes a horizontal spring having a spring constant of 160 lb/in. Determine the maximum compressive force developed in the spring.

Solution:

The total kinetic energy of the moving mass is converted to the potential energy of the spring. Note the conversion from feet to inches.

$$\frac{1}{2} m V^2 = \frac{1}{2} k S^2$$

$$\frac{(200)(4)^2 (12)}{(32.2)(2)} = \frac{160}{2} S^2$$

S = 2.72 in., maximum spring deflection

Compressive force = Sk = (2.72)(160) = 435 lb   *Answer*

The equivalent spring rate of a spring system is the ratio of the force required to act on the system to cause unit deflection. For two springs acting in parallel, $k_{eq} = k_1 + k_2$. For two springs acting in series, $k_{eq} = k_1 k_2 /(k_1 + k_2)$. If two helical springs are identical except for the number of coils, then for a given force the deflections will be proportional to the number of active coils.

$S_1 /S_2 = N_1 /N_2$

Problem 3-15 Dual-spring (in series) compression by moving weight

A 20-lb block slides down an inclined plane a distance of 6 in. before striking the first of two springs in series; see Fig. 3-17. The spring constants are $k_1 = 10$ lb/in. and $k_2 = 15$ lb/in. The coefficient of friction between the plane and the block is 0.12. Determine the maximum compressive force in springs 1 and 2.

Solution:

Assuming the block starts sliding with no initial velocity, then the total potential energy stored in the spring system at maximum compression will equal the change in the potential energy (P.E.) of the block minus the energy lost to friction.

Equivalent spring constant $k_{eq} = (10)(15)/(10 + 15) = 6$ lb/in.
Component of weight perpendicular to the plane = $20 \cos 20° = 18.8$ lb
Force of friction = (18.8)(0.12) = 2.26 lb
Change in the P.E. of the block = $20(S + 6)(\sin 20°) = 20(S + 6)(0.342)$
Energy lost to friction = (2.26)(S + 6)

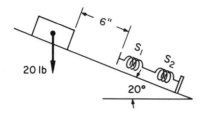

Figure 3-17

ΔP.E. of block – frictional work = P.E. stored in spring system

$$20(S + 6)(0.342) - 2.26(S + 6) = \tfrac{1}{2} k_T S^2 = 6S^2/2$$

$$S = +3.89 \text{ in. } (-2.35 \text{ in.})$$

For two springs in series, the force in both springs must be identical.

Thus, $F_1 = F_2 = (3.89)(6) = 23.34$ lb   *Answer*

3-10   VIBRATIONS

Vibrating systems are classified as either free or forced, damped or undamped systems. In a freely vibrating undamped system, no external forces act to change the mode of vibration. In a forced system, periodically applied external forces are acting. In a damped system, an external force acts to slow the velocity of the vibrating mass. In *viscous damping,* the force is proportional to the velocity. Only the freely vibrating system will be discussed in this volume.

Frequency = the number of vibrations or cycles made in unit time
Period = the length of time required to complete one cycle = 1/frequency
Displacement = the distance of any point of a vibrating system from its rest or
     equilibrium position
Amplitude = the maximum displacement

Essentially all vibrating systems are characterized by an internal restoring force that acts to restore a displaced system to the equilibrium position. The magnitude of the restoring force is directly proportional to the displacement. In a typical linear system having one degree of freedom, a constant rate spring supplies the restoring force kx. Consider the equations of motion for a spring supporting a weight W.

From Newton's Second Law,

$$\Sigma F = ma$$
$$= \frac{W}{g} a = \frac{W}{g} \frac{d^2 x}{dt^2}$$

In the equilibrium position, $a = 0$ and $F_{ST} = kS = W$, where S is the stretch of the spring when supporting a static load W. In any displaced position, $\Sigma F = W - kS - kx$, where x is the displacement from the equilibrium position.

$$W - (kS + kx) = \frac{W}{g} \frac{d^2x}{dt^2} \quad \text{or} \quad W - (W + kx) = \frac{W}{g} \frac{d^2x}{dt^2}$$

Simplifying,

$$\frac{W}{g} \frac{d^2x}{dt^2} + kx = 0$$

A general solution satisfying this differential equation is

$$x = A \sin (kg/W)^{\frac{1}{2}} t + B \cos (kg/W)^{\frac{1}{2}} t$$

The periodicity can be established as follows: The sine and cosine functions repeat every 2π rad. Calling the time to repeat one period T, then $(kg/W)^{1/2}T = 2\pi$ or $T = 2\pi(kg/W)^{-1/2}$. The frequency $f = 1/T = (1/2\pi)(kg/W)^{1/2}$. Substituting the angular frequency ω for $(kg/W)^{1/2}$, then $f = \omega/2\pi$.

The values of constants A and B of the general solution are obtained from the boundary conditions. Assume the weight is released after extending the spring X_0 from the equilibrium position, then the equations of motion reduce to the following:

Displacement = $X = X_0 \cos \omega t = X_0 \cos 2\pi ft$

Velocity = $V = -X_0 \omega \sin \omega t = -X_0 \omega \sin 2\pi ft$

Acceleration = $a = -X_0 \omega^2 \cos \omega t = -X\omega^2 = -4\pi^2 f^2 X^2$

Problem 3-16 Vibration frequency of rotating shaft

A 1.5-in. diameter 20-in.-long steel shaft carries a 50-lb steel pulley at its center. The shaft ends are mounted in ball bearings. Determine if it is safe to run the shaft and pulley combination at 2000 rpm. Neglect the weight of the shaft.

Solution:

This problem reduces to a comparison between the maximum frequency of the forced vibrations, i.e., 2000 rpm, and the natural frequency of the system. If the forced frequency is sufficiently below the lowest natural frequency, then the operation is safe.

To determine the natural frequency, the spring constant of the system must be determined. Consider the shaft as a simply supported beam.

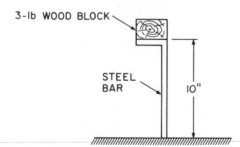

Figure 3-18

$$k = W/S \quad \text{and} \quad S = W/k = WL^3/48EI$$

For steel, $E = 30(10)^6$ psi. For a round shaft,

$$I = \pi d^4/64 = 0.248 \text{ in.}^4$$

$$S = [(50)(20)^3/48]\left[\frac{1}{(30)(10)^6\,0.248}\right] = 0.0011 \text{ in.}$$

Lowest natural frequency,

$$f = (1/2\pi)(kg/W)^{\frac{1}{2}} = (1/2\pi)(g/S)^{\frac{1}{2}}$$

$$= (1/2\pi)[(386 \text{ in./sec}^2)/(0.0011 \text{ in.})]^{\frac{1}{2}} = 94.4 \text{ cycles/sec}$$
$$= 5664 \text{ rpm}$$

Since the forced frequency is less than half the natural frequency, the system is safe from the vibration point of view.

Problem 3-17 Bullet impact on block supported on cantilevered steel bar

A 0.1-lb bullet moving horizontally at 1500 ft/min strikes and imbeds itself in a wooden block weighing 3 lb. The wooden block is supported on a cantilevered steel bar 1 in. × 4 in. in cross section; see Fig. 3-18. Assuming the bar weightless, determine the frequency and amplitude of vibration after impact.

Solution:

Using the momentum equation, the velocity of block and bullet directly after impact is obtained. This corresponds to the velocity at the equilibrium position. At this position $V = -X_0 \omega \sin \omega t$ in the previously derived equation and $\omega t = \pi/2$.

As in the previous problem, the deflection characteristic of the cantilevered beam must be determined.

$$S = WL^3/3EI = W/k$$

$$W = 3.1 \text{ lb}$$

$$L = 10 \text{ in.} \quad \text{and} \quad E = 30 \times 10^6 \text{ psi}$$
$$I = bh^3/12 = (4)(1)^3/12 = 0.333 \text{ in.}^4$$

$$S = \frac{(3.1)(10)^3}{3(30)(10)^6(0.333)} = \frac{1.04}{10^4} = 0.0001 \text{ in.}$$

$$f = (1/2\pi)(g/S)^{\frac{1}{2}} = 313 \text{ vibrations/sec} \qquad Answer$$

$$\omega = 2\pi f = 1965 \text{ rad/sec}$$

Amplitude $X_0 = V/\omega = (1500 \text{ ft/min})/(1965 \text{ rad/sec} \times 60 \text{ sec/min})$

$$= \frac{1500}{1965 \times 60} = 0.0127 \text{ ft} \qquad Answer$$

chapter 4
MECHANICS OF
INCOMPRESSIBLE FLUIDS

Two types of problems involving fluid mechanics are customarily found on examinations. The first involves the area of fluid statics—problems involving forces on dams, buoyancy, and manometry. The second area concerns itself with fluid dynamics—problems involving the Bernoulli theorem or the general energy equation, momentum concepts applied to moving fluids, the flow of fluids in pipes or channels, and fluid flow measurements. Often manometry questions combine with those of fluid flow measurements.

4-1 FLUID PROPERTIES AND FLUID STATICS

A *fluid* is a substance that deforms continuously during the application of tangential forces. A *liquid* is a fluid that occupies a definite volume, regardless of the size or shape of its container. Liquids have free surfaces. In the majority of engineering applications, liquids are considered incompressible. A *gas* is a fluid that expands to fill the container into which it is introduced. Gases are generally considered compressible fluids. The analysis of problems involving gases is found in Chap. 5.

Pressure is ratio of a force normal to a surface and the area of the surface, $P = F/A$. Usual engineering units for pressure are pounds per square inch (psi) or pounds per square foot (psf).

Atmospheric pressure refers to the pressure caused by the weight of the atmosphere. It is the ratio of atmospheric force to area. *Absolute pressure* is the ratio of total force to area. The usual designation is psia. *Gage pressure* is the ratio of all forces, except the force due to the atmosphere, to the area on which these forces act. It may also be expressed as the difference between absolute and atmospheric pressure. The usual designations for gage pressure are psi or psig. The latter designation is more exact.

The Basic Equation of Hydrostatics

The basic equation of hydrostatics is $p = wh$.

The equation shows that at any point in a liquid the pressure p is directly proportional to the product of specific weight w and the vertical distance h below the free surface of the liquid. Since the specific weight is usually considered constant, the pressure is directly proportional to the so-called "pressure head," i.e., the distance h.

The following engineering terms and units are common: p (psi), h (in.), w (lb/cu in.). Also used are $p = wh/144$, p (psi), h (ft), w (lb/cu ft). *Specific weight* w is the ratio of the weight of a fluid to its volume. For fresh water, w = 62.4 lb/cu ft; for salt water, w = 64 lb/cu ft at 60°F. *Density* d is the ratio of the mass of a fluid to its volume. For fresh water, d = 1.94 slugs/cu ft; for salt water, d = 1.99 at 60°F. *Specific gravity* is a ratio of the weight of the substance to the weight of an equal volume of a reference standard. The reference standard used for liquids and solids is water at 39.2°F and for gases the standard commonly used is air at 32°F and 14.7 psi. An alternate definition is

$$\text{Specific gravity of a substance} = \frac{\text{specific weight of substance}}{\text{specific weight of water}}$$

Manometers are meters used to determine pressure by application of the pressure head relation. The pressure at a particular location is determined by observing the height of a fluid of known specific gravity or density that is necessary to equalize the given pressure. Various forms of manometers are employed. *Open manometers* are manometers that have one end open to the atmosphere. *Differential manometers* are used to measure differences in pressure between two points to which the manometer is connected.

Problem 4-1 Balanced pressure of two different fluids in a U-tube

Water is poured into a U-tube. Then oil having a specific gravity of 0.90 is poured into one arm of the U-tube until the level of the oil is 2 cm above that of the water. The oil and water do not mix. What volume of oil will be necessary if the cross-sectional area of the U-tube is 2cm²?

Solution:

At any point in a liquid the pressure is the same in any direction. Thus, using the interface A, as seen in Fig. 4-1, between the oil and the water, the pressure due to a column h of oil must be equal to the pressure of a column of height h' of water. Note that the lower part of the U-tube has no effect on the pressure at A.

Specific weight of water = w

Oil pressure at A = 0.90hw

Water pressure at A = h'w

At A the pressures are equal, h' = 0.90h

Difference of level = h − h' = 2 cm   h − 0.90h = 2 cm

Height of the oil column h = 20 cm

Volume of oil = (20)(2) = 40 cm³   *Answer*

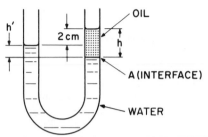

Figure 4-1

Problem 4-2 Air column length in mercury barometer tube

An accurate mercury barometer reads 75.0 cm. A second barometer tube that is 84.0 cm long is not quite filled with mercury; the space above the mercury is filled with air at atmospheric pressure. The second tube is then inverted into a bowl of mercury. The mercury column becomes 71.0 cm long. Determine the original height of the air space prior to inversion.

Solution:

The air pressure above the mercury in the second tube before inversion is 75.0 cm Hg. After inversion the combined pressure of the second mercury column and the pressure of the expanded air p' must equal atmospheric pressure.

$$75.0 = 71.0 + p'$$
$$p' = 4.0 \text{ cm Hg}$$

Assuming that $p_1 V_1 = p_2 V_2$ (Boyle's law), the volume of the expanded air is $(84.0 - 71.0)A$. The original air volume was $h(A)$. Thus, $75.0(h)(A) = 4(84.0 - 71.0)A$.

Original height h = 4(13.0)/75.0 = 0.695 cm   *Answer*

Force on a Submerged Plane

The magnitude of the resultant force F acting on a plane surface submerged in a liquid is the integral over the entire surface of the product of the liquid pressure and the differential area on which the pressure acts.

$$F = \int_A p \, dA = w \int_A h \, dA = w\bar{h}A$$

Solution of the second form ($F = w\int_A h \, dA$) shows that the force is equal to the product of the pressure at the area's centroid $w\bar{h}$ and the total area, as shown in Fig. 4-2. The forces acting on a curved submerged area are best determined as components in the vertical and horizontal directions. The vertical force is equal to the product of the volume of liquid above the surface and the specific weight of the liquid: $F_V = wV$. Its line of action passes through the centroid of the liquid volume. The horizontal force equals the force exerted on a plane vertical surface whose area and vertical location are equal to the projection of the curved surface onto a vertical plane.

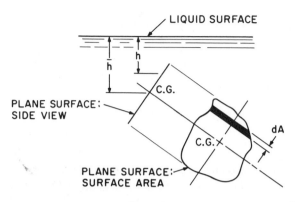

Figure 4-2

Center of Pressure (C.P.)

The point on a surface through which the line of action of the resultant force passes is defined as the center of pressure. It is located by equating the sum of the moments of the forces acting over the whole surface to the moment of the resultant force. In Fig. 4-3 the inclined distance of the C.P. below the intersection of the inclined surface and the liquid-free surface (X-X') is determined by

$$F(y_{C.P.}) = \int y \, dF = \int_A yp \, dA$$

The solution for any plane surface works out to

$$y_{C.P.} = \bar{y} + I_{1\text{-}1}/A\bar{y} = \bar{y} + k_{1\text{-}1}/y$$

where $I_{1\text{-}1}$ = moment of inertia of area A about centroidal axis 1-1, and $k_{1\text{-}1}$ = radius of gyration of area A about centroidal axis 1-1.

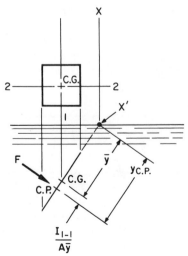

Figure 4-3

Note that except for horizontal surfaces, $y_{C.P.}$ is always greater than $\bar{y}$. To locate the C.P. in a direction parallel to line X-X$'$, moments about an axis at right angles to X-X$'$ must be taken. Then,

$$F(x_{C.P.}) = \int x \ dF = \int_A xp \ dA$$
$$x_{C.P.} = I_{1\text{-}2}/A\bar{y}$$

where $I_{1\text{-}2}$ = product of inertia about axes 1 and 2.

Note: If the surface is symmetrical about axis 2-2, $I_{1\text{-}2} = 0$ and hence the center of pressure lies on the axis of symmetry.

A few shapes recur frequently. The location of their center of gravity and center of pressure is indicated in Fig. 4-4. Note that in all cases shown, the surfaces are vertical and extend up to the liquid's free surface.

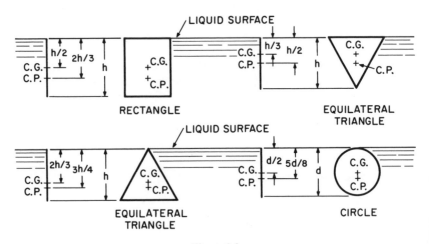

Figure 4-4

Buoyancy

Any body that is either partially or wholly immersed in a fluid will experience an upward or buoyant force. This force is equal to the difference in the upward and downward forces exerted by the fluid, respectively, on the lower and upper surfaces of the body. This upward force is always equal to the product of the volume of the liquid displaced by the body and the liquid's specific gravity. The line of action of the buoyant force acts through the *centroid of the displaced fluid.*

Problem 4-3 Foundation reaction and horizontal shearing force of concrete dam

For the concrete dam shown in Fig. 4-5 determine the foundation reaction and the horizontal shearing force that must be developed to prevent sliding. Neglect hydrostatic uplift. Assume a specific weight of 150 lb/cu ft for concrete.

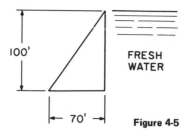

Figure 4-5

Solution:

This problem is solved using the basic equation of statics: The sum of the forces and the sum of the moments acting on a body in static equilibrium must both be zero. Since the width of the dam is not given, the calculations will be based on 1-ft width. The horizontal force exerted by the water on the dam equals the product of the pressure at the centroid of the 1-ft.-wide 100-ft-high area and the area.

$$F_H = w(h/2)A = (62.4)(50)(100)(1) = 312,000 \text{ lb}$$

The resultant horizontal force acts through the center of pressure

$$y_{C.P.} = \bar{y} + I/A\bar{y}$$
$$= 50 + (bh^3/12)/(100)(1)(50) = 66.67 \text{ ft}$$

Thus the resultant horizontal force acts at $100 - 66.67 = 33.33$ ft above the base. The water exerts no vertical force on the dam.

Weight of the dam = $(\frac{1}{2})(100)(70)(1)(150) = 525,000$ lb/ft of width

Foundation reaction = 525,000 lb ↑   *Answer*

The line of action of the foundation reaction is located by taking moments about the left edge. Calling x the distance from the edge to the line of action:

$$0 = 525,000x + 312,000(33.33) - 525,000 \, (\frac{2}{3})(70)$$

$$x = 26.9 \text{ ft}$$

Horizontal shearing force = 312,000 lb →   *Answer*

Problem 4-4 Block of wood and lead sinker in equilibrium in water

A lead sinker is attached to a block of wood weighing 21 grams. The sinker and the wood are in equilibrium when immersed in water. Find the weight of the sinker if the specific gravity of lead is 11.3 and of wood is 0.70.

Solution:

For equilibrium, weight of water displaced by sinker and wood = weight of wood and sinker.

Density of wood = specific gravity of wood × density of water
$$= 0.70 \times 1 \text{ g/cm}^3 = 0.70 \text{ g/cm}^3$$

Volume of wood $= \dfrac{\text{mass of wood}}{\text{density of wood}} = \dfrac{21\text{ g}}{0.70\text{ g/cm}^3} = 30\text{ cm}^3$

Weight of water displaced by wood $= 30\text{ cm}^3 \times 1\text{ g/cm}^3 = 30\text{ g}$

Weight of water displaced by sinker $= V_S \times 1\text{ g/cm}^3$

Weight of sinker $=$ volume $\times$ density $= V_S \times 11.3 \times 1\text{ g/cm}^3$

$$V_S \times 1\text{ g/cm}^3 + 30\text{ g} = 21\text{ g} + V_S \times 11.3 \times 1$$
$$10.3\,V_S = 9$$

Volume of sinker $V_S = 9/10.3 = 0.87\text{ cm}^3$

Weight of sinker $=$ volume $\times$ density

$\qquad\qquad\quad = 0.87\text{ cm}^3 \times 11.3\text{ g/cm}^3 = 9.9\text{ g}$ *Answer*

Problem 4-5 Buoyancy of sphere suspended in water

A 7-ton, 6-ft underwater observation sphere is suspended by a cable just below the surface of the ocean. The specific gravity of the material used in the sphere is 7.8 and that of sea water is 1.03. Find the tension in the cable if the sphere is accidentally allowed to fill with sea water.

Solution:

Once the sphere is filled with sea water, the buoyant force acting on it is only equal to the weight of the volume of water displaced that equals the sphere's net volume. In other words the spherical hollow shape is no longer effective.

Sphere net volume $=$ total weight/specific weight $= (7\text{ tons})(2000\text{ lb/ton})/(7.8)$
$$\qquad\qquad\qquad\qquad\qquad\qquad\qquad\qquad \times (62.4\text{ lb/cu ft})$$
$$= 28.78\text{ cu ft}$$

Weight of sea water displaced $=$ volume $\times$ density
$$= (28.78)(62.4)(1.03)$$
$$= 1860\text{ lb}$$

The sum of the forces acting on the filled sphere $= 0$.

$\qquad 0 =$ tension $+$ buoyant force $-$ weight of sphere

$\qquad 0 = T + 1860 - 14,000$

$\qquad T = 12,140\text{ lb}$ *Answer*

4-2   THE CONTINUITY EQUATION

For steady incompressible flow the same quantity of fluid flows past all cross sections in any given interval of time. If Q is the rate of flow, then

$\qquad Q = A_1 V_1 = A_2 V_2$

$\qquad Q =$ cu ft/sec $A =$ sq ft $V =$ ft/sec

The continuity equation also gives the relation of the velocities of the fluid at two points in a system, $V_1 = V_2 A_2 / A_1$.

4-3   THE BERNOULLI THEOREM

This theorem, based on the concept of the conservation of energy, states that the total internal energy of a fluid at any cross section 1 (upstream), plus any energy gained due to pumps (H_P), minus any energy lost due to hydraulic motors and turbines (H_M) or due to friction (H_F) and minor losses is equal to the total internal energy at section 2 (downstream). The usual engineering units for all terms are ft-lb/lb of fluid or feet of fluid.

$$P_1/w + V_1^2/2g + Z_1 + H_P - H_M - H_F - \text{minor losses} = P_2/w + V_2^2/2g + Z_2$$

where P = pressure, lb/sq ft

   w = specific weight, lb/cu ft

   V = fluid velocity, ft/sec

   g = acceleration due to gravity, cu ft/sec^2

   Z = elevation above an arbitrary horizontal datum surface, ft

4-4   FRICTION LOSSES AND THE REYNOLDS NUMBER

The frictional head loss H_F for fluids flowing in pipes is calculated by

$$H_F = fLV^2/2Dg$$

where f = friction factor (see below)

   L = pipe length

   D = pipe diameter or four times the hydraulic radius (see below)

   V = average velocity of fluid at a particular diameter

Determination of the Friction Factor f

(1) For laminar flow ($N_{Re} < 2000$), $f = 64/N_{Re}$.

(2) For turbulent flow ($N_{Re} > 2000$), determine f from Moody diagram.

(3) N_{Re}, the Reynolds number, is a dimensionless ratio whose magnitude indicates the nature of the flow:

   $N_{Re} = VDw/\mu g = VD/v$ for circular pipes

   $N_{Re} = V4Rw/\mu g$ for noncircular pipes

where μ = dynamic (or absolute) viscosity, lb-sec/sq ft

   v = kinematic viscosity, sq ft/sec

   R = hydraulic radius = (pipe cross-sectional area)/(pipe wetted perimeter)

Minor Losses

Minor losses* are all those energy losses due to turbulence that a fluid experiences on encountering valves, fittings, elbows, sudden contractions, or expansions. A fluid flowing from a reservoir into a pipe with a square-edged opening suffers

---

*Minor losses are expressed as $K(V^2/2g)$, the value of K being determined experimentally.

an energy loss of $0.5V^2/2g$. Fluids flowing from a pipe into a reservoir have a total energy loss of $V^2/2g$. In each case V represents velocity in the pipe. Usually minor losses are negligible.

Branching Systems

When a system consists of a number of parallel pipes the following must hold true. The pressure drop in each parallel pipe must be the same between junction points. The sum of all the quantities flowing toward and away from a junction point must be zero, where flow towards a junction may be considered positive. Since the friction factor f is dependent on the Reynolds number for $N_{Re} > 2000$, it is usually assumed to be about 0.015 until velocity values have been established. Unless f is known, the solution must be iterative using successively improved values of f and pipe velocity.

Problem 4-6 Pump capacity for transferring water between tanks

Water is being transferred by means of a pump from a storage tank having a surface elevation of 40 ft to one having a surface elevation of 100 ft. A 6-in.-diameter, 1250-ft-long pipeline connects the two tanks and the pump. The friction factor f for the pipeline is 0.012. Neglecting minor losses determine the pump capacity for a discharge of 4 cu ft/sec.

Solution:

This problem is readily solvable by applying the Bernoulli equation provided the following assumption is made. The velocity of the water at the surface of either tank is zero. With this assumption made, sections 1 and 2 are then located at the surfaces. We know then that $P_1 = P_2$; $Z_1 - Z_2 = -60$ ft; $V_1 = V_2 = 0$; the water velocity within the pipe = $Q/A = 4/(0.7854)(0.5)^2 = 20.3$ ft/sec.

$$Z_1 + H_P = Z_2 + H_F$$

$$H_F = f\frac{LV^2}{D2g} = 0.012\frac{(1250)(20.3)^2}{(0.5)(64.4)} = 192 \text{ ft}$$

$H_P = 60 + 192 = 252$ ft, pressure head developed by pump

Pumps are usually rated in terms of horsepower capacity. The water horsepower required is the head (in ft) through which a specified weight of water must be raised each second.

Weight rate of water = Q_w = 4 cu ft/sec × 62.4 lb/cu ft = 249.6 lb/sec

Water horsepower required = (249.6)(252)/550 = 114   *Answer*

Problem 4-7 Pressure drop of oil flowing through length of pipe

Fuel oil having a specific gravity of 0.90 and an absolute viscosity of 0.0020 lb-sec/sq ft flows through a horizontal $1\frac{1}{2}$-in. I.D. pipe at 15 gal/min. Determine the pressure drop in a 100-ft length of pipe.

Solution:

From the continuity equation and the given data, $Z_1 = Z_2$, $V_1 = V_2$, where sections 1 and 2 represent two cross sections 1000 ft apart. Then using the energy equation:

$$P_1/w = P_2/w + H_F \quad \text{or} \quad (P_1 - P_2)/w = H_F$$

The magnitude of the friction loss H_F depends on the friction factor f, which in turn is a function of the Reynolds number.

$$\text{Average oil velocity} = V = Q/A = \left(\frac{15 \text{ gal/min}}{7.48 \text{ gal/cu ft}}\right)\left(\frac{144 \text{ in.}^2/\text{ft}^2}{\frac{1}{4}\pi(1.5)^2 \text{ in.}^2}\right)\left(\frac{1}{60 \text{ sec/min}}\right)$$

$$= 2.72 \text{ ft/sec}$$

$$N_{Re} = \frac{VD}{v} = \frac{VDw}{\mu g} = \frac{(2.72)(1.5/12)(62.4)(0.90)}{(0.0020)(32.2)}$$

$$= 298$$

Since the Reynolds number is less than 2000, flow must be laminar. Therefore $f = 64/N_{Re}$ and

$$\text{Friction losses } H_F = \frac{64}{N_{Re}}\frac{LV^2}{D2g} = \frac{(64)(1000)(12)(2.72)^2}{(298)(1.5)(2)(32.2)}$$

$$= 198 \text{ ft}$$

Pressure drop $= H_F w = (198)(62.4)(0.90)/144 = 77$ psi   *Answer*

Problem 4-8 Horsepower requirements of a pump

Determine the input horsepower required by a pump that is 82% efficient if it delivers 300 gal/min of crude oil against a total head of 25 ft. The oil has a specific gravity of 0.90.

Solution:

Theoretical or output horsepower required $= 300$ gal/min $\times$ weight/gal $\times$ distance through which oil is lifted. (7.48 gal $= 1$ cu ft.)

$$hp_{output} = \frac{(300)(62.4)(0.90)(25)}{(7.48)(33,000)} = 1.7$$

Efficiency $=$ output/input

Therefore

$$hp_{input} = 1.7/0.82 = 2.1 \quad \textit{Answer}$$

Problem 4-9 Pressure differentials in junctures of parallel pipes

A cast-iron pipeline carrying 10 cu ft/sec of water divides at point A into two branches that rejoin at B. One branch consists of a 6-in. pipe 4000 ft long; the other consists of a 10-in. pipe 12,000 ft long. If point A is 20 ft above point B, find the pressure differential between points A and B. The kinematic viscosity of water may be assumed to be 1.233×10^{-5} sq ft/sec.

Solution:

This is a basic parallel pipe problem. The frictional head loss must be the same in both pipes between points A and B. Assume a friction factor of 0.015 for each pipe and apply the Bernoulli equation.

For the 6-in. pipe:

$$(V_{A6})^2/2g + Z_A + P_A/w = (V_{B6})^2/2g + Z_B + P_B/w + H_{F6}$$

But $V_{A6} = V_{B6}$ and $Z_A - Z_B = 20$ ft. Thus,

$$20 + P_A/w = P_B/w + f_6 L_6 V_6{}^2/D_6 2g$$

Similarly, for the 10-in. pipe:

$$20 + P_A/w = P_B/w + f_{10} L_{10} V_{10}{}^2/D_{10} 2g$$

Thus, $$f_6 \frac{L_6 V_6{}^2}{D_6 2g} = f_{10} \frac{L_{10} V_{10}{}^2}{D_{10} 2g}$$

$$f_6 = f_{10} = 0.015$$

$$V_{10} = V_6 [(4000/12,000)(10/6)]^{\frac{1}{2}}$$

$$= 0.75 V_6$$

The total quantity of water carried by both pipes must add to 10 cu ft/sec.

$$V_6 A_6 + V_{10} A_{10} = 10 \text{ cu ft/sec}$$
$$V_6(0.7854)(0.5)^2 + 0.75 V_6 (0.7854)(10/12)^2 = 10 \text{ cu ft/sec}$$
$$V_6 = 16.5 \text{ ft/sec}$$
$$V_{10} = 12.36 \text{ ft/sec}$$

Friction loss between points A and B = $fLV^2/D2g$

$$= 0.015 \frac{(4000)(16.5)^2}{(0.5)(64.4)} = 507 \text{ ft}$$

Total pressure differential between points A and B = $P_A/w - P_B/w$

$$= -20 + 507$$
$$= 487 \text{ ft} \qquad Answer$$

Problem 4-10 Submarine depth determined by speed and bow pressure

A submarine is driven through salt water at a speed of 15 mph. The pressure at the bow is found to be 30 psi gage. The specific weight of salt water is 64 lb/cu ft. Find the depth at which the submarine is moving.

Solution:

This problem deals with the concept of stagnation pressure; i.e., the pressure at the bow where the velocity of the water relative to the submarine is taken to be zero. Apply the Bernoulli equation between points 1 (the surface of the water some distance ahead of the bow) and 2 (the bow). (See Fig. 4-6.) For convenience the submarine is considered stationary and the water moving to the right at 15 mph or 22 ft/sec.

$$P_1/w + Z_1 + V_1{}^2/2g = P_2/w + Z_2 + V_2{}^2/2g$$
$$0 + 0 + 22^2/64.4 = (30)(144)/64.0 + Z_2 + 0$$
$$Z_2 = -59.9 \text{ ft} \qquad Answer$$

The negative value indicates a distance below the datum surface, which was taken as the free surface of the water.

Alternate Solution:

With a horizontal streamline, the elevation $Z_1 = Z_2$ and the equation is rewritten as $P_1/w + V_1{}^2/2g = P_2/w + V_2{}^2/2g$. Again $V_1 = 22$ ft/sec, $V_2 = 0$; now, however, $P_1/w = h$, the pressure head in feet of water.

$$h = P_2/w - V_1{}^2/2g$$

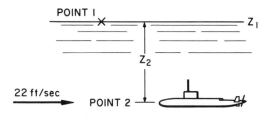

Figure 4-6

4-5   MOMENTUM CONCEPTS

The concept of linear momentum, which was previously discussed in Chap. 3, may also be applied to determine the force exerted on or by a fluid in motion. Simply restated, the impulse-momentum relation says that a force F exerted on a fluid for a time interval Δt will cause a change in the fluid's momentum ΔMV: $F(\Delta t) = \Delta MV$. For an incompressible fluid, M is constant, then $F(\Delta t) = M(\Delta V)$. But the mass of fluid moving during time interval Δt is conveniently restated as the product of the density, rate of flow, and time interval: $M = \rho Q(\Delta t)$

Then $\qquad F = \rho Q(\Delta V) = \rho Q(V_2 - V_1)$

The velocity may change either in direction, magnitude, or both. It is usually convenient to resolve both force and velocity vectors into suitable directions such as X, Y, Z, so that

$$F_X = \rho Q(V_{2X} - V_{1X}) \qquad \text{and} \qquad F_Y = \rho Q(V_{2Y} - V_{1Y}), \text{ etc.}$$

Care must be taken with the sign convention as shown in Problem 4-11. In fluids flowing through closed channels, the fluid's static pressure must be added to the dynamic pressure to determine the total pressure acting on a surface.

Problem 4-11 Force of water jet on vertical plane

A circular jet of water leaves a horizontal nozzle at 10 ft/sec striking a vertical plate a short distance away. Determine the force exerted on the plate if the jet diameter is 3 in.

Solution:

This is a simple application of the momentum equation in one direction.

The quantity of water flowing: $Q = VA = (10 \text{ ft/sec})(\pi/4)(3/12)^2$ sq ft

$$= 0.49 \text{ cu ft/sec}$$

Forces on the water: $F = \rho Q(V_2 - V_1) = \rho Q(-V_1)$

The final velocity of the water in the horizontal direction: $V_2 = 0$. The initial velocity of the water is 10 ft/sec, considering positive direction to the right, as shown in Fig. 4-7.

$$F = (62.4/32.2)(0.49)(-10) = -9.5 \text{ lb}$$

The plate exerts a force on the water (to the left) to decelerate the water. The force exerted by the water on the plate is equal in magnitude, opposite in direction. Thus, the force on the plate

$$F = +9.5 \text{ lb} \rightarrow \qquad Answer$$

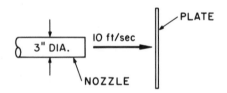

Figure 4-7

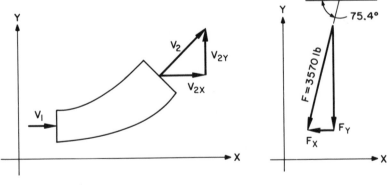

Figure 4-8   Figure 4-9

Problem 4-12 Force exerted on expanding elbow in pipeline

A 45° horizontal expanding elbow connects a 12-in.-diameter pipeline to an 18-in.-diameter line. The pressure at the 12-in. entrance is 15 psi. If water flows through the elbow at 10,000 gal/min, what force will be exerted on the elbow? Neglect friction effects.

Solution:

Resolve the entrance and exit velocities into X- and Y-components, as seen in Fig. 4-8, assuming the indicated positive directions. In addition to the forces caused by momentum change, the pressures at the entrance and exit also exert forces.

Quantity flowing = (10,000 gal/min)(1/60)(0.1337 cu ft/gal) = 22.28 cu ft/sec

Entrance area = $(\pi/4)(1 \text{ ft})^2$ = 0.785 sq ft

Exit area = $(\pi/4)(1.5 \text{ ft})^2$ = 1.77 sq ft

Entrance velocity: $V_1 = Q/A_1$ = 22.28/0.785 = +28.40 ft/sec

Exit velocity: $V_2 = Q/A_2$ = 22.28/1.77 = 12.65 ft/sec

Resolving exit velocity: V_{2X} = 12.65 cos 45° = +8.94 ft/sec

$\qquad\qquad\qquad\qquad V_{2Y}$ = 12.65 sin 45° = +8.94 ft/sec

Determine exit pressure, using the Bernoulli equation and noting that $Z_1 = Z_2$.

$$P_1/w + V_1{}^2/2g = P_2/w + V_2{}^2/2g$$
$$P_2 = (w/2g)(V_1{}^2 - V_2{}^2) + P_1$$
$$= (62.4/64.4)(28.40^2 - 12.65^2) + (15)(144)$$
$$= 2760 \text{ lb/sq ft or } 19.3 \text{ psi}$$

Force on elbow:

$$F_X = -\rho Q(V_{2X} - V_{1X}) + P_1 A_1 - (P_2 A_2)_X$$
$$= -(62.4/32.2)(22.28)(8.94 - 28.40) + (15)(144)(0.785)$$
$$- (2760)(1.77)(0.707)$$
$$= -902 \text{ lb} \leftarrow$$
$$F_Y = -\rho Q(V_{2Y} - V_{1Y}) - (P_2 A_2)_Y$$
$$= -(62.4/32.2)(8.94 - 0) - (2760)(1.77)(0.707)$$
$$= -3467 \text{ lb} \downarrow$$

The total force on the elbow is the vector sum of F_X and F_Y.

$$F = [(-902)^2 + (-3467)^2]^{\frac{1}{2}} \not\angle \tan^{-1} (-3467/-902)$$
$$= 3570 \text{ lb} \not\angle 75.4° \qquad Answer$$

See Fig. 4-9 to note the directions.

Problem 4-13 Force exerted by water through converging nozzle

A 3-in. horizontal diameter pipe is discharging water into the atmosphere through a 1-in.-diameter converging nozzle. The pressure in the pipe is known to be 80 psi. Find the force exerted by the water on the nozzle.

Solution:

The given pressure may be assumed as gage pressure; thus, the atmospheric pressure outside the nozzle is zero. Apply the Bernoulli equation for the up- and downstream conditions, noting that $Z_1 = Z_2$,

$$V_u^2/2g + P_u/w = V_d^2/2g + 0$$
$$P_u/w = (V_d^2 - V_u^2)/2g$$

From the continuity equation

$$V_u\pi(3^2)/4 = V_d\pi(1^2)/4$$
$$V_u = (1/9)V_d$$
$$P_u/w = \left\{V_d^2 - [(1/9)V_d]^2\right\}/2g$$
$$\frac{(80)(144)}{62.4} = \frac{V_d^2(1 - 1/81)}{64.4}$$
$$V_d = 110 \text{ ft/sec}$$
$$V_u = 12.2 \text{ ft/sec}$$
$$Q = V_d(\pi/4)(1/12)^2 = 0.600 \text{ cu ft/sec}$$

Applying the momentum equation

$$F = \rho Q(V_2 - V_1) = (62.4/32.2)(0.6)(110 - 12.2)$$
$$= 114 \text{ lb}$$

Assuming a positive direction for force and velocity to the right, this indicates a 114-lb force on the water to the right or a force on the nozzle of 114 lb to the left, as seen in Fig. 4-10.

Additional forces exerted on the nozzle are due to the change in pressure.

$$F_P = P_u A_u - P_d A_d$$
$$= 80\,(\pi/4)(3)^2 - 0$$
$$= 566 \text{ lb} \rightarrow$$

Net force on nozzle = $566 - 114 = 452$ lb $\rightarrow$ *Answer*

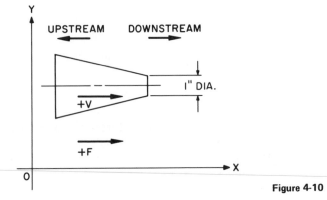

Figure 4-10

Problem 4-14 Thrust of jet plane determined by velocity of exhaust gases and fuel consumption

A jet plane operating at 600 mph discharges its exhaust gases at 4000 ft/sec. If its fuel consumption is 2 lb/sec and it requires an air-fuel ratio of 16:1, determine the thrust.

Solution:

Apply the momentum relation to determine the change in momentum for the air, noting its change in velocity is from 0 to −4000 ft/sec, and for the fuel, noting its change in velocity from +600 mph to −4000 ft/sec. Positive direction is assumed to be forward.

$$F_{air} = \rho Q(V_2 - V_1)$$
$$= (16)(2/32.2)(-4000) = -3980 \text{ lb}$$
$$F_{fuel} = (2/32.2)[-4000 - (88/60)(600)] = -303 \text{ lb}$$

Total thrust = 3980 + 303 = +4283 lb   *Answer*

Problem 4-15 Horsepower transfer to curved vane by water jet

A stream of water 3 in. in diameter with a velocity of 100 ft/sec strikes a curved vane moving in the same direction at 30 ft/sec; see Fig. 4-11. Determine the force exerted by the water on the vane and the horsepower delivered to the vane.

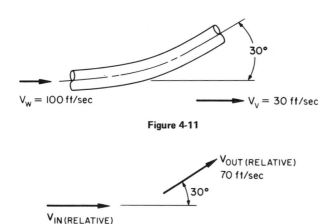

Figure 4-11

V_{OUT} (RELATIVE)
70 ft/sec

30°

V_{IN} (RELATIVE)
70 ft/sec

Figure 4-12

Solution:

To determine the change of the fluid's momentum in a problem where the deflector blade is not stationary, two methods of solution are possible. The change in momentum can be calculated by considering the change in either the absolute or the relative velocity of the fluid. Generally speaking the relative velocity approach is somewhat more convenient. It will be employed here. The relative velocity of the water with respect to the vane is $V_w - V_v$ or $100 - 30 = 70$ ft/sec to the right (as noticed by an observer moving with the vane). This is the relative velocity of the water upon entering the blade. The water's relative velocity, assuming no friction upon leaving the vane, is also 70 ft/sec but the direction is changed, as seen in Fig. 4-12.

The force on the blade in the assumed X-direction is $F_X = -\rho Q(V_{2X} - V_{1X})$. Note that Q must be the quantity of fluid actually contacting the blade which is based on the relative entering velocity.

$$F_X = -(62.4/32.2)(\pi/4)(3/12)^2(70)(70\cos 30° - 70)$$
$$= +62.6 \text{ lb} \rightarrow$$

Noting that $V_{1Y} = 0$

$$F_Y = -(62.4/32.2)(\pi/4)(3/12)^2(70)(70\sin 30° - 0)$$
$$= -233 \text{ lb} \downarrow$$

The power delivered to the vane is the product of the force exerted on the vane and the velocity of the vane in the same direction. Since the vane has only an X-direction, the horsepower is based on F_X.

$$hp = F_X V_X/550 = (62.6)(30) \text{ ft/sec}/550 \text{ ft-lb/sec}$$
$$= 3.42 \quad Answer$$

Relative Equilibrium

Another application of the momentum equation occurs in connection with relative equilibrium, i.e., the equilibrium achieved by a liquid subject to a constant accelerating force. Once the free surface of such a liquid has been established, the pressure variation may be determined as in a static liquid. Consider a tank partially filled with liquid that is acted upon by a constant horizontal force F_H. A particle of liquid at the surface is subject to the force F_H and the reaction from the surrounding water to its own weight R_W, as shown in Fig. 4-13. The direction of the free surface is normal to the resulting vector.

$$\tan\theta = F_H/R_W$$
$$F_H = m(dv/dt) = ma_H$$
$$R_W = |mg|$$
$$\tan\theta = ma_H/mg = a_H/g$$

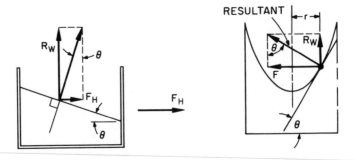

Figure 4-13   Figure 4-14

The pressure at any point h below the free surface is wh.

If the liquid is exposed to simultaneous horizontal and vertical accelerations, then $\tan \theta = a_H/(g + a_V)$. The pressure in such a case is $w(g + a_V)(h/g)$ at a distance h below the free surface.

Forced vortex rotation or the rotation of a liquid with constant angular velocity ω about a fixed vertical axis is another case of relative equilibrium. The free surface assumes and holds the shape of a paraboloid for which the direction at any point (see Fig. 4-14) is obtained by finding the forces acting on a particle at the surface:

$$\tan \theta = F/R_W$$

Centripetal force $F = m\omega^2 r$

Reaction to its weight $R_W = |mg|$

$$\tan \theta = m\omega^2 r/mg = \omega^2 r/g$$

since $\tan \theta = dy/dr = \omega^2 r/g$. Note that $\tan \theta$ is directly dependent on r. By integration, $y = \omega^2 r^2/2g$. The distance y is taken above the vertex of the paraboloid and as before the pressure at any distance h below the free surface is wh.

For a closed container containing no free surfaces, an imaginary free surface must be established through a point for which the gage pressure is known to be zero before the pressure at any point can be established.

Problem 4-16 Water spillage from accelerated cylindrical tank

Determine the volume of water spilled from a 2-ft-diameter open cylindrical tank, 6 ft high, initially filled with water which is accelerated horizontally at 8 ft/sec.

Solution:

The free surface makes an angle θ so that $\tan \theta = a_H/g = 8/32.2$. Assuming the tank has its base in the horizontal plane, as shown in Fig. 4-15, the depth of the water on the forward edge is by geometry

$$x/2 = 8/32.2$$

$$x = 0.497 \text{ ft}$$

The amount spilled out $= 1/2(\pi/4)(d^2)(x) = 1/2(\pi/4)(2)^2(0.497)$

$$= 0.780 \text{ cu ft} \qquad Answer$$

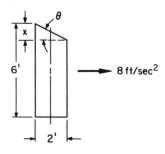

Figure 4-15

4-6 FLOW MEASUREMENT

In closed conduit flow, the pressure, velocity, or rate of flow are often to be determined. By applying the Bernoulli and continuity equations, the following meters may be used.

Quantity to be Measured	Typical Meter
Static pressure	Piezometer, static tube
Total pressure	Pitot tube
Velocity head	Combination of pitot tube with piezometer or with static tube
Flow rate	Venturi meter, flow nozzle or orifice meter

If a sudden contraction in the flow occurs as in an orifice meter, the smallest cross-sectional area of the flow known as the *vena contracta* is smaller than the least cross section. The two areas are related by a contraction coefficient.

$$\text{Area}_{\text{vena contracta}} = C_C(\text{Area of orifice or least cross section})$$

Actual flow velocity is less than ideal, thus $V_{\text{actual}} = C_V V_{\text{ideal}}$.

Actual flow rate: $Q_{\text{actual}} = C_V C_C Q_{\text{ideal}}$

$$= C_D Q_{\text{ideal}}$$

where C_D = coefficient of discharge.

For unrestrained discharge into the atmosphere under a pressure head h,

$$Q_{\text{actual}} = C_D(2gh)^{\frac{1}{2}}$$

Note that in a Venturi meter $C_C = 1$ and C_V is so close to 1 that often C_D is assumed to equal 1.

Problem 4-17 Flow characteristics of water discharging from a tank opening

Water discharges through the opening in the tank, as shown in Fig. 4-16, and strikes the ground 6 ft below. If the velocity coefficient is 0.97 and the contraction coefficient is 0.70, determine (a) the flow in cu ft/sec and (b) the horizontal distance x in feet. The diameter of the orifice is 3.0 in.

Solution:

To determine the discharge velocity, write the Bernoulli equation between the free surface of the water ($P_1 = 0$, $Z_1 = 3$ ft) and the discharge level ($P_2 = 0$, $Z_2 = 0$). Assume the water velocity at the free surface to be zero.

$$P_1/w + Z_1 + V_1{}^2/2g = P_2/w + Z_2 + V_2{}^2/2g$$
$$3 = V_2{}^2/2g$$

Discharge velocity $V_2 = 13.9$ ft/sec. This is the ideal velocity.

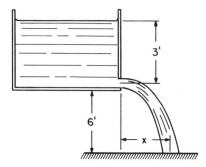

Figure 4-16

$V_{actual} = (0.97)(13.9) = 13.5$ ft/sec

Flow $= C_C V_{actual} A_{orifice} = (0.70)(13.5)(\pi/4)(3/12)^2$

$= 0.463$ cu ft/sec   *Answer*, part (a)

To find the distance in the X-direction, determine the time required for the water to drop 6 ft with zero initial velocity in the vertical direction. (See Sec. 3-3.)

$S_Y = a_Y t^2/2$

$t = (2S_Y/a_Y)^{\frac{1}{2}} = (12/32.2)^{\frac{1}{2}}$

$= 0.610$ sec

The same time is available for movement in X-direction.

$x = V_{actual}(t) = 8.23$ ft   *Answer*, part (b)

4-7   OPEN CHANNEL FLOW

In open channel flow the fluid stream has a free surface; the rest of the stream cross action is that of the confining channel. In steady, uniform, open channel flow, $V_1 = V_2$ and $P_1 = P_2$, therefore, the Bernoulli equation reduces to

Head lost due to friction $= H_F = Z_1 - Z_2$

Rate of flow in open channels depends on the slope of the channel $S = (Z_1 - Z_2)/L$, the surface condition, the hydraulic mean radius R, and the stream cross-sectional area A.

$V_{avg} = C(RS)^{\frac{1}{2}}$

$Q = AV$

Empirical values for C can be found (among others) by using the Manning formula

$C = (1.486/n)R^{\frac{1}{6}}$

where n = surface roughness factor.

Then $V = (1.486/n)\left(R^{\frac{2}{3}}\right)\left(S^{\frac{1}{2}}\right)$

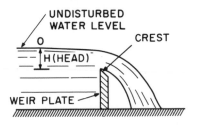
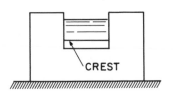

Figure 4-17

Flow Measurement—Weirs

An obstruction placed across a channel to impede water flow is called a weir. The difference in height between the undisturbed water level and the crest of the weir is a reasonably good measure of the rate of flow. Flow velocity at point 0 is assumed negligible. (See Fig. 4-17.)

$$Q_{actual} = \int V_{jet}\, dA = C \int_0^H (2gy)^{\frac{1}{2}}\, dy$$

4-8 MODEL THEORY

Models used in the study of fluid situations must usually satisfy geometric similitude, i.e., the models are scale versions of the original. Kinematic similitude, i.e., the kinematic quantities of velocity and acceleration, are identical in the model and in the original; and dynamic similitude, i.e., the forces acting on or in the model and the original, are identical. The applicable relations can always be expressed in the fundamental units of force F, length L, and time T; or mass M, length and time. The variables are usually expressed in standard fluid mechanics symbols and formed into a number of important dimensionless ratios.

1. The geometric ratio L_1/L_2 must be identical for all corresponding dimensions in the model L_1 and the original L_2 to assure geometric similitude.

2. The Reynolds number must be the same for dynamic similarity to exist in cases where the model and the original move in a fluid, or the fluid moves in a pipe. Submarines and their models are dynamically similar if the Reynolds number is the same.

$$N_{Re} = VD/v$$

3. For high-speed compressible flow near or above sonic velocities the Mach number must be identical for model and original $[V(E/\rho)^{1/2}]$.

4. The Froude number is used for open hydraulic structures, spillways, and ships.

$$N_{Fr} = (V/(Lg)^{\frac{1}{2}} = (\text{inertia forces/gravity forces})^{\frac{1}{2}}$$

Other dimensionless ratios used are

1. The Euler number = pressure forces/inertia forces
2. The Weber number = inertia forces/surface tension forces.

   Determination of the particular dimensionless ratio to be used is based on a consideration of the most important quantities for the problem under investigation.

Problem 4-18 Water model test of oil flow in pipeline

A study is to be made of the flow of crude oil through a 24-in. pipeline. The oil temperature is estimated at 60°F and the oil's velocity is to be 20 ft/sec. Model tests are to be conducted for pressure drop using water at 70°F as the test medium. If the water is to flow through a 2-in. I.D. pipe, at what velocity should it move?

Solution:

The flow must be dynamically similar to allow study of the dynamic characteristic pressure. For the flow inside of pipes, the Reynolds number is the characteristic number. It must be equal for the two cases. The characteristic length involved is the pipe diameter.

$$(N_{Re})_{oil} = (N_{Re})_{water}$$

$$N_{Re} = VD/v$$

   From the given information, V_o = 20 ft/sec, V_w = unknown, D_o = 24 in., D_w = 2 in., $v_o = 6 \times 10^{-4}$, and $v_w = 1 \times 10^{-4}$. Thus,

$$V_o D_o/v_o = V_w D_w/v_w$$

$$V_w = \frac{(20)(24)(1 \times 10^{-4})}{(2)(6 \times 10^{-4})}$$

$$= 40 \text{ ft/sec} \qquad Answer$$

chapter 5
THERMODYNAMICS

Engineering thermodynamics deals with the determination of the nature of the energy transformation and the amount of energy being transferred during a thermodynamic process. Involved in this area are the concepts of heat, heat transfer, and heat transformation to useful work.

5-1 FORMS OF ENERGY

Energy exists in two ways (neglecting the transformation of mass into energy), either stored or transient.

Examples of stored energy are: mechanical potential energy as the energy stored in a compressed spring; mechanical kinetic energy as in a mass moving at a specific velocity; or internal energy, i.e., the energy stored within a body by virtue of its atomic or molecular positioning and movement. Evidences of internal energy are the temperature, pressure, and specific volume or physical phase (solid, liquid, gas) of a substance.

Examples of transient energy are work, i.e., a force acting through a distance, or transferred heat, the transfer taking place by conduction or radiation.

5-2 THE FOUR LAWS OF THERMODYNAMICS

Four primary laws govern the study of thermodynamics. These laws are stated in many ways of which the following are typical.

Zeroth Law *When two bodies are in thermal equilibrium, there is no net heat flow from one to the other body and both are at the same temperature.*

First Law *Energy can neither be created nor destroyed. This law is also known as the Law of the Conservation of Energy.*

Second Law *The heat energy of a hot body can be made available only by interposing an engine between the hot body and a cooler one and utilizing a fraction of the energy being transferred from the hot to the cool body.*

Third Law *Every body has a finite "entropy" that is almost zero when the absolute temperature of the body is zero. (Some residual energy remains due to nuclear spin.)*

5-3 GENERAL ENERGY EQUATION

The following steady flow general energy equation pertains to both reversible and irreversible processes and is a mathematical statement of the First Law of Thermodynamics written between points 1 and 2.

$$\frac{z_1}{J} + \frac{Vel_1^2}{2gJ} + \frac{p_1 v_1}{J} + u_1 + Q = \frac{z_2}{J} + \frac{Vel_2^2}{2gJ} + \frac{p_2 v_2}{J} + u_2 + W$$

This equation is written for 1 lb of a substance and all terms are energy values expressed in Btu/lb. Note that $J = 778$ ft-lb/Btu. This equation is an accounting of all the energy transformations occurring in a system between points 1 and 2 provided that the heat Q entering (+) or leaving (−) between points 1 and 2 and the work done by (+) or on (−) the system between these two points are also accounted for. The energy terms in the above equation may be restated as difference values between points 1 and 2 as follows:

Difference in potential energy $= \dfrac{z_1 - z_2}{J}$

Difference in kinetic energy $= \dfrac{Vel_1^2 - Vel_2^2}{2}$

Difference in flow work $= \dfrac{p_1 v_1 - p_2 v_2}{J}$

Note that flow work done by a system is a function of external pressure (p_1, p_2) only. If the external pressure is zero, no flow work will be done. The specific volume of the thermodynamic fluid at points 1 and 2 is v_1, v_2.

Difference in internal energy $= u_1 - u_2$

Heat added or removed from system $= \pm Q$

Work done by or on the system $= \pm W$

Simplifications and restatements of the general energy equation are made to suit a variety of particular cases or processes. In thermodynamics the difference $z_1 - z_2$ is usually assumed to be negligible. The internal energy u and the flow work term pv/J are usually combined and expressed as "enthalpy," so that $h = u + pv/J$. Thus, a simplified form of the general energy equation that assumes $z_1 - z_2 = 0$ is

$$Vel_1^2/2gJ + h_1 + Q = Vel_2^2/2gJ + h_2 + W$$

5-4 IDEAL GAS LAWS

The *state* of a substance is thermodynamically defined by specifying any three of the four following parameters: pressure, volume, temperature, and composition. The relation between the first three parameters is contained in the ideal gas laws or characteristic equation of a perfect gas.

$$pV = wRT \qquad or \qquad pV = RT$$

The composition refers to the type of fluid being used, i.e., carbon dioxide, air, etc. Knowing this, the ideal gas constant R may be looked up in appropriate tables. For air, R = 53.3 ft-lb/lb-°Rankine. Another expression for the character-istic equation of a perfect gas uses the universal gas constant R_u that has the same value for all gases.

R_u = 1545 ft-lb/mole-°Rankine

where R_u = MR

M = w/n

M = molecular weight

n = number of moles or ratio of weight of gas to its molecular weight ex-pressed in pounds

so that $pV = nMRT = n\ R_u\ T$.

Problem 5-1 Air temperature in chamber determined by molecular weight, total weight, and volume

An air chamber measuring 10 ft X 10 ft X 8 ft is filled with 52 lb of air at 16 psia. The molecular weight of air is approximately 24. What is the temperature inside the chamber?

Solution:

Since the molecular weight, the total weight, and volume are given, use the equa-tion employing the universal gas constant and the number of moles n:

n = w/M = 52/24 = 2.16, say 2.2

$pV = n\ R_u\ T$

$T = pV/(n\ R_u) = (16)(144)(800)/(2.2)(1545) = 544°$ Rankine

= 544 − 460 = 84°F   *Answer*

Boyle's Law (T is constant)

pV = constant

$p_1 V_1 = p_2 V_2$

$p_1/p_2 = V_2/V_1$

Charles' Law (p is constant)

V/T = constant

when T is expressed in absolute values, usually °Rankine (°Rankine = 460 + °F)

$V_1/V_2 = T_1/T_2$

Charles' Law (V is constant)

p/T = constant

$p_1/T_1 = p_2/T_2$

5-5 SPECIFIC HEATS

The *heat capacity* or *specific heat* C is the quantity of heat in Btu's required to change the temperature of 1 lb of a substance by $1°$ Rankine.

$$Q = \int_{T_1}^{T_2} C \, dT$$

or if C does not vary with temperature

$$Q = C(T_2 - T_1)$$

The amount of heat required for a gas or vapor to be raised from T_1 to T_2 depends on the path or process that is used. Two commonly used paths define two commonly used specific heats, the constant volume process wherein

$$Q_V = \int_{T_1}^{T_2} C_V \, dT$$

and the constant pressure process for which

$$Q_p = \int_{T_1}^{T_2} C_p \, dT.$$

5-6 NONFLOW PROCESSES

A nonflow process is defined as a process in which no flow of fluid occurs across the boundary of a system. With this stipulation there can be no flow work term nor a kinetic energy term and the general energy equation reduces to the simple form $u_1 + Q = u_2 + W$. Again the solution of the equation depends in part on knowing the state of the working substance at points 1 and 2 and the process by which the substance passed from point 1 to 2.

Problem 5-2 Work done during expansion of gas in a cylinder

The gas in a cylinder slowly expands moving a 5-in.-diameter piston from its initial position at 3 in. to its final position at 8 in., as shown in Fig. 5-1. The pressure varies according to $p = -0.01V^2 + 8V$, where V is the volume and p is given in psi. How much work in Btu's is done during the expansion?

Solution:

This is a nonflow process; work is done because of the movement of a boundary (i.e., the piston).

The volume of the gas at points 1 and 2 is

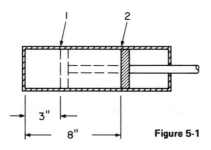

Figure 5-1

$$V_1 = (\pi d^2)L_1/4 = (\pi 5^2)(3/4) = 59 \text{ cu in.}$$
$$V_2 = (\pi d^2)L_2/4 = (\pi 5^2)(8/4) = 157 \text{ cu in.}$$
$$\text{Work} = \int_{V_1}^{V_2} p \, dV = \int_{V_1}^{V_2} (-0.01V^2 + 8V) \, dV$$
$$= \left[\frac{-0.01V^3}{3} + \frac{8V^2}{2} \right]_{59}^{157}$$
$$= 71{,}885 \text{ in.-lb} = \frac{71{,}885 \text{ in.-lb}}{12 \text{ in./ft} \times 778 \text{ ft-lb/Btu}} = 7.70 \text{ Btu} \qquad Answer$$

Problem 5-3 Internal energy of Freon vapor determined from conditions

Determine the internal energy of 1 lb of saturated Freon vapor having an absolute pressure of 313.00 psi, a temperature of 170°F, a volume of 0.1187 cu ft/lb, and an enthalpy of 91.36 Btu/lb.

Solution:

Given the absolute pressure and the temperature of a saturated vapor, the specific volume, enthalpy, and often also the internal energy (for example, for steam) can be looked up in appropriate tables. However, to determine the internal energy u recall

$$h = u + pv/J$$
$$u = h - pv/J = 91.36 - (313)(144)(0.1187)/778$$
$$= 91.36 - 6.84 = 84.52 \text{ Btu/lb} \qquad Answer$$

Problem 5-4 Heat absorbed by steel during drilling of hole

Ninety seconds are required to drill a $\frac{1}{4}$-in.-diameter hole through a $\frac{3}{4}$-in. piece of steel weighing 2 lb. The power required for the drilling operation is 0.25 hp. Determine the final temperature of the steel if it absorbs 0.70 of the heat generated during drilling. The room temperature is 75°F and the specific heat of steel is 0.118.

Solution:

$$\text{Work} = 0.25 \text{ hp} \times \frac{33{,}000 \text{ ft-lb}}{\text{hp} \times \text{min}} \times 1.5 \text{ min} = 12{,}380 \text{ ft-lb}$$

Assume all the work is transferred to heat energy

$$Q = W/778 \text{ ft-lb/Btu} = 12{,}380/778 = 15.9 \text{ Btu}$$
$$Q' = 15.9/2 = 7.95 \text{ Btu/lb}$$

Assume, furthermore, all the heat absorbed remains within the steel during the drilling operation. The specific heat value in engineering work is normally quoted in terms of Btu/lb/°F. The final temperature

$$Q' = C(T_2 - T_1)$$
$$T_2 = (Q'/C) + T = 7.95/0.118 + 75 = 142.4 \qquad Answer$$

Problem 5-5 Cylinder gas pressure affected by heat

An air cylinder, originally at 90 psi and 60°F, has been standing in the sun so that its temperature is raised to 95°F. Determine the pressure in the air cylinder.

Solution:

This is a straightforward application of Charles' Law, i.e., a constant-volume process. Note that pressure must be expressed as an absolute value.

$$p_2 = p_1 T_2/T_1 = (90 + 14.7)(460 + 95)/(460 + 70)$$

$$= 110 \text{ psia}$$

$$= (110 - 14.7) = 95.3 \text{ psi} \qquad Answer$$

A *reversible process* is a process in which a substance can proceed from state 1 to state 2 along a specific path after which the substance may be returned to state 1 with all conditions upon return being identical to the initial conditions. For a reversible process to take place, no friction or fluid turbulence can be present and the pressures and/or temperatures must be such that an infinitesimal change in either will reverse the process. An *irreversible process* is, of course, one that does not fit these conditions.

The *difference in internal energy* of a perfect gas can be determined by using the nonflow energy equation in combination with the equation for the specific heat at constant volume: $Q = u_2 - u_1 + W$. In a constant volume process, $W = 0$. Therefore,

$$Q_v = u_2 - u_1 = \int_{T_1}^{T_2} C_v \, dT$$

or, if C_v is constant, the change in internal energy is directly related to the change in temperature: $u_2 - u_1 = C_v(T_2 - T_1)$. It is seen that $u_2 - u_1$ is dependent only on the initial and final state of the gas. The difference in internal energy with respect to an arbitrary datum level may be found in the thermodynamic tables and diagrams.

The *difference in enthalpy* of a perfect gas is obtained from the definition of enthalpy $h = u + pv/J$. Therefore,

$$h_1 - h_2 = u_1 - u_2 + \frac{p_1 v_1 - p_2 v_2}{J}$$

Note that the difference of enthalpy is also dependent only on the initial and final states of the gas.

Using the general energy equation for a nonflow constant-pressure process, we find

$$Q_p = u_2 - u_1 + W = u_2 - u_1 + p(v_2 - v_1)/J$$

$$= h_2 - h_1$$

Since $\qquad Q_p = C_p(T_2 - T_1)$

$$h_2 - h_1 = C_p(T_2 - T_1)$$

The Relation of C_p to C_v

The ratio of specific heats C_p/C_v is denoted k, having approximately the value of 1.67 for monatomic gases and 1.40 for diatomic gases.

For a nonflow constant-pressure process, the flow work per pound is evaluated by $W = p \, dv = p(v_2 - v_1)$ and using the characteristic equation for a perfect gas $W = R(T_2 - T_1)/J$. Therefore, substituting in the general energy equation for a constant-pressure nonflow process

$$Q = u_2 - u_1 + W$$

or $C_p(T_2 - T_1) = C_v(T_2 - T_1) + R(T_2 - T_1)/J$

Therefore, $C_p = C_v + R/J$. Using $C_p/C_v = k$

$$C_p = kR/(k-1)J \qquad \text{and} \qquad C_v = R/(k-1)J$$

Entropy s is the ratio of the heat transferred to the constant temperature at which this transfer occurs in a reversible process. For an infinitesimal change $ds = Q_{rev}/T$ and for a finite change at constant temperature $\Delta s = Q_{rev}/T$. Entropy increases when heat passes into a system (i.e., positive Q) and decreases for heat leaving the system. Note that entropy, like enthalpy, and internal energy, is a function of state only.

If a process is irreversible, entropy, which is sometimes defined as a measure of unavailable energy, is greater than the ratio of heat input to temperature. This is caused by the increase in unavailable energy caused by friction in a reversible process.

$$\Delta s > Q_{irr}/T$$

Thermodynamic Reversible Nonflow Processes with Constant Specific Heats

An understanding of the change of properties of the working substances and the addition or rejection of energy in the form of heat or work is desirable for the solution of problems in thermodynamics. In addition to the equations suitable for a particular process, a plot of the process on a p-V or on a T-S (temperature-entropy) diagram is desirable for obtaining a graphical presentation of the energy requirements of a cycle. The area under the process curve on a p-V plane is indicative of the work requirement of a process from the equation work = $\int p \, dv$. The area under the process curve on a T-S plane is indicative of the heat requirements of a process from the equation $\int dQ = \int T \, ds$. These curves are plotted for all processes in Figs. 5-2 through 5-6. The relations governing the various processes are outlined in the succeeding paragraphs. The words internal energy, enthalpy, and entropy refer to the change occurring in these quantities between the beginning and end of the process.

Constant-volume process is one in which the volume of the gas is held constant while heat is being added or removed, thereby raising or lowering the pressure and temperature. It is an application of Charles' Law, $p_1/p_2 = T_1/T_2$.

CONSTANT-VOLUME PROCESS

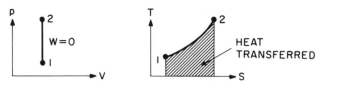

Figure 5-2

CONSTANT-PRESSURE PROCESS

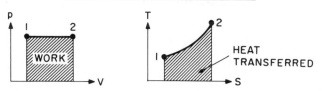

Figure 5-3

CONSTANT-TEMPERATURE PROCESS

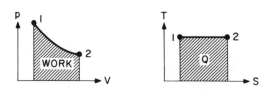

Figure 5-4

ISENTROPIC PROCESS

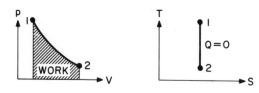

Figure 5-5

POLYTROPIC PROCESS

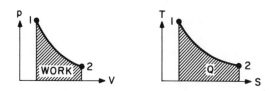

Figure 5-6

Work: $W = 0$ (Fig. 5-2)

Internal energy: $u_2 - u_1 = C_v(T_2 - T_1)$

Heat transferred: $Q = C_v(T_2 - T_1)$

Energy equation: $Q = u_2 - u_1$

Enthalpy $= h_2 - h_1 = \int_{T_1}^{T_2} C_p \, dT = C_p(T_2 - T_1)$ if C_p is constant

Entropy $= s_2 - s_1 = \int_{T_1}^{T_2} dQ/T = C_v \int_{T_1}^{T_2} dT/T = C_v \ln(T_2/T_1)$

Constant-pressure process is one in which the pressure of the gas is held constant while heat is being added or removed, Fig. 5-3, thereby increasing or decreasing the volume and temperature. It is another application of Charles' Law: $V_1/V_2 = T_1/T_2$.

Enthalpy $= h_2 - h_1 = C_p(T_2 - T_1)$; also $h_2 - h_1 = Q$

Heat transferred: $Q = C_p \int_{T_1}^{T_2} dt = C_p(T_2 - T_1)$

Entropy $= s_2 - s_1 = \int_{T_1}^{T_2} dQ/T = C_p \int_{T_1}^{T_2} dT/T = C_p \ln(T_2/T_1)$

Isothermal or constant-temperature process is a process taking place at constant temperature; therefore, $p_1 V_1 = p_2 V_2 = C$. This plots as an equilateral hyperbola on the p-V plane, whereas on the T-S plane it is represented by a horizontal line, as see in Fig. 5-4.

Work: $W = (1/J) \int p \, dv = (C/J) \int_{v_1}^{v_2} dv/v = (C/J) \ln(v_2/v_1)$

Internal energy $= u_2 - u_1 = 0$ (because $T_2 - T_1 = 0$)

Heat transferred: $Q = W = (s_2 - s_1)T$

Energy equation: $Q = W$

Enthalpy $= h_2 - h_1 = 0$ (because $T_2 - T_1 = 0$)

Entropy $= s_2 - s_1 = (R/J) \ln(v_2/v_1)$

Specific heat is infinite for an isothermal process because heat may be added to a substance without causing a corresponding rise in temperature.

Isentropic process is a process during which the substance undergoes no change in entropy (Fig. 5-5). This is accomplished by making the process completely reversible and adiabatic. Reversibility indicates that there will be no losses resulting from turbulence or friction; adiabatic indicates that the process takes place without any heat being transferred in any direction. Energy gains or losses during the process result only from work. Changes in the internal energy of the substance result only from work being done on or by the substance. During the process all fundamental properties, i.e., pressure, volume, and temperature, vary. This variation may be obtained by considering the simple nonflow energy equation $Q = U + W$ and, realizing that for this process $Q = 0$; therefore $U = -W$ or $wC_v \, dT = (-p \, dv)/J$.

Recalling the characteristic equation for a perfect gas $pV = wRT$, the relations between two variables at a time may be written as follows, using the relation $C_p/C_v = k$:

$$(V_1/V_2)^k = p_2/p_1 \qquad pV^k = C$$
$$T_2/T_1 = (V_1/V_2)^{k-1}$$
$$= (p_2/p_1)^{(k-1)/k}$$

Work: $W = C/J$

$$\frac{dV}{V^k} = \frac{p_2 V_2 - p_1 V_1}{J(1-k)}$$

Internal energy: $u_2 - u_1 = C_v(T_2 - T_1)$

Heat transferred = 0, by definition

Enthalpy $= h_2 - h_1 = C_p(T_2 - T_1)$

Entropy = 0, by definition

Polytropic process is the most general form of process during which expansion or compression of a working substance can take place. As in an isentropic process, the fundamental properties continuously vary; however, heat may be added or removed during the process. The equations are fundamentally those of the isentropic process with the substitution of the value of n for k; the value of n has to be given or determined for a particular process. This value of n may vary from 0 to infinity. Some interesting results are tabulated below for various values of n:

$0 > n < 1$ temperature rises during expansion, falls during compression

$n > 1$ temperature falls during expansion, rises during compression

$n < k$ heat must be added during expansion

$n > k$ heat rejected during expansion

The cause for the apparent paradox in the last inequality is that work is being done by the gas at a faster rate than that at which heat is being added to the gas. Pressure, volume, and temperature relations are

$$\text{Work} = \frac{p_2 v_2 - p_1 v_1}{J(n-1)}$$

Internal energy: $u_2 - u_1 = C_v(T_2 - T_1)$

Heat transferred: $Q = n = C_v(T_2 - T_1)(n-k)/(n-1)$

Enthalpy $= h_2 - h_1 = C_p(T_2 - T_1)$

Entropy $= s_2 - s_1 = C_v(n-k)/(n) \ln (T_2/T_1) = C_n \ln (T_2/T_1)$

Throttling process is an irreversible adiabatic steady flow process. The general energy equation applied to this is

$$h_1 + (\text{Vel}_1)^2/2g = h_2 + (\text{Vel}_2)^2/2g$$

Because the velocity at the entrance and exit (points 1 and 2) of a throttling device are usually very nearly equal, the equation reduces to $h_1 = h_2$. Most often a throttling process is used in connection with a fluid such as steam which changes phase during the throttling.

Problem 5-6 Volume and pressure of gas affected by adiabatic compression

Five cubic feet of a gas initially at 2 psig and 70°F are compressed causing a 19-fold increase in pressure. The compression is adiabatic, $k = 1.4$. If the barometric pressure is 33 ft of water, determine the final volume and pressure of the gas.

Solution:

To express the pressure in absolute values, note that 34 ft of water = 14.7 psi.

$p_1 = 2 + (33/34)(14.7) = 16.22$ psia

$p_2 = 19p_1 = 308$ psia

For adiabatic expansion

$(V_1/V_2)^k = p_2/p_1$

$(5/V_2)^{1.4} = 308/16.22 = 19.0$

$5/V_2 = 19.0^{1/1.4} = 8.2$

$V_2 = 5/8.2 = 0.61$ cu ft   *Answer*

$p_2 = 308 - (33/34)(14.7) = 293.8$ psig   *Answer*

Problem 5-7 Temperature rise of gas under conditions of constant pressure or constant volume

In a laboratory experiment 50 Btu were required to raise 1 lb of air at constant pressure (14.7 psi) from 32°F to 253°F while the volume changed from 12.33 cu ft to 17.90 cu ft. If in another experiment the initial volume (12.33 cu ft) were kept constant, how much heat would be required to cause the same temperature rise?

Solution:

This problem involves the difference in energy requirements for the two processes. The energy equations for the two processes are

Constant-pressure process = $Q_p = u_2 - u_1 + W$

Constant-volume process = $Q_v = u_2 - u_1$ $(W = 0)$

Since the change in internal energy $u_2 - u_1$ is the same for all processes provided the temperatures are the same, the difference in heat added is the additional work done during the constant-pressure process.

$Q_p - Q_v = W$

$W = p(v_2 - v_1)/J$

$$= \frac{(14.7 \times 144)\ \text{lb/sq ft} \times (17.90 - 12.33)\ \text{cu ft}}{778}$$

$= 15.2$ Btu

Heat required for constant volume process = $Q_p - W = 50 - 15.2$

$= 34.8$ Btu   *Answer*

Problem 5-8 Work required and heat transferred during compression of nitrogen

Five pounds of nitrogen are compressed in a nonflow process from an initial volume of 137.5 cu ft at 14.7 psia to a volume of 50 cu ft at 60 psia. The gas constant for nitrogen is 55.15 ft-lb/lb-°Rankine. Determine (a) the process used for compression, (b) the amount of work required, and (c) the heat transferred.

Solution:

For all processes except the constant-volume and constant-pressure processes, which are incidentally ruled out by the statement of the problem, the relation between pressure and volume is given by

$$p_1/p_2 = (V_2/V_1)^n \qquad (-\infty < n < \infty)$$

$$\frac{14.7}{60} = \left(\frac{50/5}{137.5/5}\right)^n = \left(\frac{50}{137.5}\right)^n$$

$$0.245 = (0.364)^n$$

$$n = 1.395 \approx 1.4 = k$$

(a) Since n equals the specific heat ratio for nitrogen, the compression is adiabatic. *Answer*

(b) Work: $W = (p_2 V_2 - p_1 V_1)/(k - 1)$ ft-lb. *Note:* V_1, V_2 are the total volumes.

$$W = \frac{144[(60 \times 50) - (14.7 \times 137.5)]}{(1.4 - 1)}$$

$$= 353,000 \text{ ft-lb} \qquad Answer$$

(c) Heat transferred: $Q = 0$ (for any adiabatic process) *Answer*

Problem 5-9 Weight, volume, and temperature of air determined from constants

Air in a room is at 60°F and atmospheric pressure. Barometer reading is 20.37 in. Hg. For air: $C_v = 0.1715$, $C_p = 0.24$, $R = 53.3$.
(a)   What is the weight of the air in lb/cu ft?
(b)   What would be the resulting volume if 1 cu ft of the room air were compressed to 50 psig at 320°F?
(c)   What would be the resulting volume if 1 cu ft of the room air were heated at constant pressure to a temperature of 580°F?
(d)   What would be the resulting temperature if 1 cu ft of the room air were compressed according to $pV = C$ to a pressure of 90 psig?
(e)   What would be the resulting temperature if 1 cu ft of the room air were compressed isentropically to 90 psig?

Solution:

(a) Determine the weight per cubic foot from the characteristic equation $pV = wRT$.

$$p = 20.37 \text{ in. Hg} \times 0.490 \text{ psi/in. Hg} = 9.98 \text{ psia}$$

(Incidentally, 9.98 psia is an extremely low atmospheric pressure.)

$$w/V = p/RT = (9.98)(144)/(53.3)(460 + 60) = 0.052 \text{ lb/cu ft} \qquad Answer$$

(b) From (a) 1 cu ft weighs 0.052 lb. Using this information and again applying the characteristic equation

$$V = \frac{wRT}{p} = \frac{(0.052)(53.3)(460 + 320)}{(50 + 9.98)(144)} = 0.251 \text{ cu ft} \qquad Answer$$

(c) Assuming the constant pressure refers to atmospheric pressure and starting at $T = 60°F$

$$V_1/V_2 = T_1/T_2$$

$$V_2 = \frac{V_1 T_2}{T_1} = \frac{(1)(460 + 580)}{(460 + 60)} = 2 \text{ cu ft} \qquad Answer$$

(d) The process defined by $pV = C$ is a constant-pressure process; therefore,

$$T_2 = T_1 = 60°F \qquad Answer$$

(e) For the isentropic process the following relation holds between pressure and temperature:

$$\frac{T_2}{T_1} = \left(\frac{p_2}{p_1}\right)^{(k-1)/k}$$

$$T_2 = T_1 \left(\frac{p_2}{p_1}\right)^{(k-1)/k} = (460 + 60) \left(\frac{90 + 9.98}{9.98}\right)^{0.4/1.4}$$

$$= 1005 - 460 = 545°F \qquad Answer$$

Cycles

A thermodynamic cycle is a succession of processes in which the working substance starting with initial conditions works or is worked upon after which the substance is returned to its original conditions. Essential elements of the cycle are the working substance or medium that serves to transform energy, the hot and cold bodies that act, respectively, as a source and as a receiver of heat energy, and the heat engine or heat pump that either delivers energy to or removes energy from the working substance. Cycles may be classified as open or closed, flow or nonflow. In an open cycle nature returns the working substances to their original conditions as, for example, in a diesel engine, where the working substance is exhausted to the atmosphere. In a closed cycle the same working substance is used continually, always returning to its original state. In all thermodynamic cycles the working substance must proceed by more than one process from the original conditions back to them.

Power cycle efficiency is the ratio of the energy output or work done to the energy input.

$$\text{Efficiency} = \frac{\text{energy output}}{\text{energy input}} = \frac{Q_{in} - Q_{rejected}}{Q_{in}} = \frac{\text{work done}}{Q_{in}}$$

The maximum conceivable cycle efficiencies occur in a reversible cycle where no losses or inefficiencies occur due to irreversibilities.

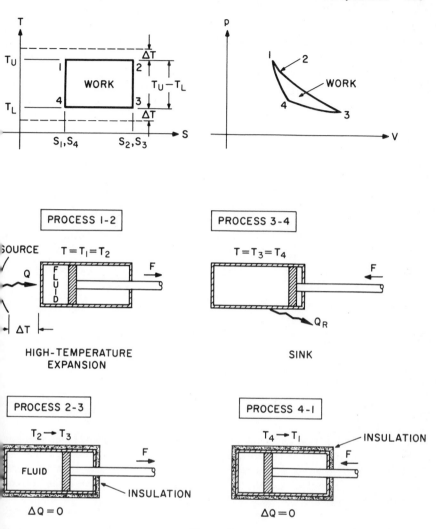

Figure 5-7

Carnot Cycle

An interesting example of such a reversible nonflow cycle, one often used for comparisons, is the Carnot cycle, as shown in Fig. 5-7. It consists of four separate processes as follows: (1) isothermal expansion during which heat is added to the working substance from the source; (2) reversible adiabatic or isentropic expansion; (3) isothermal compression of the working substance with heat rejection to the sink; and (4) reversible adiabatic or isentropic compression. For this cycle the heat added, the heat rejected, the work done, and the efficiency may all be determined by appropriate area measurements on the T-S plane; see Fig. 5-7. The total heat added is the area between the line indicating states 1 and 2 and the S-axis. Thus, the total heat added is the rectangular area defined by the upper temperature T_U, the two isentropic lines S_1 and S_2, and an arbitrary lower datum, the S-axis.

$$Q_A = T_U(S_2 - S_1)$$

The heat rejected is the area between the line indicating states 3 and 4 and the S-axis. The heat rejected is $Q_R = T_L(S_3 - S_4)$. The usable energy or the work done during the cycle is the algebraic difference between Q_A and Q_R

$$\begin{aligned}
\text{Work} = Q_{net} &= T_U(S_2 - S_1) - T_L(S_3 - S_4) \\
&= T_U(S_2 - S_1) - T_L(S_2 - S_1) \\
&= (T_U - T_L)(S_2 - S_1)
\end{aligned}$$

The efficiency is then

$$\frac{\text{Usable energy}}{\text{Total energy input}} = \frac{Q_A - Q_R}{Q_A} = \frac{T_U - T_L}{T_U}$$

The p-V plane may similarly be used to obtain the work done during the cycle as the work enclosed in the p-V diagram of Fig. 5-7. Calculation of the work proceeds by calculating the work for each process and summing these quantities.

W_{1-2}, an isothermal process $= p_1 V_1 \ln(V_2/V_1)$

W_{2-3}, an isentropic process $= (p_3 V_3 - p_2 V_2)/(1 - k)$

W_{3-4}, an isothermal process $= p_3 V_3 \ln(V_4/V_3)$

W_{4-1}, an isentropic process $= (p_1 V_1 - p_4 V_4)/(1 - k)$

Net cycle work $= W_{1-2} + W_{2-3} + W_{3-4} + W_{4-1}$

Note that in working out the above statements, $p_1 V_1$ may be substituted for $p_2 V_2$ and $p_3 V_3$ for $p_4 V_4$ from isothermal relations. Then $W_{2-3} = -W_{4-1}$. Cycle efficiency is $(W_{1-2} + W_{3-4})/W_{1-2}$, which equals $(T_U - T_L)/T_U$.

In connection with cycle analysis, the following terms are frequently used: displacement volume, the volume swept out during one piston stroke, $V_3 - V_1$ (Fig. 5-7); and mean effective pressure p_m, the average pressure that would be required to produce the net cycle work when forcing the working substance through the displacement volume, $p_m = W_{net}/V_{dis}$.

Refrigeration Cycles—Heat Pumps

By reversing all the processes of the Carnot cycle, the Carnot engine can be turned into an ideal refrigeration machine or heat pump, wherein the net work has to be an energy input and the amount of heat rejected is greater than the amount added. Heat pumps utilize the rejected heat; refrigeration machines obtain their utility from the heat added, which is primarily heat removed from the substance under refrigeration.

To judge the effectiveness of the reversed cycle, the coefficient of performance COP is used.

$$COP_{refr} = \frac{\text{heat added}}{\text{net work done}} \qquad COP_{heating} = \frac{\text{heat rejected}}{\text{net work done}}$$

This value is always greater than 1.

For the reversed Carnot cycle, tracing the processes in reversed direction on the T-S plane (1-4-3-2-1), the coefficient of refrigeration performance is

$$COP_{refr} = \frac{Q_2}{Q_1 - Q_2} = \frac{T_L(S_2 - S_1)}{T_U(S_2 - S_1) - T_L(S_2 - S_1)} = \frac{T_L}{T_U - T_L}$$

and of heating performance

$$COP_{heating} = \frac{T_U}{T_U - T_L}$$

Corresponding to the horsepower rating for engines, refrigeration machines are rated in terms of the "standard commercial ton" (Std. Com. Ton). One standard commercial ton = 200 Btu/min. The unit is derived from the heat required to turn 1 ton of water at 32°F into ice at 32°F in one day.

Characteristically, examination problems can be classified as follows: problems in which the fundamental properties are stated at various points in the cycle and the efficiency and/or work performed during a cycle have to be determined. This type of problem is often combined with economic aspects, but the essentials remain thermodynamic. A second class of problems gives the properties of the working substance at one point of a cycle, then gives information about the efficiency, the work done, or the amount of heat added or rejected and requires the determination of the properties of the working substance at the ends of various processes. Knowledge of the various cycles in common use will prove helpful.

Problem 5-10 Heat rejection and entropy of Carnot cycle

A Carnot engine utilizing an ideal gas operates at an efficiency of 45% when receiving 250 Btu at a constant temperature of 700°F. (a) How much heat does this engine reject? (b) At what temperature is the heat rejected? (c) What is the change in entropy during the isothermal expansion of the gas?

Solution:

The efficiency of a Carnot engine is expressed either in terms of upper and lower temperatures or in terms of the quantities of heat added and rejected.

(a) Efficiency = $(Q - Q_R)/Q = (T_U - T_L)/T_U$

$$250 - Q_R = 250 \times 0.45$$

$$Q_R = 250 - 113 = 137 \text{ Btu} \qquad Answer$$

(b) $460° + 700 - T_2 = (460 + 700)0.45$

$$T_2 = 639° \text{Rankine}$$

$$= 179°F \qquad Answer$$

(c) For a reversible process at constant temperature, the change in entropy can be calculated by

$$S_2 - S_1 = 1/T \int_1^2 dQ = Q/T_U = +250/1160 = +0.216 \text{ Btu/°R}$$

Note: There is no net change in the entropy of the Carnot cycle. Therefore, the increase in entropy during the isothermal (upper temperature) expansion equals the absolute value of the decrease in enthropy during the isothermal (lower temperature) process.

Check:

$$S_4 - S_3 = Q_{3-4}/T = -137/639 = -0.215 \text{ Btu/}^\circ R$$
$$S_4 - S_3 = |S_2 - S_1|$$

Problem 5-11 Temperature, work, and pressure of a Carnot engine

A Carnot engine using 5 lb of air operates between a source temperature of $600^\circ F$ and a sink temperature of $150^\circ F$. The pressure at the beginning of the isothermal expansion is 350 psia. The ratio of isothermal expansion is 2.8. The gas constant for air is 53.34 ft-lb/$^\circ R$.

(a) Find the pressure at the end of the isothermal expansion.
(b) Find the pressure at the end of isentropic expansion.
(c) Find the net work done.
(d) Find the mean effective pressure.
(e) What is the effect of either raising the source temperature $100^\circ F$ or lowering the sink temperature $100^\circ F$ on the cycle efficiency?

Solution:

(a) For isothermal expansion, $p_1 V_1 = p_2 V_2$. The ratio of expansion is $V_2/V_1 = 2.8$. Therefore,

$$p_2/p_1 = V_1/V_2 = 1/2.8$$
$$p_2 = 350/2.8 = 125 \text{ psia} \qquad Answer$$

(b) For isentropic expansion,

$$T_L/T_U = (p_3/p_2)^{(k-1)/k}$$
$$= \frac{150 + 460}{600 + 460} = \frac{1}{1.74}$$

Using k = 1.4,

$$(p_3/125)^{0.4/1.4} = 1/1.74$$
$$p_3 = (1/1.74)^{1.4/0.4} \times 125$$
$$= 18.05 \text{ psia} = 18 \text{ psia} \qquad Answer$$

(c) The work may be found in several ways, for example, as the area inside the p-V curve, or as the difference between the heat added and the heat rejected.

$$W = p_1 V_1 \ln (V_2/V_1) + p_3 V_3 \ln (V_4/V_3)$$
$$= wRT_U \ln (p_1/p_2) + wRT_L \ln (p_4/p_3)$$

To find p_4, note that

$$V_2/V_1 = V_3/V_4$$

Therefore,

$$V_4/V_1 = V_3/V_2 \quad \text{and} \quad (p_1/p_4)^{1/k} = (p_2/p_3)^{1/k}$$

$$p_4/p_1 = p_3/p_2$$

$$p_4 = \frac{350 \times 18}{125} = 50.4 \text{ psia}$$

$$W = (5)(53.34)(1060 \ln 2.8 + 610 \ln 2.8) = 458,000 \text{ ft-lb} \qquad Answer$$

(d) Mean effective pressure = work displacement volume

Displacement volume = $V_3 - V_1$

From the characteristic equation

$$V_3 = \frac{wRT_L}{p_3} = \frac{(5)(53.34)(610)}{(18)(144)}$$

$$= 62.5 \text{ cu ft}$$

$$V_1 = \frac{(5)(53.34)(1060)}{(350)(144)}$$

$$= 5.6 \text{ cu ft}$$

$$V_3 - V_1 = 56.9 \text{ cu ft}$$

Mean effective pressure = 458,000/56.9 = 8080 lb/sq ft

$$8080/144 = 56.2 \text{ lb/sq in.} \qquad Answer$$

(e) The effect of changing source or sink temperature on efficiency can be generalized.

$$\text{Efficiency} = \frac{T_U - T_L}{T_U}$$

If a change $+\Delta T$ occurs in T_U,

$$\text{Eff} = \frac{T_U + \Delta T - T_L}{T_U + \Delta T}$$

If a change $-\Delta T$ occurs in T_L,

$$\text{Eff} = \frac{T_U - (T_L - \Delta T)}{T_U} = \frac{T_U + \Delta T - T_L}{T_U}$$

For both cases the numerator is the same, but the denominator increases when the upper temperature is increased. This decreases the efficiency.

Problem 5-12 Mean effective pressure and compression ratio of 4-cylinder engine

(a) A 4-cylinder, 2-cycle engine has a 3.5-in. piston and a 4-in. stroke. What would be the mean effective pressure (mep) required to develop 150 hp at 3000 rpm?

(b) If this engine takes air at 16 psia and 70°F and has a compression ratio of 6.25 to 1, what would be the temperature of the compressed air? (Assume $n = 1.3$.)

Solution:

(a) The power delivered by an engine is the product of the work per cylinder, the number of cylinders, the number of power strokes per revolution, and the number of revolutions per minute. A 2-cycle engine has one power stroke per revolution. (*Note:* a 4-cycle engine has one power stroke for every 2 revolutions.)

$$150 \text{ hp} = \frac{(\text{mep}) \times (\pi/4)(3.5 \text{ in.})^2}{33,000 \text{ ft-lb/min}} \times \frac{4 \text{ in.}}{12 \text{ in./ft}} \times 4 \text{ cylinders} \times 3000 \text{ rpm}$$
$$\times 1 \text{ stroke/rev}$$

$$\text{mep} = \frac{150 \times 33,000 \times 12 \times 4}{3.5^2 \times \pi \times 4 \times 4 \times 3000}$$

$$= 128.8 \text{ psi} \qquad Answer$$

(b) The compression ratio = initial volume/final volume = V_1/V_2 = 6.25. For polytropic expansion

$$\frac{T_2}{T_1} = \left(\frac{V_1}{V_2}\right)^{n-1}$$

$$T_2 = (460 + 70)(6.25/1)^{(1.3-1)} = 915°\text{R} = 455°\text{F} \qquad Answer$$

Problem 5-13 Pressure and temperature of gas following adiabatic expansion

A room at a pressure of 15 psi and 30°C contains a cylinder of oxygen with a pressure of 1000 psi. The valve is suddenly opened. After the pressure in the cylinder has dropped to room pressure the valve is closed and the enclosed gas returns to the temperature of the room. What is the pressure of the gas in the cylinder at the end of this time? (Assume the expansion to be adiabatic.)

Solution:

To work this problem, change the temperature to absolute units. Rankine units are used here as being the most familiar.

$$T_1 = (30° \times 9/5) + 32° + 460 = 546°\text{R}$$

Adiabatic expansion = isentropic expansion:

$$T_2 = T_1(p_2/p_1)^{(k-1)/k}$$

Assume all pressures are absolute:

$$T_2 = 546 \left(\frac{15}{1000}\right)^{0.4/1.4} = 164°\text{R} = -296°\text{F}$$

The temperature inside the container is now 164°R, the pressure is 15 psi. Now the valve is closed and the gas returns to room temperature. This must be a constant-volume process since the volume of the tank is fixed when the valve is shut. Thus

$$p_3/p_2 = T_3/T_2$$
$$p_3 = 15 \times 546°\text{R}/164°\text{R} = 50 \text{ psi} \qquad Answer$$

Otto or Gasoline Engine Cycle

This cycle consists of an isentropic compression followed by a constant-volume increasing pressure process, then an isentropic expansion, followed by a constant-volume decreasing pressure process. For this cycle, efficiencies may again be calculated as work (heat added).

Heat added = $wC_v(T_3 - T_2)$

Work = $wC_v(T_3 - T_2) - (T_4 - T_1)$

Efficiency = $1 - (T_4 - T_1)/(T_3 - T_2) = 1 - (V_2/V_1)^{k-1}$

Because V_2/V_1 represents the adiabatic compression ratio r_k, the efficiency is sometimes expressed in terms of r_k.

$$\text{Efficiency} = 1 - \frac{1}{r_k^{k-1}}$$

Diesel Cycle

This cycle is identical to the Otto cycle except that the constant-volume increasing pressure portion of the Otto cycle with piston at top dead center and ignition causing increasing pressure is replaced in the Diesel cycle by a constant-pressure increasing volume process that occurs after the piston has left the top dead-center position and fuel is being injected. Burning of the air-fuel mixture maintains the pressure during this part of the expansion process.

Heat added = $wC_p(T_3 - T_2)$

Work = $wC_p(T_3 - T_2) - wC_v(T_4 - T_1)$

Efficiency = $1 - (T_4 - T_1)/k(T_3 - T_2)$

Note that k is always greater than 1 and, therefore, the efficiency of the Diesel cycle operating between the same temperature limits is always greater than that of the corresponding Otto cycle.

Erickson Cycle

This is a hot air cycle utilizing a regenerative effect wherein the hot air leaves the cylinder at the upper temperature T_1, and rejects the heat to a storage chamber during the constant-pressure cooling process. Isothermal cooling with heat rejection to the sink occurs next, then constant-pressure expansion during which the gas removes heat from the storage device to the fourth and final process, an isothermal expansion with addition of heat from the source.

Heat added = $(wRT_1/J) \ln (V_b/V_a)$

Heat rejected = $(wRT_2/J) \ln (V_d/V_c) = -(wRT_2/J) \ln (V_c/V_d)$

Work = $(T_1 - T_2)(w\,R/J) \ln (V_b/V_a)$

Efficiency = $(T_1 - T_2)/T_1$

Note that the storing of heat in the storage device does not affect the theoretical efficiency of this cycle, which has the same value as the Carnot cycle.

Reciprocating Compression Cycle

Reciprocating compressors, although steady-flow devices, are ordinarily analyzed by process steps as were the previous cycles, the kinetic energy of the working substance at entrance and exit being neglected. The process steps may be followed on the corresponding p-V diagram, Fig. 5-8. Intake or suction work is a constant-pressure process, $W_{4-1} = p_1(V_1 - V_4)$. Compression is an isentropic or polytropic process, $W_{1-2} = (p_2V_2 - p_1V_1)/1 - n$.

Delivery or discharge is a constant-pressure process, $W_{2-3} = p_2(V_3 - V_2)$. The net work equals the area 1-2-3-4 on the p-V diagram. Analytically, after recognizing that $V_4 = V_3$, the net work is defined by

$$W_{net} = \sum_{i=1}^{i=4} W_i = \frac{n}{1-n} (p_2V_2 - p_1V_1)$$

The above result is an ideal case representing in addition to the zero change in kinetic energy, a compressor without clearance, i.e., $V_4 = V_3 = 0$. Actual reciprocating compressors have some clearance volume V_c, the space between the piston and cylinder, when the cylinder is at the end of the delivery stroke. Clearance c is defined thus, $c = V_c/V_{displacement} \times 100$. The clearance volume does not change the net work requirement of the engine.

Rotary Compressor

The steady flow energy equation applies directly to the rotary compressor with a steady in and out flow of a gas as well as a constant work input and heat output. The mass rate of flow is typically expressed by w = lb/min

$$Q = w(h_2 - h_1) + \frac{w(Vel_2^2 - Vel_1^2)}{2gJ} + \frac{W}{J}$$

Adiabatic compression efficiency Eff_{ad} is the compression efficiency most commonly used. Its definition is

$$Eff_{ad} = \frac{\text{isentropic work of compression}}{\text{compression work as obtained from an indicator card}}$$

Brake thermal efficiency, another commonly used value, is

$$Eff_{BT} = \frac{\text{work output as measured on output shaft}}{\text{total energy input}}$$

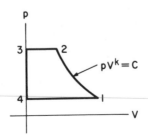

Figure 5-8

Problem 5-14 Displacement and brake thermal efficiency of 2-stroke diesel engine

For a 2-stroke cycle Diesel engine that will operate at 1500 rpm, estimated values at rated load are 90 psi for the brake mean effective pressure and 0.50 lb/bhp-hr for the brake specific fuel consumption when burning fuel with a lower heating value of 18,000 Btu/lb. From these figures, determine for a 1000-hp engine: (a) the displacement needed and (b) the brake thermal efficiency.

Solution:

The engine is running at rated load; its output is 1000 hp.

$$hp = \frac{pressure_{mep}}{33,000} \times volume \times \frac{power\ strokes}{min}$$

A 2-stroke cycle engine uses one power stroke per revolution

$$\text{Displacement volume} = \frac{1000 \times 33,000}{90 \times 144 \times 1500}$$

$$= 1.695\ cu\ ft \qquad Answer,\ part\ (a)$$

Total energy input = (0.50 lb/bhp-hr)(1 hr/60 min)(18,000 Btu/lb)
$$\times (1000\ bhp)$$

$$= 150 \times 10^3\ Btu/min$$

$$= 150 \times 10^3\ Btu/min \times 778\ ft\text{-}lb/Btu$$

$$= 117 \times 10^6\ ft\text{-}lb/min$$

Brake thermal efficiency = output (bhp)/energy input

$$= \frac{1000\ hp \times 33,000\ ft\text{-}lb/min\text{-}hp}{117 \times 10^6\ ft\text{-}lb/min} \times 100\%$$

$$= 28.2\% \qquad Answer,\ part\ (b)$$

5-7 THE USE OF VAPOR TABLES (STEAM, AIR, AMMONIA, ETC.)

The discussion so far has been concerned with an ideal gas. In many thermodynamic problems, however, the gas may be in equilibrium with a liquid, in which case it is usually called a "vapor." A number of concepts and terms must be understood to deal effectively with substances undergoing phase changes (i.e., going from liquid to gas, solid to liquid or gas, or vice versa). Steam is commonly used as an example, although other vapors could serve as well.

Saturation temperature is the temperature at which a particular liquid at a given pressure will begin boiling.

Saturated liquid is a liquid that is at the saturation temperature. *Saturated vapor* is a vapor that is at the saturation temperature and is no longer in equilibrium with a liquid. Its quality (defined later on) is 100%. *Superheated vapor* is a vapor at a temperature higher than the saturation temperature. *Degrees of superheat* refer to the difference between the temperature of the superheated vapor and that of the saturated vapor when both vapors are at identical pressures.

Wet mixture is a combination of a substance in its liquid and gaseous phases. *Quality* refers to the percent by weight of existence of vapor in a wet mixture.

A 60% quality (x = 60%) indicates that 0.60 lb of a 1.00-lb wet mixture is vapor. *Percent moisture* is an expression giving similar information as quality but referred to the liquid. A 40% moisture (y = 40%) indicates that 0.40 lb of a 1.00-lb wet mixture is liquid.

By using tables such as those in Keenan and Keyes, *Thermodynamic Properties of Steam* (New York: John Wiley & Sons, Inc., Second Edition, 1969) numerical values of the vapor properties for a 1.00-lb mass in a specified state may be determined. For a change of state the change in the properties can be ascertained as the difference between two readings taken for the initial and final states. The tables convey the following information directly:

| Variables | | Related Properties |
Independent	Dependent	
	Saturated Steam	
Temperature	Pressure	Specific volume, enthalpy, entropy
Pressure	Temperature	Specific volume, enthalpy, entropy, internal energy
	Superheated Steam	
Pressure	Temperature	Specific volume, enthalpy, entropy

In the tables for saturated steam, the entries for specific volume, enthalpy, entropy, and internal energy are further subdivided into three columns, or for internal energy into two columns, which give the values for saturated liquid, saturated steam, and the difference between these two values. If interpolation between values is necessary, straight-line interpolation will be satisfactory. When two phases are in equilibrium, as when a vapor exists in equilibrium with a liquid, both phases must be at the same pressure. The total value of the properties, such as specific volume, enthalpy, entropy, and internal energy may be found if the quality x or the percent moisture y is known from the following typical equation for enthalpy and entropy:

$$h = xh_g + yh_f \qquad \text{and} \qquad s = s_{fg} + ys_f$$

where the subscripts g and f refer to the liquid and gaseous phases, respectively.

For instance, let us determine the total enthalpy of steam having a quality of 60% and a temperature of 100°F. From the tables $h_f = 67.97$ and $h_g = 1105.2$. Therefore, the total enthalpy is $0.60(1105.2) + 0.40(67.97) = 690.3$. Similarly $h = h_f + xh_{fg} = 67.97 + 0.60(1037.2) = 690.3$

For steam having a high quality (x = 75%) a preferred way when using the slide rule of obtaining values is to write the equation in terms of percent moisture y: $h = h_g - yh_{fg}$.

In connection with obtaining the various point functions such as enthalpy, entropy, pressure, etc., of steam or other vapors, three graphs are in common use: the p-V diagram (Fig. 5-9), the T-S diagram (Fig. 5-10), and the h-S or Mollier diagram (Fig. 5-11).

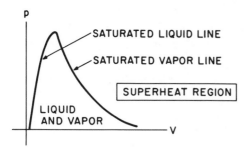

Figure 5-9

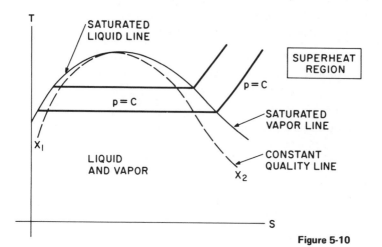

Figure 5-10

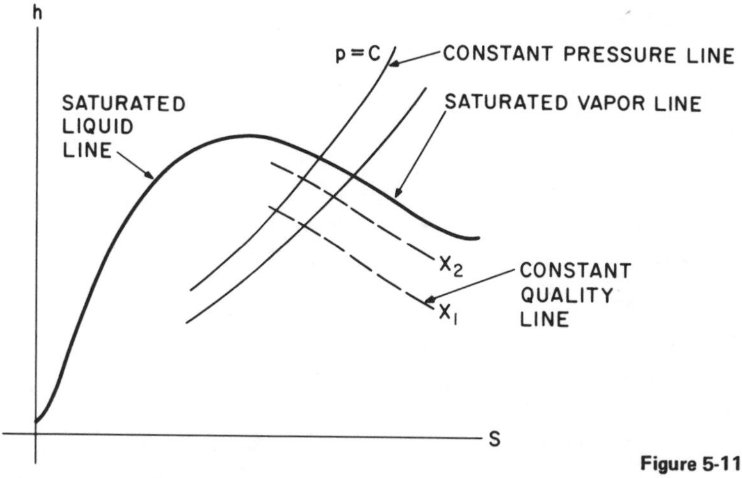

Figure 5-11

5-8   VAPOR CYCLES

Rankine Cycle

This is one of several vapor cycles particularly suited to steam cycles. It consists of a series of reversible steady-flow processes performed on separate pieces of equipment as follows:

Constant-pressure heating in boiler from the mix temperature to the saturation temperature, P-1 (Fig. 5-12)
Constant-pressure–constant-temperature evaporation in the boiler, 1-2
Possible superheating, 2-a
Isentropic expansion in the engine, 2-3, if no superheating occurred
Isentropic expansion in the engine, a-b, if superheating occurred
Constant-pressure condensation in condenser, 3-4 or b-4
Isentropic pumping, 4-P
Heat added $= Q_A = h_2 - h_p$
Heat rejected $= Q_r = h_3 - h_4$
Net work $= Q_A - Q_r = h_2 - h_p - (h_3 - h_4) = h_2 - h_3 + (h_4 - h_p)$

Theoretical pump work $= h_p - h_4 = v/J \int_4^p dp$
Actual pump work $= (h_p - h_4)/Eff_{pump}$

In the Rankine cycle, the work to operate the pump must be accounted for thus:

$$Eff_{Rankine\ cycle} = \frac{h_2 - h_3 - W_{pump}}{h_2 - h_4 - W_{pump}} = \frac{h_2 - h_3 - W_{pump}}{h_2 - h_p}$$

For the Rankine engine

$$Eff_{Rankine\ engine} = \frac{h_2 - h_3}{h_2 - h_{f3}} = \frac{h_2 - h_3}{h_2 - h_4}$$

Steam rate is another performance characteristic of a steam engine defined as the pounds of steam per unit of output work:

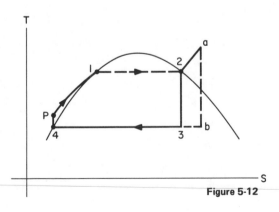

Figure 5-12

$$\text{Steam rate} = \frac{2544 \text{ Btu/hp-hr}}{W \text{ Btu/lb steam}} = \frac{2544 \text{ lb steam}}{W \text{ hp-hr}}$$

$$= \frac{3412 \text{ lb steam}}{W \text{ kWhr}}$$

Problem 5-15 Thermal efficiency of a Rankine cycle

The maximum pressure in a Rankine cycle is 350 psia, the minimum is 10 psia. The steam as exhausted may be considered a saturated vapor. Find the thermal efficiency of the cycle.

Solution:

Sketch the cycle on the T-S plane (Fig. 5-13) and on a Mollier diagram (Fig. 5-14).

The expansion in the engine proper (prime mover) is indicated by the line a-b. Point a corresponds to 350 psia, up vertically (because of constant entropy expansion) above point b, which lies on the saturated vapor line but at the same pressure as c, 10 psia.

$s_a = s_b = 1.788$ from steam tables

$s_c = 0.2835$ from steam tables

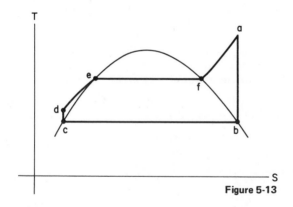

Figure 5-13

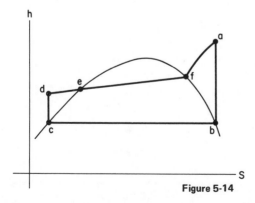

Figure 5-14

Since no pump work is indicated

$$Eff = (h_a - h_b)/(h_a - h_c)$$

where $h_a = 1545.4$ Btu/lb obtained either from Mollier diagram or from superheat table by interpolation, knowing that p = 350 psia and s = 1.788.

$h_b = 1143.4$ Btu/lb either from Mollier diagram or directly from saturated steam vs. pressure tables for p = 10 psia, the liquid value

$$Eff = [(1545.4 - 1143.4)/(1545.4 - 161.2)] \times 100\%$$
$$= 29.1\% \quad \textit{Answer}$$

Ammonia Refrigeration Cycle

This is a specific case of a vapor cycle applied to refrigeration using ammonia as the fluid. The sequence of processes that make up the cycle are:

1. Constant-pressure evaporation, 1-2 (Fig. 5-15), where the heat from the material to be cooled is absorbed by wet low-temperature vapor. The ammonia leaves the evaporation as a warmer dry saturated vapor.
2. Isentropic compression, 2-3, for the ideal case or more typically adiabatic compression 2-3′ to a higher temperature.
3. Condensation, 3-4 or 3′-4, wherein heat from the vapor is rejected, usually to water circulating through the condensor. The vapor decreases in temperature from the superheated to the dry saturated vapor, then at constant temperature and pressure to the saturated liquid state.
4. Constant enthalpy expansion, 4-1, through a throttling valve.

Heat added = $h_2 - h_1 = (h_2 - h_4)$Btu/lb. (This equals the heat absorbed from the material to be cooled.)

Heat rejected = $h_3 - h_4$ or $h_{3'} - h_4$

Work = heat rejected − heat added = $h_3 - h_4 - h_2 + h_1 = h_3 - h_2$
    or for adiabatic compression

Work = $h_{3'} - h_2 - Q$

Coefficient of performance = $(h_2 - h_1)/(h_3 - h_2)$

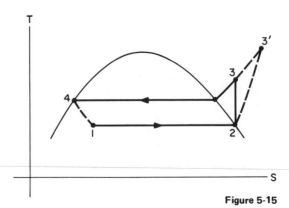

Figure 5-15

Problem 5-16 Evaporation of ammonia for refrigerating effect

Liquid ammonia at 5°F is evaporated and superheated 20°F at constant pressure. How many pounds of ammonia must be circulated per minute for 10 tons of refrigerating effect?

Solution:

Since 1 ton of refrigeration = 200 Btu/min, 10 tons = 2000 Btu/min, which equals the amount of heat to be absorbed by the ammonia.

The refrigerating effect per pound of ammonia equals the difference between the quantity of heat removed by cooling and the work done by the compressor, or is the increase in heat content between the saturated liquid at 5°F and the superheated vapor.

Using ammonia tables at 5°F

h = 48.3 Btu/lb

p = 34.27 psia

At 34.27 psia and 20° superheat

h = 622.2 Btu/lb

$\quad$ = 622.2 − 48.3 = 573.9 Btu/lb

Let x = lb/min of ammonia required; then

$$\left(573.9 \ \frac{Btu}{lb}\right) x = 2000 \ Btu/min$$

$$x = 2000/573.9 = 3.49 \ lb/min \qquad Answer$$

These values could also have been obtained from a Mollier chart of p-h as published in Bureau of Standards Handbook No. 142, similar to Fig. 5-16.

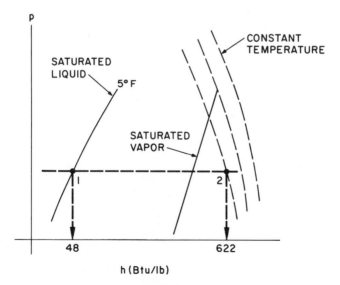

Figure 5-16

5-9   FLOW NOZZLES AND ORIFICES

The equations for flow in nozzles and orifices are derived from the four basic equations for fluid flow: (1) the general energy equation, (2) the continuity equation, (3) the momentum equation, and (4) equations of state. For all flow problems, consider inlet conditions as condition 1, outlet as condition 2. Nozzles are flow passages designed for fluids having small inlet velocities and converging or converging-diverging cross sections.

Isentropic flow nozzle provides for adiabatic expansion without work. From the simplified general energy equation

$$\text{Vel}_1{}^2/2gJ + h_1 = \text{Vel}_2{}^2/2gJ + h_2$$

For small inlet velocities $\text{Vel}_1 = 0$; then

$$\text{Vel}_2 = 223.8(h_1 - h_2)^{\frac{1}{2}}$$
$$= 223.8 \left\{ C_p T_1 [1 - (p_2/p_1)]^{(k-1)/k} \right\}^{\frac{1}{2}}$$

Other expressions may be evolved by the substitution $C_p = [k/(k-1)]R/J$. If the inlet velocity is not negligible, using the continuity equation

$$A_1 \text{Vel}_1/V_1 = A_2 \text{Vel}_2/V_2$$

yields

$$\text{Vel}_2 = 223.8 \left\{ (h_1 - h_2)/\left[1 - (A_2/A_1)^2 (V_1/V_2)^2 \right] \right\}^{\frac{1}{2}}$$

or

$$= 223.8 \left\{ (h_1 - h_2)/\left[1 - (A_2/A_1)^2 (p_2/p_1)^{2/k} \right] \right\}^{\frac{1}{2}}$$

Using the relation for weight (or mass) rate of flow

$$W = A_1 \text{Vel}_1/V_1 = A_2 \text{Vel}_2/V_2$$

The preceding expressions may be restated as flow rate equations by multiplying the right side of the equations by Vel_1/V_1 or Vel_2/V_2. For example,

$$W_2 = A_2 \left\{ 2g\left(\frac{k}{k-1}\right)\frac{p_1}{V_1}\left[\left(\frac{p_2}{p_1}\right)^2 - \left(\frac{p_2}{p_1}\right)^{(k+1)/k} \right]^{\frac{1}{2}} \right\}$$

For a given inlet pressure and specific volume, the flow rate may be maximized by differentiating the term $(p_2/p_1)^2 - (p_2/p_1)^{(k+1)/k}$ and setting the result equal to zero. Then

$$\frac{p_2}{p_1} = \left(\frac{2}{k+1}\right)^{k/(k-1)}$$

the value of p_2 is the critical pressure p_c. For $p_2 < p_c$, flow rate will be the same as if $p_2 = p_c$, i.e., the flow rate will attain its maximum value. $p_2/p_1 = 528$ for air and diatomic gas at ordinary temperatures. For $p_2 > p_c$, the flow will be smaller than the maximum attainable value. The ratio of velocity at a point to the velocity of sound at the same point in a fluid of the same conditions is called the Mach number.

$$M = \text{Vel}/\text{Vel}_{\text{sound}}$$

If $M > 1$, the velocity is greater than that of sound. The velocity of sound $= (gkRT)^{1/2}$ in any gaseous medium. For air this amounts to $Vel_{air} = 49T^{1/2}$. With this information and a set of gas tables such as Keenan and Keyes, property changes across shock boundaries can be determined.

Problem 5-17 Missile velocity determined from altitude, pressure, and temperature

A missile is traveling at an altitude of 6500 ft where the atmospheric temperature and pressure are known to be 4°F and 7.0 psia. A sensing element mounted at the nose of the missile indicates a temperature at the nose of 770°F. Determine the missile's velocity.

Solution:

Assuming that the missile is moving at supersonic speeds, the Mach number should be determined based on the ratio r of the stagnation (i.e., nose) temperature and the air temperature.

$$T_A/T_S = r$$

$$r = (460 + 4)/(460 + 770) = 0.378$$

From the gas table, Mach number = 2.50

Acoustic velocity $= (49)(464)^{\frac{1}{2}} = 1050$ ft/sec

Missile's velocity $= 2.5 \times 1050 = 2620$ ft/sec   *Answer*

Convergent-Divergent Nozzle

For a convergent-divergent nozzle, the convergent portion is normally very short and expansion takes place without loss. At the throat of such a nozzle, the critical pressure exists.

The continuity equation gives the weight rate of flow, $W = A_t Vel_t / V_t$, where the subscript t refers to the throat. For steam initially superheated a convenient expression gives

$$W_{steam} \text{ (lb/sec)} = 0.3155 \, A_t \text{ sq in } (p_1/V_1)^{\frac{1}{2}}$$

where p_1 = inlet pressure, psia

V_1 = inlet specific volume, cu ft/lb

Throat velocity $= Vel_t = 72.24 \, (p_1 V_1)^{\frac{1}{2}}$

Two additional definitions are often used:

$$\text{Nozzle efficiency} = \frac{\text{actual kinetic energy}}{\text{ideal kinetic energy}}$$

$$= \frac{(Vel_2')^2/2gJ}{h_1 - h_2 + (Vel_1)^2/2gJ}$$

where $Vel_2' = $ actual final velocity

$\quad Vel_1 = $ inlet velocity

Nozzle coefficient $= N_c = Vel_2'/Vel_2 = $ actual velocity/ideal velocity

Problem 5-18 Steam rate and throat area for nozzles in a steam turbine

A steam turbine with six nozzles is to be supplied with steam at 300 psia and 900°F. The steam will exhaust at 2.2 psia. Assuming a velocity coefficient of 0.92 and a 23% efficiency of converting the steam's kinetic energy to brake horsepower determine (a) the steam rate in lb/sec and (b) the required throat area for the nozzles if the turbine is to deliver 80 hp.

Solution:

Using the inlet and outlet conditions for the steam and considering isentropic expansion, the change in the steam's enthalpy is determined.

$\quad h_i = 1473$ Btu/lb

from the superheated vapor tables or Mollier chart for p = 300 psi and t = 900°F.

$\quad h_o = 1182$ Btu/lb

following the isentropy line from the above conditions to p = 22 psia.

Actual kinetic energy $= C_v \times 223.8(h_i - h_o)^{\frac{1}{2}} = 0.92 \times 223.8(1473 - 1182)^{\frac{1}{2}}$

$$= 3510 \text{ ft/sec}$$

Horsepower delivered $= \text{Eff} \times \frac{1}{2} m \times Vel^2$

$$80 = 0.23 \times w/2g \times (3510)^2/550$$

$$w = \frac{64.4 \times 80 \times 550}{0.23 \times (3510)^2} = 1.00 \text{ lb/sec} \qquad \textit{Answer, part (a)}$$

Throat area: $A_t = wV_i^{\frac{1}{2}}/0.316p_i^{\frac{1}{2}}$

$\quad V_i = 2.65 \qquad$ (from tables for p = 300 psia and t = 800°F)

$\quad A_t = (1.00/0.316)(2.65/300)^{\frac{1}{2}}$

$$= 0.298 \text{ sq in.}$$

Throat area per nozzle $= 0.298/6 = 0.0497$ sq in.   *Answer*, part (b)

5-10   GAS-VAPOR MIXTURES

Typical environmental conditioning problems require an understanding of the behavior of a mixture of gases and vapors. The pressure of the vapor in the mixture is its partial pressure. Usually this pressure is very low; consequently, the vapor may be treated as an ideal gas.

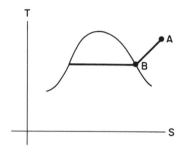

Figure 5-17

On lowering the temperature of a mixture the vapor will condense to a liquid if the partial pressure is above the triple point, to a solid if the pressure is below.

The most commonly encountered gas-vapor mixture is the air-water mixture. A review of some of the terminology used in connection with mixture or air-conditioning problems is helpful.

Dewpoint is the temperature at which a vapor condenses or solidifies when it is cooled at constant pressure, i.e., the point of intersection of the constant pressure line with the saturated vapor line on a T-S diagram. (See Fig. 5-17, point B.)

Saturated air is a mixture of air and water vapor where the vapor is at saturation pressure and temperature.

$$\text{Relative humidity} = p_v/p_g = \frac{p_A}{p_B} \qquad \text{(See Fig. 5-17)}$$

where p_v = partial pressure of vapor assumed acting as an ideal gas

p_g = saturation pressure at the same temperature

Other definitions of relative humidity are

$$p_v/p_g = \rho_v/\rho_g = v_g v_v$$

where $\rho_v \rho_g$, = partial and saturation density

v_v, v_g = partial and saturation specific volume

Humidity ratio = m_v/m_a = specific humidity

where m_v = mass of water vapor

m_a = mass of dry air or other gas exclusive of vapor

Humidity ratio = $R_a p_v/R_v p_a$ = (53.34/85.76)(p_v/p_a) = 0.622 p_v/p_a

where R_a = gas constant for air

R_v = gas constant for water vapor

p_a = partial pressure of air

Usually wet bulb-dry bulb thermometer readings are used to obtain air-humidity values from psychrometric charts.

Problem 5-19 Weights of air and water vapor in a mixture

A tank contains a mixture of air and water vapor such that the relative humidity is 75%. The temperature of the mixture is 70°F. Find (a) the weight of air and (b) the weight of water vapor in the tank if the volume is 100 cu ft and the pressure of the mixture is 5 lb/in.^{2} abs. (*Note:* The saturation pressure of water vapor corresponding to 70°F is 0.363 psia.)

Solution:

Using the definition of relative humidity as the ratio of the partial and saturation densities, the density of the water vapor may be determined.

$$\rho_v/\rho_g = 0.75$$

From steam tables for dry saturated steam at 70°

$$\rho_g = 1/v_g = 1/(867.9 \text{ cu ft/lb})$$
$$= 0.001152 \text{ lb/cu ft}$$
$$\rho_v = 0.75(0.001152)$$
$$= 0.000865 \text{ lb/cu ft}$$

Weight of water vapor = 100(0.000865) = 0.0865 lb   *Answer*, part (b)

The partial pressure of the air is determined as the difference of the total tank pressure and the water vapor pressure. The latter is determined by using the relative humidity definition and establishing the value of the saturation pressure at 70°.

$$p_g = 0.363 \text{ psi (at } 70°)$$
$$p_v = 0.75 (0.363)$$
$$= 0.272 \text{ psi}$$

Partial pressure of air = 5 − 0.272 = 4.728 psi
Now, using the ideal gas law,

$$v_a = \frac{RT_a}{p_a} = \frac{53.3(460 + 70)}{4.728 \times 144}$$
$$= 41.6 \text{ cu ft/lb}$$

Air density = $1/v_a$ = 1/41.6
$$= 0.0240 \text{ lb/cu ft}$$

Weight of air = (0.0240)(100) = 2.40 lb   *Answer*, part (a)

6-1   THERMAL CONDUCTIVITY

Heat may be transferred from a hot to a cold region by one or more of the following three modes: conduction, convection, and radiation. In conduction the heat passes through a solid or nonmoving fluid from a high to a low temperature region, the mechanism of energy transfer being primarily molecular agitation. The fundamental equation governing steady-state heat transfer by conduction is

$$Q = -kA \ \Delta t/\Delta x$$

where k = thermal conductivity = $\dfrac{Btu/(hr)(sq\ ft)}{^\circ F/ft} = \dfrac{Btu}{(hr)(ft)(^\circ F)}$

A = area normal to the flow of heat

Δt = temperature difference between surfaces

Δx = distance between surfaces

The ratio $k/\Delta x$ is often expressed as the conductance C. If several layers of material of different conductivity are to transmit heat, their total conductance can be found by

$$1/C_T = 1/C_1 + 1/C_2 + 1/C_3 + \cdots$$
$$= \Delta x_1/k_1 + \Delta x_2/k_2 + \Delta x_3/k_3 + \cdots$$

Steady-state heat transfer through a layered wall, as shown in Fig. 6-1, can be written as

$$Q = C_T A \ \Delta t = \frac{A \ \Delta t}{(x_2 - x_1)/k_1 + (x_3 - x_2)/k_2 + (x_4 - x_3)/k_3}$$

where $\Delta t = t_4 - t_1$. The quantity of heat entering the left wall equals the quantity leaving the right wall per unit time. The preceding discussion is applicable to the

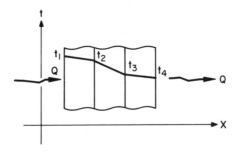

Figure 6-1

transfer of heat from a moving fluid to a conducting wall as, for example, in a heat exchanger. The fluid will have a thin static film adhering to the conducting wall that typically has a low conductance or high resistance. Again, on the other side of the wall there may be a thin film, for example, air. Then the total conductance must take into account thin-film conductance in two layers. These values are usually determined experimentally and are supplied in problem statements or determined from appropriate references.

Problem 6-1 Temperature maintenance inside an insulated steel drum

The temperature inside an insulated steel drum is to be maintained at $120°F$ for 48 hr by an electric coil. The drum is 3 ft high and has a diameter of 1.2 ft. The outside temperature is $68°F$. Determine the cost of maintaining the temperature difference for 48 hr if the insulated steel wall has a conductance value of 0.25 Btu/sq ft/hr/$°F$ and electricity costs 4.5¢/kWhr.

Solution:

The conductance value is merely the ratio of the thermal conductivity to the thickness, $C = k/\Delta x$, and is expressed for the particular material and thickness. The conductance equation then reads $Q = CA \Delta t$.

The area involved consists of the two ends of the drum and the circumferential area

$$A = (2\pi/4)(1.2)^2 + \pi(1.2) 3$$
$$= 13.56 \text{ sq ft}$$

The heat required per hour

$$Q = \frac{0.25 \text{ Btu } (120° - 68°F)(13.56 \text{ sq ft})}{(\text{sq ft})(\text{hr})(°F)}$$
$$= 176 \text{ Btu/hr}$$

Total energy requirement in Btu's

$$Q' = 176 \times 48 \text{ hr} = 8450 \text{ Btu}$$

Converting this to an electrical energy requirement and then multiplying by the cost factor

$$\text{Cost} = \frac{8450(4.5)}{3413 \text{ Btu/kWhr}}$$

$$= 11\cancel{c} \qquad Answer$$

A more precise way of expressing heat transfer is given by expressing Fourier's law as the differential equation

$$Q = -kA \, dt/dx \qquad \text{or} \qquad Q \, dx = -kA \, dt$$

If a layer has a thickness $(x_2 - x_1)$ and the temperature is t_2 at x_2, t_1 at x_1, then

$$Q \int_{x_1}^{x_2} dx = -kA \int_{t_1}^{t_2} dt$$

$$Q(x_2 - x_1) = -kA(t_2 - t_1)$$

As before

$$Q = \frac{-kA(t_2 - t_1)}{(x_2 - x_1)} = \frac{kA(t_1 - t_2)}{(x_2 - x_1)}$$

Because the area normal to the heat flow is greater on the outside than on the inside of curved surfaces, Fourier's equation applied to unit lengths of cylindrical walls works out to

$$Q = \frac{-2\pi k(t_2 - t_1)}{\ln (r_2/r_1)} = \frac{2\pi k(t_1 - t_2)}{\ln (r_2/r_1)}$$

For a multilayered wall the term $2\pi k/\ln (r_2/r_1)$ represents the conductance of one layer. The total wall conductance is determined as in the preceding case. Thus, for n layers,

$$Q = \frac{2\pi(t_n - t_1)}{1/k_1 \ln (r_2/r_1) + 1/k_2 \ln (r_3/r_2) + \cdots + 1/k_n \ln (r_{n+1}/r_n)}$$

After the heat transfer across the entire wall has been calculated, the temperature difference between individual layers is determined from

$$t_1 - t_2 = \frac{Q \ln (r_2/r_1)}{2\pi k_1}$$

$$t_2 - t_3 = \frac{Q \ln (r_3/r_2)}{2\pi k_2}$$

6-2 NONLINEAR TEMPERATURE DIFFERENCE

In most examples of convective heat transfer a temperature distribution exists across the points of a region and a nonlinear temperature difference exists between points of the hot and cold regions. A convenient method to arrive at a usable value of temperature difference is to use the logarithmic mean temperature difference.

$$t_m = \frac{t_a - t_b}{\ln (t_a/t_b)} = \frac{t_a - t_b}{\ln t_a - \ln t_b}$$

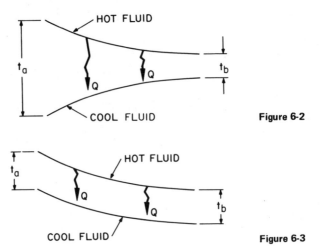

Figure 6-2

Figure 6-3

where t_a, t_b = temperature differences between the fluids at points a and b, respectively. This would apply, for example, to the heating of water in a heat exchanger where cool water enters at one point of a tube and hot water exists at a second point. The outside of the tube may be heated by a second fluid that may be flowing in the same direction (parallel flow) or in the opposite direction (counterflow) to the water. The mean temperature difference equation applies to either case. In parallel flow, cool water and the hot fluid pass one point, the water warms up, and the fluid cools off as they progress along the tube. The initial and final temperature differences t_a and t_b, respectively, are shown for the parallel flow condition in Fig. 6-2 and for counterflow in Fig. 6-3.

6-3   SURFACE COEFFICIENT OF CONVECTION

The previously mentioned thin film that adheres to a stationary boundary when a fluid flows by it sets up a heat resistance. This resistance is usually expressed as a surface coefficient of convection. This coefficient depends on the type of flow involved, i.e., laminar or turbulent, the temperature difference whether moderate or not, the direction of flow, and the Reynolds and Prandtl numbers. Typically, for horizontal pipes, the film conductance or surface coefficient for forced convection in pipes is given by

$$h = 0.0225(k/D)(N_{Re})^{0.8}(N_{Pr})^{0.4} \text{ Btu/(hr)(sq ft)(°F)}$$

where k = fluid thermal conductivity

D = actual inside diameter, ft

N_{Re} = Reynolds number = $(DV\rho/\mu)$

V = fluid velocity, ft/hr

ρ = density, lb/cu ft

μ = viscosity, lb/(ft)(hr)

N_{Pr} = Prandtl number = $C\mu/k$

   C = specific heat, Btu/lb

Simplified expressions for the surface coefficient are often used.

   For water at temperatures below 180°F

$$h = 0.00134 \, (t + 100) \, V^{0.8}/D^{0.2}, \text{ where } t = \text{average water temperature}$$

For oil an empirical formula reads

$$h = 0.03V/\mu^{0.63}$$

A number of published tables also give characteristic values for the overall coefficients of heat transfer for various classes of surface.

Problem 6-2 Counterflow and parallel flow heat exchangers

A heat exchanger is to be designed to transfer heat from a hot to a cold oil. The hot oil is to be cooled from 300°F to 200°F while heating the cold oil from 80°F to 150°F.

(a) Can this be accomplished by either of the following types of heat exchangers: (1) counterflow exchanger, (2) parallel flow exchanger?

(b) Which heat exchanger would require the greatest surface area to accomplish the above heat exchange?

(c) If the hot oil is to be cooled from 300°F to 100°F can this be done by either type heat exchanger?

Solution:

Assuming that the heat transfer coefficient is identical for all cases, then:

(a) In the counterflow heat exchanger the oil tube cooled is hottest (300°F) at the same point where the oil which is heated is at its maximum temperature (150°F). As long as the oil to be cooled is at every point at a temperature above the oil which is being heated up, heat exchange takes place. Thus counterflow can be used. Taking the parallel flow, the highest temperature of the cold oil is less than the lowest temperature of the hot oil; therefore a parallel flow heat exchanger can be used only for the first case.

(b) The surface area to be used for the same rate of heat transfer depends only on the mean temperature difference assuming the heat-transfer coefficient to be constant.

$$Q = Ah \, \Delta t$$
$$A = Q/h \, \Delta t$$
$$\approx 1/\Delta t$$

The greater the temperature difference, the smaller will be the required surface area.

   For counterflow

$$\Delta t_{mean} = \frac{t_a - t_b}{\ln (t_a/t_b)}$$

where $t_a = 300 - 150 = 150°F$

$\quad\quad t_b = 200 - 80 = 120°F$

$\Delta t_{mean} = (150 - 120)/\ln(150/120) = 30/\ln 1.25 = 134°F$

For parallel flow

$$\Delta t_{mean} = \frac{t_a - t_b}{\ln(t_a/t_b)}$$

where $t_a = 300 - 80 = 220°F$

$\quad\quad t_b = 200 - 150 = 50°F$

$\Delta t_{mean} = (220 - 50)/\ln(220/50) = 170/\ln 4.4 = 115°F$

Since $\Delta t_{mean} = 134°F$ is the higher value, proportionally *less* surface area is needed for the counterflow exchanger.

(c) As can be seen from the temperature difference, if the hot oil is to be cooled to $100°F$, this condition *cannot* be met in the parallel flow exchanger; however, it is possible with the counterflow exchanger since $t_a = 300 - 150°F$ and $t_b = 100 - 80° = 20°F$, and a temperature gradient exists at all points.

chapter 7
ELECTRICITY AND ELECTRONICS

The areas embraced by the term electricity are so large and broad that a careful selection was made by the author to develop theory and discuss problems most pertinent to the licensing examinations. The guide for this has been primarily the topics covered in previous examinations and the author's judgment on areas soon to be included.

7-1 ELECTROSTATICS

The basic electrical unit is the *electron*. The more customarily used unit is the *coulomb*. One electron = 1.60×10^{-19} coulomb. The basic law of electrostatics is Coulomb's Law:

The force between two charged particles is directly dependent on the product of the charges and inversely proportional to the square of the distance between the particles.

$$F = q_1 q_2 / cr^2$$

where F = force

q₁, q₂ = charges on particles 1 and 2
q_1, q_2 = charges on particles 1 and 2

c = constant dependent on units and dielectric

r = distance between particles

The force is one of attraction if the particles are oppositely charged; two negatively or two positively charged particles will exert a mutually repulsive force. The direction of the force is on the line connecting the centers of the charged particles. In the case of several charged particles acting simultaneously, the resultant force acting on any one particle is equal to the vectorial sum of all forces acting on that particle.

Problem 7-1 Force exerted by charged pith balls

Two equally charged pith balls are suspended from a point by strings 15 cm long. Each string makes an angle of 5° with the vertical. The pith balls weigh 1.5 g each. Determine the charge on the pith balls.

Solution:

Since the pith balls are not touching, the charges must be identical in sign, either positive or negative. The forces on each ball are exerted by (1) the string, (2) gravity, and (3) electrostatic repulsion. The resultant of (2) and (3) must be in the same direction as the string, as shown in Fig. 7-1.

$$R \cos 5° = F_g = 1.5 \text{ g}$$
$$R = 1.5/0.9962 = 1.501 \text{ g}$$
$$R \sin 5° = F_e$$
$$F_e = 1.501 \text{ g} (0.0872) = 0.1308 \text{ g}$$
$$F_e = q_1 q_2/cr^2$$

where $c = 1$ for a system where F is expressed in dynes, q in statcoulombs, r in centimeters

$$1 \text{ g} = 980.7 \text{ dyn}$$
$$q_1 = q_2$$
$$r = 2(15 \sin 5°) = 30(0.0872) = 2.616 \text{ cm}$$

Thus, $q^2 = 0.1308(980.7) (2.616)^2$

$q = 29.7$ statcoulombs, positive or negative   *Answer*

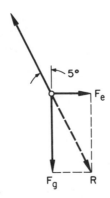

Figure 7-1

The *electric field* E is determined as the ratio of the force to charge: $E = F/q$, where the force is that exerted on a positively charged particle which is located in the field under study. The charge refers to the magnitude of charge.

Electric potential, actually the difference in electric potential between points A and B, is the ratio of the work required to move a unit positive charge q from B to A, to the charge q.

$$V_A - V_B = V_{AB} = W/q = - \int_A^B F \cos \theta \, dr/q = - \int_A^B E \cos \theta \, dr$$

where θ is the angle between force F or field E and direction r. If $V_A - V_B$ is positive, then work was done to move the charge from B to A and A is at a higher potential than B.

Absolute electric potential at a point A assumes that the positive charge has been moved from a region of zero potential to A. The earth is usually assumed to be such a region.

Capacitance C is the name given to the ratio of the charge on a conductor and its potential C = q/V. A capacitor is a pair or a group of pairs of oppositely charged conductors separated by a dielectric or insulator whose dielectric constant is ϵ. The formulas for three typical capacitors are

1. Parallel plate: $C = \epsilon A/d$
2. Spherical—two concentric spherical shells having an inner radius a and an outer radius b: $C = 4\pi\epsilon ab/(b-a)$
3. Cylindrical—two concentric cylindrical shells of radii a and b, and a length L $(a < b)$: $C = 2\pi\epsilon L/\ln(b/a)$

The work required to charge a capacitor or the energy possessed by a charged capacitor can be determined thus:

1. The voltage of a capacitor having a charge q is $V = q/C$.
2. To add a small amount of charge dq requires dw work: $dw = Vdq = (q/C)dq$.
3. Then the total amount of work to charge a capacitor to a value Q is

$$W = \int_0^Q (q/C) \, dq = \frac{1}{2} \, Q^2/C \text{ (in joules, when other values are in mks units)}$$

$$= \frac{1}{2} \, CV^2 = \frac{1}{2} \, QV$$

Capacitors in Parallel and in Series

(a) *In parallel.* The voltage across each capacitor must be the same, as shown in Fig. 7-2. Since the size of a capacitor is directly dependent on the area of its plates (see parallel plate capacitors) and since these plates are in parallel, the total capacitance is the sum of the individual capacitances, $C_T = C_1 + C_2 + C_3$.

(b) *In series.* The charge on each capacitor must be the same and the voltages are additive across the combination, as shown in Fig. 7-3. Therefore,

$$q_T = q_2 = q_3$$
$$V_T = V_1 + V_2 + V_3$$
$$1/C_T = 1/C_1 + 1/C_2 + 1/C_3$$

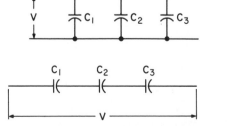

Figure 7-2

Figure 7-3

7-2 DIRECT-CURRENT CIRCUITS

Electric current i is the ratio of the quantity of charge transferred through a cross section of a conductor per unit time, $i = dq/dt$. The current is expressed in amperes when q is in coulombs and t is in seconds.

Direct steady current I occurs when neither the direction nor the magnitude of a current changes with time, $I = \Delta q/\Delta t$.

Circuit Analysis

Fundamental laws of circuit analysis are Ohm's law and Kirchhoff's laws. *Ohm's law* stipulates that the current passing through a conductor is directly dependent on the voltage across the conductor and inversely proportional to the resistance of the conductor, $I = V/R$. The resistance of the conductor in turn depends directly on its resistivity and its length, and reciprocally on its cross-sectional area, $R = \rho L/A$. A term often found useful is the conductance G. It is the reciprocal of the resistance, $G = 1/R$.

Resistance of a Group of Conductors

(a) *In series:* $R_T = R_1 + R_2 + R_3$

(b) *In parallel:* $1/R_T = 1/R_1 + 1/R_2 + 1/R_3$

Total conductance $= G_T = G_1 + G_2 + G_3$

Problem 7-2 Equivalent resistance of parallel resistors
Determine the equivalent resistance for three resistances of 5 ohms each connected in parallel.

Solution:
$1/R_e = 1/R_1 + 1/R_2 + 1/R_3 = 1/5 + 1/5 + 1/5$

$R_e = 5/3$ ohms   *Answer*

Problem 7-3 Battery formed by cells in series
A number of cells, each having an emf of 2.20 V and an internal resistance of 0.05 ohm, are to be used to form a battery. How many of these cells, used in series, are required to provide a current of 28 amp for a load having a resistance of 0.20 ohm?

Solution:
Since the cells are in series with each other and with the load, the total resistance of the circuit for n cells is $R_T = 0.20 + 0.05n$. Using Ohm's law and noting that the total emf or voltage is the sum of the individual voltages for cells in series,

$$I = V/R$$
$$28 = 2.20n/(0.20 + 0.05n)$$
$$5.6 + 1.4n = 2.20n$$
$$n = 7 \text{ cells in series} \qquad Answer$$

Kirchhoff's current law specifies that the algebraic sum of the currents at a point is zero. Assume a convenient sign convention; for example, currents toward a point are positive, away, negative. Then, in Fig. 7-5 at point A, $I_1 - I_2 - I_3 = 0$.

Kirchhoff's second or voltage law specifies that the algebraic sum of the voltage drops or potential differences around a closed circuit is zero. Consider the voltage drop across a resistor in the direction of a current as negative and the voltage drop across a source of emf such as a cell or generator when going from negative to positive terminal as positive.

Problem 7-4 Kirchhoff's current law

(a) Determine the current in the 4-ohm resistor of Fig. 7-4. (b) Determine the difference in potential between points A and B in the same circuit.

Solution:

Assume currents I_1, I_2, and I_3 to exist at the T-connection at point A. Their direction is arbitrary, as seen in Fig. 7-5. Applying Kirchhoff's current law at point A, $I_1 - I_2 - I_3 = 0$. Applying the voltage law to loops 1 and 2 and tracing the loops clockwise

Loop 1: $+ 10 - 2I_1 - 3I_2 = 0$
Loop 2: $0 - 4I_3 + 3I_2 = 0$

Now there are three independent simultaneous equations available for the three unknowns and we can solve for the currents. These are calculated to be

$I_1 = 35/13$ amps
$I_2 = 20/13$ amps
$I_3 = 15/13$ amps   *Answer*, part (a)

A positive sign on the current value indicates that the proper direction had been assumed. The difference in potential $V_A - V_B$ equals the voltage drop across the resistor in the direction of the current.

$$V_A - V_B = I_2 R = 3(20/13) = +60/13 \text{ volts} \qquad Answer, \text{ part (b)}$$

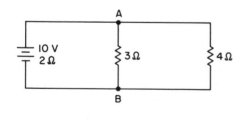

Figure 7-4

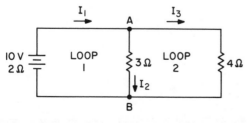

Figure 7-5

Circuit analysis using loop currents includes Kirchhoff's current law automatically, and thereby reduces by one the number of independent simultaneous equations necessary for solving a network. The following procedure is followed when using loop currents.

1. Assign a current to each loop, for example, I_1 and I_2 in Fig. 7-6. It is convenient but not necessary to assume the currents to be in the same direction initially.
2. Apply Kirchhoff's second law remembering that the current for the portions of the network belonging to two loops is the algebraic sum of the current in each loop.

Loop 1 (proceeding clockwise): $+10 - 2I_1 - 3(I_1 - I_2) = 0$
Loop 2 (proceeding clockwise): $0 - 4I_2 - 3(I_2 - I_1) = 0$

Thus two simultaneous equations in two unknowns are produced. Solving these, one obtains

$I_1 = 35/13$ amp
$I_2 = 15/13$ amp

Then $V_A - V_B = I_1 R - I_2 R = 3(35/13) - 3(15/13) = 60/13$ volts as before.

Problem 7-5 Kirchhoff's first and second laws

For the network shown in Fig. 7-7 determine (a) the resistance R_{AB} and (b) the voltage V_{GH}. These values are to be used:

$$V_{AB} = 110 \text{ VDC}$$
$$R_1, R_2, R_3, R_4 = 5 \ \Omega \text{ each}$$
$$R_5, R_6 = 10 \ \Omega \text{ each}$$

Solution:

Sketch in assumed currents and their direction. (See Fig. 7-8.) The total resistance will be determined first to find the line current. Resistance R_{EF} consists of resistor R_5 in parallel with the two series-connected resistors R_3 and R_4:

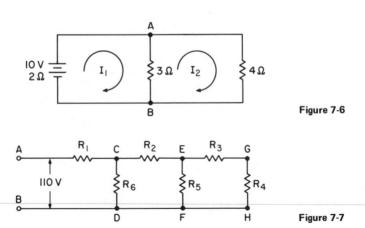

Figure 7-6

Figure 7-7

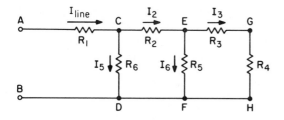

Figure 7-8

$$1/R_{EF} = 1/10 + 1/(5 + 5) \qquad R_{EF} = 5 \ \Omega$$
Similarly $\qquad 1/R_{CD} = 1/10 + 1/(5 + 5) \qquad R_{CD} = 5 \ \Omega$
$$R_{AB} = R_1 + R_{CD} = 5 + 5 = 10 \ \Omega \qquad Answer, \text{part (a)}$$
Line current $= V_{AB}/R_{AB} = 110/10 = 11$ amps

Now, with the line current known, Kirchhoff's first and second laws are applied:

$$V_{CD} = V_{line} - I_{line}R_1 = 110 - 11(5) = 55 \text{ volts}$$
$$I_5 = V_{CD}/R_5 = 55/10 = 5.5 \text{ amps}$$
$$I_2 = I_{line} - I_5 = 11 - 5.5 = 5.5 \text{ amps}$$
$$V_{EF} = V_{CD} - I_2 R_2 = 55 - 5.5(5) = 27.5 \text{ volts}$$
$$I_6 + I_3 = I_2$$
$$I_6 = I_3 \quad \text{(because } R_5 = R_3 + R_4\text{)}$$
$$I_3 = I_2/2 = 5.5/2 = 2.75 \text{ amps}$$
$$V_{GH} = I_3 R_4 = 2.75(5) = 13.75 \text{ volts} \qquad Answer, \text{part (b)}$$

Power consumption depends on the product of the square of the current through a resistive device and the resistance, $P = I^2 R = VI$. *Energy consumption* depends on the product of power and time. The usual units are watthours. Energy $= I^2 Rt = VIt$.

7-3 DIRECT-CURRENT METERS

Direct-current ammeters are placed in a circuit as a series element; thus the total current in a circuit will flow through an ammeter. Because an ammeter's current capacity is limited by its heat capacity, ammeters are provided with shunts for measuring large currents.

Problem 7-6 Determination of ammeter shunt

A current that is known not to exceed 60 amps is to be measured. An internal shunt 5-scale ammeter with a resistance of 0.01 ohm is available. What should be the resistance of an additional shunt to be used with this instrument for measuring the current?

Solution:

A 5-scale ammeter produces full-scale deflection at 5 amps. The current through the instrument coil is negligible so the maximum current through the internal shunt is 5 amps. The voltage drop across the internal shunt is $IR = 5(0.01) =$

0.05 V. Since the external shunt is connected in parallel with the internal shunt, its voltage drop must be the same. The current through the external shunt from Kirchhoff's current law = 60 − 5 = 55 amps.

$$55R_{ext} = 0.05 \text{ V}$$
$$R_{ext} = 0.05/55 = 0.00091 \ \Omega \qquad Answer$$

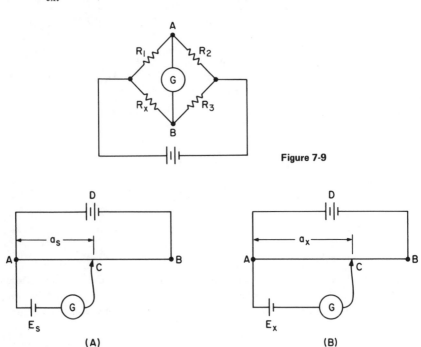

Figure 7-9

Figure 7-10

Direct-current voltmeters are placed in parallel with the elements for which the potential difference is to be determined. To protect a voltmeter from excess current when measuring large potential differences, a known resistance is placed in series with it.

Wheatstone bridges are measuring devices for determining the values of unknown resistances. The bridge consists of three known resistances, one of which is variable, the unknown, and a galvanometer. With the bridge arranged as shown in Fig. 7-9, the value of the unknown may be determined from the equation shown provided the galvanometer reading is zero indicating zero current in branch A-B.

$$R_x = \frac{R_1}{R_2} \ R_3$$

Potentiometers are measuring devices for determining the value of an unknown potential by comparing it with a known one. In its simplest form it consists of a slide wire AB in Fig. 7-10(A) and (B), a battery D, a standard cell E_s whose potential or emf is known, the source of unknown potential E_x, and a galvanometer. The slide point C is so adjusted with either the unknown E_x or the known E_s in the circuit so that the galvanometer indicates zero current. From this condition the potential of the unknown is $E_x = a_x E_s/a_s$.

7-4   ELECTROLYSIS

The *Faraday law of electrolysis* relates the mass of an element or ion liberated at an electrode by the passage of a current through an electrolyte. The mass liberated equals the product of the total charge q passing through the electrolyte and the electrochemical equivalent of the element or ion ϵ.

$$M = \epsilon q = \epsilon \int_{T_1}^{T_2} i \, dt$$

The electrochemical equivalent of an element is its gram equivalent weight divided by 96,500 coulombs. Finally, the gram equivalent weight of an element or ion is its atomic weight divided by its valence.

Problem 7-7 Metal deposited in an electrolytic cell

A 20-amp current passes through an electrolytic cell for 5 hr. The electrolyte is copper sulfate and the electrodes are made of copper. The atomic weight of copper is 63.5 and it has a valence of 2. Determine the total weight of copper deposited on the cathode.

Solution:

Electrochemical equivalent: $\epsilon = 63.5/(2)(96,500) = 329 \times 10^{-6}$ g/C

Total charge passing through solution = 20 C/sec $\times$ 3600 sec/hr $\times$ 5 hr = 360,000 C

Mass of copper liberated: $M = 329 \times 10^{-6} \times 360,000 = 118$ g   *Answer*

7-5   ELECTROMAGNETICS

Electromagnetics is concerned with the interaction of magnetic fields, charged particles in motion, and the electrical and magnetic fields surrounding charged particles.

Coulomb's Equations for Magnets. Two like poles will repel each other, with a force F as follows:

$$F = \frac{\mu m_1 m_2}{4\pi (r_{1-2})^2}$$

where F = force, N

   μ = permeability (depends on medium), Wb/amp-m. In free space

     $\mu = \mu_0 = 4\pi \times 10^{-7}$ Wb/amp-m.

   r_{1-2} = distance between poles, m

m_1, m_2 = two distinct poles

Magnetic flux density **B** is a measure of the force exerted on unit magnetic pole in any medium, $\mathbf{F}_1 = \mathbf{B}m_1$ or $\mathbf{B} = \mathbf{F}_1/m_1$.

Force on a moving charged particle is

$$F = qvB \sin \theta < {}^{v}_{B}$$

or vectorially, $\mathbf{F} = q\mathbf{v} \times \mathbf{B}$ where v = velocity of particle.

Force on a current-carrying conductor of length L in a uniform field, as shown in Fig. 7-11:

$$F = ILB \sin \theta < {}^{L}_{B}$$

or vectorially, $\mathbf{F} = \mathbf{IL} \times \mathbf{B}$.

Left-Hand Rule (Motor)   *If the THumb, FORefinger, and Center finger of the left hand are held mutually perpendicular then the THumb will indicate the THrust on the conductor, if the FORefinger is held in the direction of the field* **B** *and the Center finger in the direction of the current I.*

Torque on a coil in a uniform magnetic field:

$T = InAB \sin \alpha$

$\mathbf{T} = In\mathbf{A} \times \mathbf{B}$

where A = area of coil, sq m

n = number of coils

α = angle between the direction of the flux density vector and the area vector

Magnetic flux density due to a wire conducting current:

$$d\mathbf{B} = \frac{\mu I \, d\mathbf{L} \times \mathbf{r}}{4\pi r^3}$$

At the center of a circular coil this amounts to

$B = \mu n I/2r$

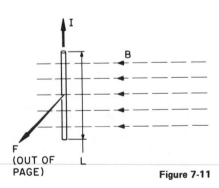

Figure 7-11

where r is the distance from the wire to the point where the magnetic flux density is to be determined, and n is the number of coils.

Electromagnetic Induction–Induced emf's. The scalar product of the magnetic flux density and the surface through which it passes is known as magnetic flux ϕ_m:

$$\phi_m = \int_A B \, dA \cos \alpha = \int_A \mathbf{B} \cdot d\mathbf{A}$$

If the magnetic flux changes with respect to time as it passes through a closed loop of n coils, an emf ϵ will be produced.

$$\epsilon = -n \frac{d\phi_m}{dt}$$

7-6   ALTERNATING-CURRENT CIRCUITS

Alternating Currents

As previously discussed, when a coil experiences a change of magnetic flux either due to a change of its position or due to a changing magnetic flux intensity, an emf is induced in the coil. If the coil is part of a closed circuit, the induced emf will generate a corresponding current. A coil that is turned at a constant angular velocity ω in a field of uniform flux density will have a sinusoidally varying emf induced in it according to the derivation

$$\epsilon = -\frac{d}{dt} \, \alpha \, (BA \cos \alpha) = BA \sin \alpha \, \frac{d\alpha}{dt} = BA\omega \, \sin \alpha$$

Because the angle α is time dependent, this may be written as $BA\omega$ sin ωt or, realizing that $BA\omega$ represents the maximum value of induced emf, $\epsilon = \epsilon_m$ sin ωt. Applying this emf to a simple series circuit (Fig. 7-12) consisting of a resistance R, a capacitance C, and an inductance L, the circuit may be analyzed using Kirchhoff's second law:

$$Ri + L \, di/dt + 1/C \int i \, dt = \epsilon_m \sin \omega t$$

The solution to this equation neglecting transients is

$$i = \left[\epsilon_m / \sqrt{R^2 + (X_L - X_C)^2} \right] [\sin (\omega t - \theta)]$$

where X_L = inductive reactance (= $2\pi fL$), ohms

X_C = capacitive reactance [= $1/(2\pi fC)$], ohms

θ = phase angle between voltage and current

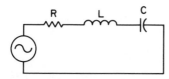

Figure 7-12

The total quantity under the radical sign is called the impedance Z. Therefore, $i = \epsilon_m [\sin (\omega t - \theta)]/Z$. The value of Z is minimum when $X_L = X_C$. This is called *resonance* and is the condition at which the current for a particular series circuit is maximum. A circuit that contains resistors, inductances, and capacitances of known value can be brought to resonance by adjusting the frequency f so that

$$2\pi fL = 1/(2\pi fC) \qquad \text{or} \qquad f_r = 1/(2\pi\sqrt{LC})$$

Phase Relations in Alternating-Current Circuits

In an a-c circuit it is not unusual to have the voltage and the current reach their maximum values at different instances. If they do reach it at the same instant, the voltage and current are said to be "in phase." If not, they are "out of phase." If the inductance reactance exceeds the capacitive reactance, the voltage will reach its maximum value first. The voltage is then said to lead the current. This is caused by the inductance's inertial resistance to change in its current-created magnetic flux. Oppositely, if the capacitance is dominant, then the current will lead the voltage because of the relative ease for having a time related change of the charge on a capacitance, i.e., a current.

Phasors

A graphical representation of the voltage in a series circuit can be made by drawing to scale the voltage for each element of the circuit. We know that the voltage across a resistance is in phase with the current through the resistance. We also know that the voltage leads or lags the current by 90°, respectively, for the inductance or the capacitance. From Kirchhoff's second law, the sum of the voltages must add to the total impressed voltage so that these voltages must be added keeping in mind their phase relation. The conventional procedure is to lay out the voltage across the resistance horizontally (in phase with the current), those across the inductance and capacitance vertically. (See Fig. 7-13.)

The total voltage V_T may then be scaled from the graph or determined analytically. These graphical representations of the voltage are called phasors

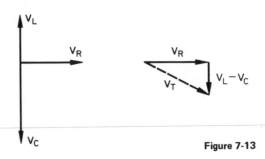

Figure 7-13

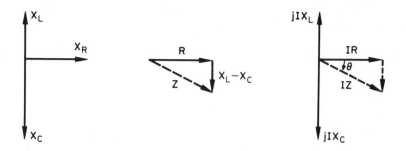

| **Figure 7-14** | **Figure 7-15** |

rather than vectors, which they resemble, because unlike vectors they are continuously rotating so that only an instantaneous value of voltage for each element is shown. Usually this is the rms value. Because the current in a series circuit is the same in each element, the phasor diagram can also be laid out in terms of the values of resistance, inductance, and reactance. The phasor sum of these is the previously mentioned impedance. (See Fig. 7-14.)

$$Z = V_T/I$$
$$X_L = V_L/I$$
$$X_C = V_C/I$$
$$R = V_R/I$$
$$V_T = \sqrt{V_R{}^2 + (V_L - V_C)^2}$$
$$Z = \sqrt{R^2 + (X_L - X_C)^2}$$

Complex Number Notation

The ease with which complex numbers can be algebraically manipulated invites their use for solving circuit problems. Thus

$$\mathbf{Z} = R + j(X_L - X_C) \quad \text{and} \quad \theta = \tan^{-1}(X_L - X_C)/R$$

This plots as shown in Fig. 7-15.

The effective value of a-c current is defined as that value of a-c current that produces the same heating effect as a steady direct current of the same magnitude.

Heat produced $= I^2 R$ (steady d-c current)

For a sinusoidally varying current, the instantaneous value i is related to the maximum as $i = I_{max} \sin 2\pi ft$. Equating the heating effects produced:

$$I_{dc}{}^2 R = I_{eff}^2 R = 1/T \int_0^T i^2 R \; dt$$

$$I_{eff}^2 = 1/T \int_0^T I_{max}^2 \sin^2 2\pi ft \; dt = I_{max}^2/2$$

$$I_{eff} = 0.707 I_{max}$$

The effective (or rms, i.e., root mean square value) for a sine wave is seen to be 0.707 times the maximum value of the sine wave. Therefore, the effective voltage for sinusoidally varying voltages is $V_{eff} = 0.707V_{max}$.

The *average value* of a-c current is defined as

$$I_{avg} = 1/T \int_0^T I_{max} \sin 2\pi ft \, dt$$

For one cycle this value is zero, whereas for one-half cycle

$$I_{avg} = 2/T \int_0^{T/2} I_{max} \sin 2\pi ft \, dt = (2/\pi)I_{max} = 0.63I_{max}$$

Note: In a-c work when values of current or voltage are given these invariably refer to the effective or rms value unless otherwise specifically indicated.

Volt-Amperes and Watts

In a d-c circuit, whenever current passes through a resistance, an energy dissipation occurs that equals I^2R and is expressed in watts when I is in amperes and R is in ohms. The product I^2R equals the product of the voltage drop across the resistance and the current through it, $I^2R = VI$.

In an a-c circuit, energy storage occurs in the capacitance as electrostatic energy (i.e., the energy for an electric field) and in the inductance as electromagnetic energy (i.e., the energy for the magnetic flux) in addition to the energy dissipation in the resistance. These facts are recognized by use of the term volt-ampere, which is the product of the total voltage and current in a circuit. Unlike the d-c case the volt-amperes do not represent total energy dissipation in a circuit. For a series circuit, watts = $I^2R = V_R I$ = real power, or energy dissipation, and volt-amperes = $V_T I = I^2 Z$.

Power Factor

The ratio of watts to volt-amperes, V_R/V_T or R/Z, is called the *power factor* (p.f.). From the relation p.f. = R/Z it may be seen that p.f. = 1 indicates that $Z = R$, which is the resonance condition mentioned previously. Three problems typifying many of these concepts follow.

Problem 7-8 Determination of capacitor for power factor correction

An inductive load is connected across a 100-V, 60-Hz single-phase line drawing 5 amps at a power factor of 0.7. (a) Determine the size of the capacitor required in series with the load to correct the power factor to 1.0. (b) Determine the power used prior to power factor correction. (c) Determine the volt-amperes used prior to power factor correction. (d) Determine the power used after installation of the capacitor.

Solution:

(a) To correct the power factor to unity, the capacitative reactance must have the same value as the inductive reactance which is therefore determined first.

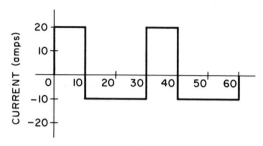

TIME (sec)

Figure 7-16

$Z = V/I = 100/5 = 20 \ \Omega$

$R = Z \cos \theta = Z(\text{power factor}) = 20(0.7) = 14 \ \Omega$

$X_L = \sqrt{20^2 - 14^2} = 14.3 \ \Omega$

Therefore,

$X_C = X_L = 14.3 \ \Omega$

$C = 1/(2\pi f X_C) = 1(2)(3.14)(60)(14.3) = 1.85 \times 10^{-4} \ \text{F}$

$$= 185 \ \mu\text{F} \qquad Answer$$

(b) Power used $= I^2 R = 5^2 \ (14) = 350 \ \text{W}$ *Answer*

(c) Volt-amperes $= VI = 100 \ (5) = 500 \ \text{VA}$ *Answer*

(d) Current after installation of capacitor $= 100/14 = 7.15$ amps

Power used $= I^2 R = (7.15)^2 \ 14 = 715 \ \text{W}$ *Answer*

Note that the power used after installation of the capacitor is greater than before. However, if the volt-amperes are determined for this by $I^2 Z$, it will be noticed that this value must be the same as the watts, namely 715 volt-amperes, since the p.f. = 1.00.

Problem 7-9 Effective value of pulsating square wave

Determine the effective value of current of the pulsating square wave current shown for one cycle, as shown in Fig. 7-16.

Solution:

The value of effective current (or voltage) is the root mean square value. The complete period is 30 sec. As a discontinuous curve this must be integrated for each part.

$$I_{eff} = \sqrt{\frac{1}{T} \int_0^T i^2 \ dt}$$

$$= \sqrt{\frac{1}{30} \int_0^{10} 20^2 \ dt + \frac{1}{30} \int_{10}^{30} (-10)^2 \ dt}$$

$$I_{eff} = \sqrt{\frac{1}{30}[4000 + (3000 - 1000)]}$$

$$= 14.14 \text{ amp} \qquad Answer$$

Problem 7-10 Determination of reactance from current measurements

When 100 VDC are impressed across the terminals of a series circuit, a 1.0-amp current is drawn. Using the same circuit with a 100-V 60-Hz a-c source, the a-c current is noted to be 0.5 amp. Find the values of (a) the resistance R, (b) the inductive reactance X_L, and (c) the capacitive reactance X_C.

Solution:

Since a current is present when a d-c voltage is impressed across the series circuit, it is evident that there is no capacitance in the circuit; hence neglecting transients,

$$X_C = 0 \qquad Answer, \text{ part (c)}$$

Since X_L is always 0 in a d-c circuit, the resistance can be determined.

$$R = 100/1.0 = 100 \ \Omega \qquad Answer, \text{ part (a)}$$

Impedance $= Z = V_{a\text{-}c}/I_{a\text{-}c} = 100/0.5 = 200 \ \Omega$

The impedance is the phasor sum of the reactive and resistive elements of the circuit.

$$Z = \sqrt{R^2 + (X_L - X_C)^2}$$

$$200 = \sqrt{100^2 + X_L^2}$$

$$X_L = 173 \ \Omega \qquad Answer, \text{ part (b)}$$

Parallel Circuit Analysis

In a parallel circuit, Kirchhoff's current law that the sum of the currents at a point must equal zero, holds true. However, phase relations between currents must be observed. Consider the circuit of Fig. 7-17. The voltage drops across AB, CD, and EF are equal. The total circuit current in 0-A is the phasor sum of the currents in AB, CD, and EF.

$$I = V/R - V/jX_C + V/jX_L$$

$$V = \frac{I}{1/R - 1/jX_C + 1/jX_L}$$

A more typical case consists of two parallel branches consisting of a capacitor and resistance in one branch, and an inductance and resistance in series in the other branch, as shown in Fig. 7-18. The current in each branch is the total voltage divided by the branch impedance

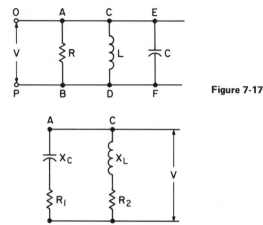

Figure 7-17

Figure 7-18

$$I_{AB} = \frac{V}{Z_{AB}} = \frac{V}{R_1 - jX_C} = \frac{V}{R_1 - jX_C} \times \frac{R_1 + jX_C}{R_1 + jX_C} = \frac{V(R_1 + jX_C)}{R_1{}^2 + X_C{}^2}$$

$$I_{CD} = \frac{V}{Z_{CD}} = \frac{V}{R_2 + jX_L} = \frac{V}{R_2 + jX_L} \times \frac{R_2 - jX_L}{R_2 - jX_L} = \frac{V(R_2 - jX_L)}{R_2{}^2 + X_L{}^2}$$

The total current is the phasor sum of both branch currents

$$I = V \left(\frac{1}{Z_{AB}} + \frac{1}{Z_{CD}} \right) = V \left(\frac{Z_{CD} + Z_{AB}}{Z_{CD}Z_{AB}} \right)$$

The last expression in parentheses is a general expression for $1/Z_T$, which is applicable to any two-branch parallel circuit.

Admittance, conductance, and *susceptance* are the a-c circuit counterparts to the term conductance (= $1/R$) for a d-c circuit. Thus, admittance is defined as the reciprocal of impedance.

$$Y = \frac{1}{Z} = \frac{1}{R + jX} = \frac{1}{R + jX} \times \frac{(R - jX)}{(R - jX)} = \frac{R - jX}{R^2 + X^2}$$

Recalling that $| R^2 + X^2 | = Z^2$, the last term is expanded to

$$Y = R/Z^2 - jX/Z^2$$

It is seen that admittance, like impedance, consists of two general terms: the conductance $G = R/Z^2$, and the susceptance $B = X/Z^2$. Note that when there is no reactance ($X_L = X_C = 0$), then $G = R/R^2 = 1/R$, which is the form for conductance in the case of direct current.

Sign convention is such that G is always positive, but B is positive for a capacitive susceptance and negative for an inductive susceptance, the signs being opposite to those found in reactances due to rationalization.

Problem 7-11 Power loss in an alternating-current circuit

Determine the power loss in the parallel circuit of Fig. 7-19.

Solution:

The power loss in an a-c circuit is the product of the voltage and the current in phase with the voltage. The total current is easily determined by finding the current in each branch and adding these by phasor addition.

I_C = current in the branch with capacitance

I_L = current in the branch with inductance

$$I_C = \frac{V}{Z_1} = \frac{100}{3-j4} = \frac{100}{3-j4} \times \frac{3+j4}{3+j4} = 12+j16 = 20\angle+53.17° \text{ amps}$$

$$I_L = \frac{V}{Z_2} = \frac{100}{6+j8} \times \frac{6-j8}{6-j8} = 6-j8 = 10\angle-53.17° \text{ amps}$$

$$I_T = I_C + I_L = 18+j8 \text{ amps}$$

The current in phase with the voltage is 18 amps.

$$P = VI = 100(18) = 1800 \text{ W} \qquad Answer$$

Alternate Solution:

The total power used may also be determined by finding the effective current in each branch and then finding the $I_{eff}^2 R$ loss in each branch.

Effective current, capacitance branch = $\sqrt{(12-j16)(12+j16)}$

$$I_{eff} = 20 \text{ amps}$$

Loss in capacitance branch = $(20)^2 3 = 1200$ W

Effective current, inductance branch = $\sqrt{(6+j8)(6-j8)}$

$$I_{eff} = 10 \text{ amps}$$

Loss in inductance branch = $(10)^2 6 = 600$ W

$$\text{Total loss} = 1800 \text{ W}$$

Note: Total value of line current = $\sqrt{18^2+8^2}$ = 19.7 tan^{-1} (8/18)° amps. The voltage current phase relation is shown in Fig. 7-20 using the voltage as datum.

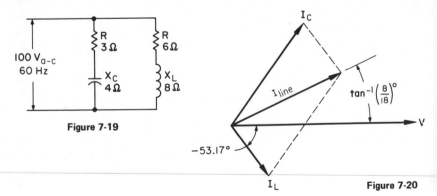

Figure 7-19

Figure 7-20

Problem 7-12 Alternating-current loads in parallel

Two parallel loads are connected across a single-phase 60-Hz, 220-V line, as shown in Fig. 7-21. Find (a) the line current, (b) the power used, and (c) the potential difference V_{BE}.

Solution:

(a) Total impedance Z_T for a parallel circuit:

$$\frac{1}{Z_T} = \frac{1}{Z_1} + \frac{1}{Z_2} = \frac{1}{50 + j50} + \frac{1}{50 - j50}$$

$$\frac{1}{Z_T} = \frac{50 + j50 + 50 - j50}{(50 + j50)(50 - j50)} = \frac{100}{2500 + 2500} = \frac{1}{50}$$

$$Z_T = 50 \ \Omega$$

$$I_{line} = V_{line}/Z_T = 220/50 = 4.4 \ amps \angle 0° \qquad Answer$$

(b) Power used = $V_{line}I_{line} \cos \theta$

$$= 220 \times 4.4 \times 1 = 968 \ W \qquad Answer$$

(c) $$I_{AC} = \frac{V_{line}}{Z_{AC}} = \frac{220}{50 + j50} = \frac{220}{50 + j50} \times \frac{(1 - j1)}{(1 - j1)} = \frac{220 - j220}{50 + 50} = 2.2 - j2.2$$

$$I_{DF} = \frac{V_{line}}{Z_{DF}} = \frac{220}{50 - j50} = 2.2 + j2.2$$

Alternate Solution:

$$I_{DF} = I_{line} - I_{AC}$$

$$= 4.4 - (2.2 - j2.2) = 2.2 + j2.2$$

$$V_{AB} = I_{AC}X_L = (2.2 - j2.2)(j50) = 110 + j110 \ volts$$

$$V_{DE} = I_{DF}X_C = (2.2 + j2.2)(-j50) = 110 - j110 \ volts$$

$$V_{BE} = V_{BA} + V_{DE} = -110 - j110 + 110 - j110 = -j220 \ volts$$

$$= 220 \ V \angle -90° \qquad Answer$$

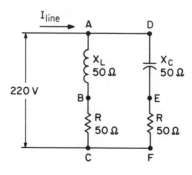

Figure 7-21

Resonance in Parallel Circuits

In contrast to the series circuit, the resonant condition in a parallel circuit will result in a *minimum* line current provided the conductances are equal. At resonance, the line current will be in phase with the applied or line voltage; the reactive portion of the current in both branches must be equal and opposite, thus canceling each other. In the preceding problem, a resonant condition was indicated. Note the unity power factor. The general solution for obtaining a parallel circuit resonance follows.

The parallel impedance Z_p for a two-branch circuit is

$$Z_p = \frac{Z_1 Z_2}{Z_1 + Z_2}$$

Resonance occurs when the absolute values of Z_1 and Z_2 are equal:

$$|Z_1| = |Z_2|$$
$$|R_1 \pm jX_1| = |R_2 \pm jX_2|$$

and $R_1 = R_2 \quad X_1 = -X_2$

For the resonant condition, the parallel impedance is determined by

$$Z_p = \frac{R_1^2 + X_1^2}{2R_1}$$

In Problem 7-12, the total impedance Z_T is also the parallel impedance for a resonant network so that it could have been calculated as above. Thus,

$$Z_1 = 50 + j50$$
$$Z_2 = 50 - j50$$
$$Z_p = \frac{50^2 + 50^2}{2 \times 50} = 50 \angle 0° \ \Omega$$

Similarly, if two branches in parallel consists of 10-ohm resistances and a 100-ohm inductance or capacitance so that

$$Z_1 = 10 + j100 \quad \text{and} \quad Z_2 = 10 - j100$$

then $Z_p = \dfrac{10^2 + 100^2}{2 \times 10} = 505 \angle 0° \ \Omega$

In case resonance has to be obtained by adjusting the frequency using given capacitors and inductances, resonance will occur when the resistances in both branches are equal and when the frequency is adjusted so that

$$f_r = \frac{1}{2\pi\sqrt{LC}}$$

which is the same condition as in a series circuit.

Problem 7-13 Maximum power transfer with complex impedances

In a low-current application, a generator having an impedance of $2 + j4$ ohms is generating 15 V at 1000 Hz. It is connected to a load having an impedance of $5 + j4$ ohms. The connecting line has an impedance of $2 + j2$ ohms. Maximum power transfer is desired. (a) Determine the value of the additional line components needed for maximum power transfer. (b) What is the maximum current, (c) the power dissipated in the generator, and (d) the power delivered to the load?

Solution:

Maximum power transfer occurs in a tuned circuit, i.e., one in which the imped-ance of the load matches the impedance of the generator and transmission line, and the reactive elements cancel out: $Z_{gen} + Z_{line} = Z_{load}$.

For the case in question, the equation does not initially balance

$$(2 + j4) + (2 + j2) \neq 5 + j4$$
$$4 + j6 \neq 5 + j4$$

To match the impedances and have the reactive elements cancel, the following are necessary

$$R_{gen} + R_{line} + R_{Bal\ Comp} = R_{load}$$
$$X_{gen} + X_{line} + X_{Bal\ Comp} = -X_{load}$$

The additional components must therefore be

$$R = 1\ \Omega \qquad X = -j10\ \Omega$$

A capacitive reactance of 10 Ω is required.

$$C = 1/\omega X_C = 1/(1000 \times 10 \times 2\pi) = 100/2\pi\ \mu F = 16\ \mu F$$

Additional line components needed:

$$R = 1\ \Omega \qquad C = 16\ \mu F \qquad \textit{Answer, part (a)}$$

Maximum current $= 15\ V/(R_{gen} + R_{line} + R_{Bal\ Comp} + R_{load})$
$$= 15/(2 + 2 + 1 + 5) = 1.5\ \text{amps} \qquad \textit{Answer, part (b)}$$

Power dissipated in generator $= I_{max}^2 R_{gen} = (1.5)^2 2 = 4.5\ \text{W} \qquad \textit{Answer, part (c)}$

Power delivered to load $= I_{max}^2 R_{load} = (1.5)^2 5 = 11.25\ \text{W} \qquad \textit{Answer, part (d)}$

7-7 TRANSFORMERS, MOTORS, GENERATORS, AND POLYPHASE CIRCUITS

Transformers

Transformers are often used in a-c circuits because of the ease with which they allow voltage transformation with very small accompanying power losses. These power or core losses in a transformer are due to (1) hysteresis losses, (2) eddy current losses, and (3) copper or I^2R losses occurring in both the primary and secondary of the transformer. The first two losses are dependent on the frequency f of imposed alternating emf, the maximum flux density B_{max}, and the configuration and material expressed by constants a and b. Thus

Hysteresis loss $= aB_{max}^{1.6}$

Eddy current loss $= bfB_{max}^2$

Knowing the power losses and the input to a transformer, its efficiency can be determined by

$$\frac{Output}{Input} = \frac{input - losses}{input}$$

and its voltage regulation is expressed by

$$\frac{(\text{no-load secondary voltage}) - (\text{full-load secondary voltage})}{(\text{full-load secondary voltage})}$$

The functioning of a transformer depends on the fact that a harmonically alternating voltage applied to a transformer primary will be accompanied by a harmonically alternating current that creates a magnetic flux density in the primary. This flux density will also alternate harmonically.

In a typical transformer the coils are so wound that all the flux from the primary links the coils of the secondary so that the coefficient of coupling $K = 1$. Therefore, $K = 1 = M = \sqrt{L_1 - L_2}$. As the flux is the same in both the primary and secondary winding, the induced emf per turn for each winding must be the same. Then the total induced emf in each winding is proportional to its number of turns, $E_1/E_2 = N_1/N_2$. The terminal voltage is essentially equal to the induced emf, therefore, $V_1/V_2 = N_1/N_2$ and from energy considerations, the input energy must equal the output energy (neglecting losses). Therefore

$$V_1 I_1 = V_2 I_2 \quad \text{and} \quad I_1/I_2 = -N_2/N_1$$

The negative sign in the above equations indicates that the secondary current and voltage are $180°$ out of phase with their primary counterpart, assuming the coils are wound in the same sense.

Circuit Equations for Transformers

Using Kirchhoff's second or voltage law, a transformer circuit analysis including the generator in the primary loop and the load in the secondary loop (see Fig. 7-22), consists of two simultaneous equations:

Loop 1: $I_1 Z_1 + I_2 j\omega M = V_{gen}$

Loop 2: $I_1 j\omega M + I_2 Z_2 = 0$

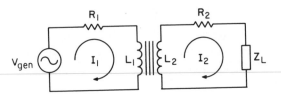

Figure 7-22

where $Z_1 = Z_{gen} + R_1 + j\omega L_1$

$\quad\quad Z_2 = Z_{load} + R_2 + j\omega L_2$

Solutions for I_1 and I_2 are

$$I_1 = \frac{\begin{vmatrix} V_{gen} & j\omega M \\ 0 & Z_2 \end{vmatrix}}{\begin{vmatrix} Z_1 & j\omega M \\ j\omega M & Z_2 \end{vmatrix}} \quad = \quad \frac{V_{gen}Z_2}{Z_1Z_2 + \omega^2 M^2}$$

$$I_2 = \frac{\begin{vmatrix} Z_1 & V_{gen} \\ j\omega M & 0 \end{vmatrix}}{\begin{vmatrix} Z_1 & j\omega M \\ j\omega M & Z_2 \end{vmatrix}} \quad = \quad \frac{-V_{gen}j\omega M}{Z_1Z_2 + \omega^2 M^2}$$

For an *idealized* case, neglecting core losses an equivalent circuit may be drawn (see Fig. 7-23) in which all secondary impedances are reflected into the primary circuit by transforming the product I_2Z_2 to I_1 $(N_1/N_2)^2$ so that

$$V_{gen} - I_1 [R_1 + j\omega L_1 + (N_1/N_2)^2 Z_2] = 0$$

The term $(N_1/N_2)^2 Z_2$ is the equivalent impedance reflected into the primary circuit. It may be broken down into equivalent resistance $(N_1/N_2)^2 R_2$, and equivalent reactance $(N_1/N_2)^2 X_{L2}$.

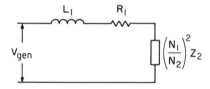

Figure 7-23

Problem 7-14 Determination of transformer efficiency

A 2200/220-V transformer has an iron loss of 400 W at 60 Hz. Its primary and secondary resistances are 0.6 and 0.0064 ohm, respectively. If the transformer delivers a full-load current of 114 amps at an 85% power factor, determine its efficiency at full load.

Solution:

The ratio of primary to secondary currents is essentially equal to the inverse ratio of primary to secondary emf's, therefore

$I_p = I_s(N_s/N_p)$

$\quad = 114(220/2200) = 11.4$ amps

Power output $= 220 \times 114 \times 0.85 = \quad\quad\quad$ 21,300 W

Power loss (iron loss) $= \quad\quad\quad$ 400 W

Copper loss in the primary $= I^2 R = (11.4)^2 \times 0.6 = \quad\quad$ 78 W

Copper loss in the secondary = $I^2R = (114)^2 \times 0.0064 = 83$ W

Power input, the sum of the above =   21,861 W

Efficiency = $(21,300/21,861) \times 100\% = 97.4\%$ *Answer*

Problem 7-15 Determination of input conditions for transformer with centertapped secondary

A 2200/220-volt transformer has its secondary centertapped as shown in Fig. 7-24. Determine the input power and kVA for this circuit.

Solution:

The secondary current in the pure resistance circuit is $110/10 = 11$ amps in phase with the voltage. Similarly, the current in the capacitive circuit is $110/15 = 7.35$ amps leading the voltage by 90°.

The corresponding primary currents are

$$(I_R)_p = 110/2200 \times 11 = 0.55 \text{ amp}$$

in phase with the primary voltage;

$$(I_C)_p = \frac{110}{2200} \times 7.35 = 0.37 \text{ amp}$$

leading the primary voltage by 90°.

Total primary current = $\sqrt{(I_R)_p{}^2 + (I_C)_p{}^2} = 0.662$ amp (see Fig. 7-25)

To determine the power factor, the phase angle must be found between the total primary current and the voltage.

$$\tan \theta = 0.37/0.55 = 0.672$$
$$\theta = 33.9°, \text{ leading}$$
$$\cos \theta = 0.83$$

Power factor = 0.83

$$\text{Input kVA} = \frac{2200 \times 0.662}{1000} = 1.455 \text{ kVA} \qquad Answer$$

Input power = kVA $\times$ power factor = $1.455 \times 0.83 = 1.210$ kW   *Answer*

Note that in this example the transformer losses are neglected since no information about them is available. This is satisfactory since losses tend to be very small.

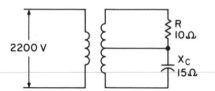

2200 V

R
10Ω

X_C
15Ω

Figure 7-24

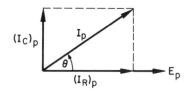

Figure 7-25

Generators

The essentials of a generator consist of a coil in which an emf is induced by varying the flux through the coil. The instantaneous value of emf is given by the expression $E = (d\phi/dt)10^{-8}$ V, where $d\phi/dt$ represents the time rate of change of flux through the coil. For a uniformly rotating coil in a uniform constant magnetic field, the average emf produced in a quarter turn is $E = N(\phi/t)10^{-8}$ V, where N = number of turns per coil, and t = time required to complete a quarter revolution.

A useful generator equation for the generated armature voltage is $E = \phi PS(N/P_a)10^{-8}$ V, where ϕ = flux in lines or maxwells, P = number of magnetic poles, S = revolutions per second, and N/P_a = number of conductors in series, with N as the total number of conductors and P_a the number of parallel paths.

Note that in a simplex lap winding there are as many paths as poles.

Problem 7-16 Direct-current generated voltage determined from flux density

A six-pole generator has a simplex lap winding and a 600-conductor armature revolving at 450 rpm. If the pole's cross-sectional area is 80 sq in. and the average flux density is 40,000 lines/sq in., determine the emf induced between brushes.

Solution:

Total flux per pole = $40,000 \times 80 = 3.2 \times 10^6$ lines or Mx.

Generated emf = $3.2(10)^6 \times 6 \times 450/60 \times (600/6)(10)^{-8}$

$\qquad$ = 144 V   *Answer*

The line voltage of a d-c generator is always less than the generated emf. The reduction is due to the potential drop in just the armature if shunt connected, or in the armature and series field if series or compound connected, i.e.,

$E_{line} = E - I_a R_a$ (shunt connected)

$E_{line} = E - I_a(R_a + R_s)$ (compound connected)

where I_a = armature current

$\qquad R_a$ = armature resistance

$\qquad R_s$ = field resistance in series with armature

$\qquad a$ = subscript indicating armature

$\qquad s$ = subscript indicating series field

The line current equals the armature current in a series connected generator or, from Kirchhoff's law, equals the sum of armature and shunt field currents in shunt or compound connected generators.

Direct-Current Motors

The same equations as developed in the preceding paragraphs apply to d-c motors except that the line voltage is always greater than the generated emf (or so-called back voltage E_b) in a motor by an amount equal to the potential drop due the armature circuit resistances.

$E_{line} = E_b + I_a R_a$ (shunt wound motor)

$E_{line} = E_b + I_a(R_a + R_s)$ (series or compound motor)

Problem 7-17 Armature emf and armature current in a direct-current shunt generator

A 110-V shunt generator operating at 1200 rpm is delivering 10 kW of power. If the field resistance is 40 ohms, the armature resistance is 0.10 ohm, determine the armature emf and the armature current.

Solution:

Line current   = 10,000 W/110 V = 90.8 amps

Field current   = 110/40 = 2.75 amps

Armature current = $I_{line} + I_f$

= 90.8 + 2.75 = 93.55 amps   *Answer*

Armature emf   = line voltage + armature potential drop

= 110 + 93.55(0.10) = 119.36 V   *Answer*

Problem 7-18 Direct-current shunt motor operated as generator at higher speed

A 110-V 2-kW shunt motor has an armature resistance of 0.06 ohm and a field resistance of 250 ohms. Its full-load (2 kW) operating speed is 900 rpm. If this motor is operated as a generator at 930 rpm, determine its available power if the field current is 0.50 amp.

Solution:

The load (2 kW) of the 110-V shunt motor allows calculation of the line current, therefore also of field current. With the field current known and the speed known for both motor and generator operation, the generated emf for both cases can be determined and thus so can the available power as a generator.

(a) Performing as a motor

Line current   = 2000 W/110 V = 18.2 amps

Field current   = 110 V/250 Ω = 0.44 amp

Armature current = $I_{line} - I_f = 17.76$

Back emf   = $110 - I_a R_a = 110 - (17.76 \times 0.06) = 108.93$ V

Since E = emf = $\phi PS(N/P_a)10^{-8}$ and P and N/P_a are constants, the emf is proportional to flux and speed, $E = k(\phi S)$. The flux ϕ is dependent on the field current. Since the magnetization curve for the field winding is not available, assume a direct proportion between flux and field current. Then, the flux for generator operation is

$$\phi_{gen} = \phi_{mot} \times \frac{(I_f)_{gen}}{(I_f)_{mot}}$$

(b) Performing as a generator

$$E_{gen} = E_{mot} \times \frac{S_{gen}}{S_{mot}} \times \frac{(I_f)_{gen}}{(I_f)_{mot}}$$
$$= 108.93(930/900)\,(0.50/0.44) = 127 \text{ V}$$
$$E_{line} = 127 - I_a R_a$$

Since the field current is 0.50, the line voltage can be calculated as

$$E_{line} = I_f R_f = 0.5 \times 250 = 125 \text{ V}$$
$$I_a = \frac{127 - 125}{R_a} = \frac{2}{0.06} = 33 \text{ amps}$$
$$I_{line} = 33 - 0.5 = 32.5 \text{ amps}$$

Power delivered = $(I_{line})(E_{line}) = \dfrac{32.5 \times 125}{1000} = 4$ kW   *Answer*

Torque-Current-Speed Relations

A current-carrying conductor located in a magnetic field will experience a force F so that

$$F = BLI \sin \theta$$

where F = force on conductor, B = field density, L = length of conductor, I = current in conductor, and θ = angle between flux lines and conductor.

Similarly, if a current passes through a coil or loop of many turns N, which is located in a magnetic field, the coil experiences a torque,

$$T = BrLI(\sin \theta)N$$

where r = radial distance from center of rotor shaft to conductor. Since in a motor or generator the terms r, L, θ, and N are constants, armature torque is proportional to the product of flux and current, i.e.,

$$T = kBI = k'\phi I$$

Using the previously established relation for back emf and the torque relation, the torque-current-speed relations for particular machines can be determined.

Problem 7-19 Load increase on direct-current shunt motor reduces speed

A shunt-wound 5-hp motor is drawing an armature current of 60 amps. The line voltage is 110 V. The armature resistance is 0.08 ohm. (a) Determine the back emf for this condition. (b) The load is then increased causing a 5% reduction motor speed. Determine the new armature current.

Solution:

(a) The armature voltage, resistance, and armature current are known, allowing direct calculation of the back emf.

$$\text{Back emf} = V_{line} - I_a R_a$$
$$= 110 - 60(0.08)$$
$$= 105.2 \text{ V} \qquad Answer$$

(b) For the increased load, $S_2 = 0.95 S_1$. In a shunt-wound motor, the field is directly connected across the line; thus unless reference is made to an adjustable field resistance, it may be assumed constant and hence the field current and the field ϕ itself remain constant. Since

$$E = KS\phi$$
$$E_{b2} = KS_2\phi \qquad \text{and} \qquad E_{b1} = KS_1\phi$$
$$E_{b2}/E_{b1} = S_2/S_1 = 0.95 S_1/S_1 = 0.95$$
$$E_{b2} = 0.95(105.2) = 100 \text{ volts}$$
$$= V_{line} - I_{a2}R_a$$
$$I_{a2} = \frac{V_{line} - E_{b2}}{R_a} = \frac{110 - 100}{0.08} = 125 \text{ amps} \qquad Answer$$

Alternating-Current Circuits

In single-phase circuits there is only one impressed line voltage, whereas in polyphase circuits such as two- or three-phase circuits several out-of-phase voltages are generated simultaneously and impressed on a number of lines. In a balanced two-phase system, two equal voltages that are $90°$ out of phase are generated. Similarly in the more popular balanced three-phase system three equal voltages are generated $120°$ out of phase. The advantage of polyphase circuitry is the higher power to copper ratio for the transmission system.

A two-phase, three-wire system using a common neutral and connected to both single-phase and two-phase loads is illustrated in Fig. 7-26.

A three-phase, four-wire system using a common neutral with single and three-phase loads is illustrated in Fig. 7-27. And a three-phase, delta-connected load is shown in Fig. 7-28. Note that the delta-connected load cannot use a neutral line.

In Fig. 7-27 the voltages from the lines A, B, C to neutral are called phase voltages; line voltages are, as implied, from line to line. These may be determined by phasor addition, Fig. 7-29. Note the inversion of letters from E_{NB} to E_{BN} to denote changed directions.

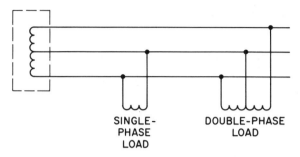

SINGLE-
PHASE
LOAD

DOUBLE-PHASE
LOAD

Figure 7-26

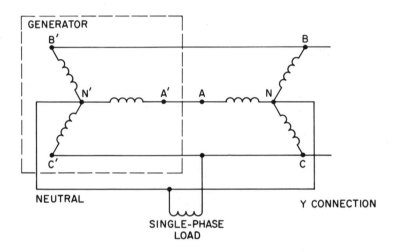

GENERATOR

B'

B

N'

A'   A

N

C'

C

NEUTRAL

Y CONNECTION

SINGLE-PHASE
LOAD

Figure 7-27

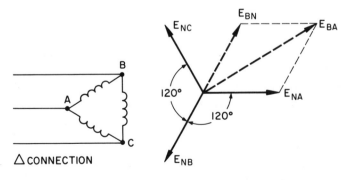

△ CONNECTION

Figure 7-28

Figure 7-29

For a balanced Y load, the magnitude relationship of the phase and line voltage is

Line voltage = $(\sqrt{3})$ phase voltage
$$E_{BA} = |\sqrt{3}\ E_{NA}| = |\sqrt{3}\ E_{NB}|$$

In a general four-wire, three-phase system, the following hold true, using the load current in load Z_{AN} as an example:

$$I_{AN} = E_{AN}/Z_{AN}$$

Phase angle for the same load: $\theta_{AN} = \cos^{-1}(R_{AN}/Z_{AN})$

Line current = phase current

Current in neutral: $I_N = I_{AN} + I_{BN} + I_{CN}$ (phasor addition)

For a balanced condition, $I_N = 0$:

Power per phase: $P_{AN} = E_{AN} I_{AN} \cos \theta_{AN}$

Total power: $P_T = P_{AN} + P_{BN} + P_{CN}$ (scaler addition)

For a balanced delta load, the following relations hold true:

Line current = $\sqrt{3}$ (phase current)

Line voltage = phase voltage

For a more general circuit, i.e., unbalanced loads, recourse to Kirchhoff's laws is necessary.

Problem 7-20 Current and power in three-phase balanced system

A three-wire, three-phase 220-V line supplies power to a balanced Y (wye) load. Each phase of the load consists of an impedance of $6 + j8$ ohms. Determine (a) the phase current, (b) the line current, (c) the total power used, and (d) the total power used if the loads were delta connected.

Solution:

In a three-phase wye system, the phase voltage is

$$V_{phase} = V_{line}/\sqrt{3} = 220/\sqrt{3} = 127 \text{ volts}$$

$$I_{line} = I_{phase}$$

(a), (b) $I_{phase} = I_{line} = \dfrac{127 + j0}{6 + j8} = 7.62 - j10.16$ amps

$$= 12.7 \angle -53.13° \text{ amps} \qquad Answer$$

(c) Volt-amperes per phase = $I_{phase} \times V_{phase}$
$$= (7.62 - j10.16)(127 + j0)$$
$$= 967.74 + j1290$$

Power per phase = 967.74 W

Total power = $3 \times 967.74 = 2903.22$ W   *Answer*

For a delta connection,

Phase voltage = 220 V

Phase current = $\dfrac{220 + j0}{6 + j8}$ = 13.2 − j17.6 amps

Power per phase = 13.2 × 220 = 2904 W

Total power = 3 × 2904 = 8712 W   *Answer*

Note that the power consumed in a balanced delta-connected load is three times the power consumed for the same wye-connected load.

Alternating-Current Motors

Two types of a-c motors are in general use: the synchronous motor and the induction motor. Of these, the latter is the more widely used because of its inherent ruggedness and simplicity. A further categorization of common a-c motors follows:

(a) Polyphase machines
  1. Squirrel cage
  2. Wound rotor
    a. Slip ring
    b. Brush shifting

(b) Single-phase machines
  1. Split phase
  2. Repulsion-induction
  3. Universal
  4. Capacitor
  5. Series

Alternating-current machines generally have stationary field windings that produce the effect of rotating magnetic field. This is accomplished in a single-phase machine by various devices such as a capacitor that causes the current in adjacent field coils to be out of phase and thus the flux from the coils to be out of phase. Phasor summation of the flux from two coils, spaced say 90° (physical degrees) apart, will give rise to the rotating field if the coils have an alternating variation in current. For a polyphase machine the field coils are directly connected to the different incoming phases, thereby automatically having a difference in phase between coils. The rotating magnetic field induces voltages in the conductors on the rotor, which in turn cause currents to exist in these conductors. Interaction between the rotor current and the field causes the force that acts on the rotor's conductors and hence the necessary torque. No direct electrical energy input to the rotor is required; consequently there is no need for slip rings, commutators, or brushes.

Slip. Since the induced emf's in the rotor exist only when the stator's magnetic field is moving relative to the rotor's conductors, the rotor cannot deliver torque unless it is moving slower than the magnetic field. The lag between field speed (the so-called synchronous speed N_s) and rotor speed is known as slip and is expressed either in rpm or in percent. This value is usually less than 10%.

Field or synchronous speed: $N_s = 120f/p$ rpm   *freq*
                                                         poles

Slip percent: $s = (N_s − N)(100)/N_s$

Torque at standstill: $T_{st} = K(V_{line})^2$

Power output, single-phase: $P = (Eff)I_{line}V_{line}$ (p.f.) W

Power output, three-phase: $P = (Eff)\sqrt{3} \, I_{line}V_{line}$ (p.f.) W

Conversion factor: 746 W = 1 hp

Torque, operating: $T = hp(33,000)/2\pi N$ lb-ft

where f = line current frequency or voltage frequency, typically 60 Hz

    N = rotor speed, rpm

    Eff = efficiency

    p.f. = power factor = $\cos \theta$

The following factors contribute to the overall losses from input.

1.   Stator copper losses—$I^2 R$ losses
2.   Friction and windage losses
3.   Core losses
4.   Rotor copper losses—$I^2 R$ losses

Output power = input power—losses

Rotor power input = total input—stator copper and core losses

Rotor power input = output + rotor copper losses and friction and
                    windage losses

    The slip may also be determined as follows: slip = rotor copper losses/
rotor input. The frequency of rotor currents f_2 is determined thus: f_2 = sf.

Problem 7-21 Frequency of rotor currents in induction motor

Determine the frequency of the rotor currents in a 60-Hz, six-pole (per phase)
induction motor. The measured rotor speed is 1164 rpm.

Solution:

First find the field or synchronous speed:

$N_s = 120f/p = (120)(60)/6 = 1200$ rpm

The percent slip is then: $s = \dfrac{1200 - 1164}{1200} (100) = 3\%$

The frequency of the current can now be determined

$f_2 = sf = (0.03)(60) = 1.8$ Hz   *Answer*

It might be recalled that the induction motor can be used as a frequency
changer by driving the motor mechanically at the proper speed.

Problem 7-22 Horsepower and phase quantities in a three-phase induction motor

A three-phase wye-connected induction motor operating on 220 V has a power
factor of 70% and an efficiency of 85%. If the line current is 4 amps, what are
(a) the phase voltage, (b) the phase current, and (c) the output horsepower of
the motor?

Solution:

Phase voltage (in wye connections) = $V_{line}/\sqrt{3}$ = $220/\sqrt{3}$

$\qquad\qquad\qquad\qquad\qquad\qquad\qquad$ = 127 V   *Answer*, part (a)

Phase current (in wye connections) = line current = 4 amps   *Answer*, part (b)

kVA delivered to the motor = $3I_{phase}V_{phase}$

$\qquad\qquad\qquad\qquad\qquad$ = $3(4)(127)(10^{-3})$

$\qquad\qquad\qquad\qquad\qquad$ = 1.52 kVA

Power delivered (in kilowatts) = kVA (power factor)

$\qquad\qquad\qquad\qquad\qquad\qquad$ = 1.52(0.70)

$\qquad\qquad\qquad\qquad\qquad\qquad$ = 1.07 kW

Horsepower delivered = (power)(efficiency)

$\qquad\qquad\qquad\qquad$ = 1.07(0.85)/0.746

$\qquad\qquad\qquad\qquad$ = 1.2 hp   *Answer*, part (c)

Problem 7-23 Torque, speed, and current of three-phase induction motor

A three-phase, 220-V, six-pole, 60-Hz induction motor delivers 20 hp at full load with an efficiency of 90% and a power factor of 85%. Its slip is 0.02. Calculate (a) the torque, (b) the speed, and (c) the current drawn by this motor.

Solution:

Power delivered = 20 hp(746) W/hp = 14,920 W

Line current = $\dfrac{P}{\sqrt{3} \times E_{line} \times \cos\theta \times Eff}$

$\qquad\qquad$ = $\dfrac{14,920}{\sqrt{3} \times 220 \times 0.85 \times 0.90}$

$\qquad\qquad$ = 51 amps   *Answer*, part (c)

Synchronous speed = N_s = 120f/p

$\qquad\qquad\qquad\qquad$ = (120)(60)/6 = 1200 rpm   *Answer*, part (b)

Slip = s

$\qquad$ = $\dfrac{N_s - N}{N_s} \times 100$

$\quad$ 0.02 = $\dfrac{1200 - N}{1200}$

$\quad$ 24 + N = 1200

$\qquad$ N = 1176 rpm   *Answer*, part (b)

$\qquad$ T = hp(33,000)/$2\pi N$

$\qquad\quad$ = (20)(33,000)/$2\pi(1176)$

$\qquad\quad$ = 89.3 lb-ft   *Answer*, part (a)

Problem 7-24 The effect of losses on speed and torque of induction motor

A 10-hp, three-phase, six-pole, 60-Hz, 220-V induction motor operates with an efficiency of 80%. A tabulation of known losses is

Stator copper loss	360 W
Friction and windage loss	650 W
Core loss	450 W

Calculate the speed and torque at (a) full load and at (b) half load.

Solution:

(a) From the output (10 hp) and the efficiency, the input power is determinable. Comparing this value to output, the remaining losses can be determined. Once rotor copper loss is known, speed and torque are readily determined.

Input = (10) (746)/0.80 = 9320 W

Total losses = input − output = 9320 − 7460 = 1860 W

Sum of known losses = 360 + 650 + 450 = 1460 W

Rotor copper loss = 1860 − 1460 = 400 W

Synchronous speed = 120f/p = (120) (60)/6 = 1200 rpm

Rotor power input = total input − (stator copper and core losses)

$$= 9320 − (360 + 450) = 8510 \text{ W}$$

Slip = rotor copper loss/rotor input = 400/8510 = 0.047

Rotor speed = (synchronous speed)(1 − s)

$$N = 1200(1 − 0.047) = 1140 \text{ rpm} \quad \text{(at full load)} \qquad Answer$$

Torque = hp(33,000)/2πN = (10)(33,000)/2π (1140)

$$= 46 \text{ lb-ft} \quad \text{(at full load)} \qquad Answer$$

(b) At one-half load the following situation is encountered. The mechanical losses and the core loss remain approximately constant; however, the copper losses are proportionate to the square of the load. Therefore, the stator and copper losses are $(\frac{1}{2})^2 = \frac{1}{4}$ of their full-load values.

Output = (5)(746) = 3730 W

Stator copper loss = $(\frac{1}{4})$(360) = 90 W

Friction and windage losses = 650 W

Core loss = 450 W

Rotor copper loss = $(\frac{1}{4})$(400) = 100 W

Rotor input = output + rotor copper loss + friction and windage = 3730 + 100 + 650

$$= 4480 \text{ W}$$

Slip = 100/4480 = 0.022 = 2.2%

Rotor speed = 1200(1 − 0.022) = 1174 rpm   *Answer*

Torque = (5)(33,000)/2π(1174) = 22.2 lb-ft   *Answer*

7-8 ELECTRONICS

A simple vacuum tube and a few transistor circuits will be found in the examinations. Vacuum tubes are classified by the number of elements they contain; a two-element tube consisting of a filament and a plate is called a *diode*. Similarly, a three-element tube is a *triode*.

In a diode the filament or cathode is heated causing electrons to boil off and become attracted to the cold collection plate. The plate is also called the *anode* and is kept at a positive potential with respect to the filament. Unlike circuits previously discussed, Ohm's law does not apply to tubes or transistors. Instead *characteristic curves* are plotted showing the relation between voltage and current, the latter being plotted as the dependent variable. (See Fig. 7-30.) For the portion of the curve that is concave upward, the current is proportional to $V^{3/2}$.

Note the saturation level, where despite increasing voltage no corresponding increase in current occurs. Since diodes allow electrons to pass only in one direction, they are primarily used for rectification. Conventional current flow is from anode to cathode, whereas actual electron flow is in the reverse direction.

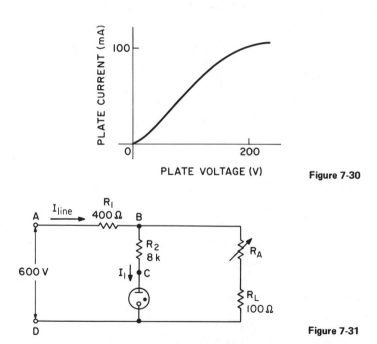

Figure 7-30

Figure 7-31

Problem 7-25 Glow discharge tube to regulate voltage

A glow discharge tube is to be used in the circuit of Fig. 7-31 to maintain the voltage between points C and D at 150 ± 4 V, while the current through the load R_L is to range from 150 to 300 mA. Current regulation is obtained by varying R_A. Determine the minimum and maximum values of R_A and the current range for the glow tube.

Solution:

A glow discharge tube maintains almost a steady voltage over a wide range of small current values. The actual solution requires two separate series of steps, one for each value of current. Using the 150-mA value first and writing current and voltage equations,

$$I_{line} = I_1 + 0.150$$
$$V_{BD} = 8000I_1 + 150 \text{ volts} \qquad \text{(voltage drop BCD)}$$
$$= 0.150(R_A + R_L) = 0.150R_A + 15 \qquad \text{(voltage drop through } R_A, R_L)$$

$$V_{BD} = V_{AD} - V_{AB} = 600 - 400I_{line}$$

Then

$$8000I_1 + 150 = 600 - 400I_{line}$$
$$8000(I_{line} - 0.150) + 150 = 600 - 400I_{line}$$
$$I_{line} = 0.196 \text{ amp}$$
$$I_1 = 0.196 - 0.150$$
$$= 0.046 \text{ amp or 46 mA}$$
$$I_1 R_2 = (0.046)(8000) = 368 \text{ V}$$
$$V_{CD} = 600 - 400I_{line} - 368$$
$$= 600 - (0.196)(400) - 368$$
$$= 154 \text{ V}$$
$$V_{BD} = 600 - 78$$
$$= 522 \text{ V}$$
$$0.150(R_A + 100) = 522$$
$$0.150R_A + 15 = 522$$
$$R_A = 507/0.150 = 3380 \ \Omega \qquad Answer$$

For the 0.300-amp current, the solution is worked in the identical manner:

$$8000(I_{line} - 0.300) + 150 = 600 - 400I_{line}$$
$$I_{line} = 338.0 \text{ mA}$$
$$= 0.3380 \text{ amp}$$
$$I_1 = 338.0 - 300$$
$$= 38.0 \text{ mA} = 0.0380 \text{ amp}$$
$$I_1 R_2 = (0.0380)(8000) = 304.0 \text{ V}$$
$$V_{CD} = 600 - 304.0 - 400(0.3380)$$
$$= 600 - 304.0 - 135.2$$
$$= 160.8 \text{ V}$$
$$V_{BD} = 600 - 135.2$$
$$= 464.8 \text{ V}$$
$$0.300(R_A + 100) = 464.8$$
$$R_A = 434.8/0.300 = 1450 \ \Omega \qquad Answer$$

The voltage range is thus within the allowed range, the current range is from 38 to 46 mA, and the corresponding resistance values are 1450 and 3380 ohms.

In a triode a grid is inserted in the space between the filament and plate. The grid is kept at a negative potential with respect to the filament. This is called the *grid bias*. It causes a retardation in the flow of electrons from the filament to the plate. Small changes in the grid potential cause large changes in the electron flow. The small power requirement of the grid and the amplification of the change in grid potential make triodes and tubes with even more elements highly suitable for amplifiers.

Three ratios or parameters are often discussed in connection with triodes. These are the a-c plate resistance, the mutual conductance, and the amplification factor. All three are determined from tube characteristic curves.

The a-c plate resistance or dynamic resistance r_p is the ratio of a small change in plate voltage to the corresponding change in plate current, the grid voltage being held constant.

$$r_p = \Delta e_b / \Delta i_b \qquad \text{for } \Delta e_c = 0$$

It is measured in ohms. It is essentially the value of the slope of the plate current vs plate voltage curve at a particular point on the curve.

Mutual conductance or grid-plate transconductance g_m is the ratio of the change in plate current produced by a small change in grid voltage; the plate voltage being held constant. It is a measure of the grid effectiveness in controlling plate current.

$$g_m = \Delta i_b / \Delta e_c \qquad \text{for } \Delta e_b = 0$$

It is measured in reciprocal ohms or mhos.

The amplification factor μ is the ratio of the change in plate voltage produced by a small change in grid voltage while the plate current is held constant. It is a measure of the effectiveness of the grid as compared to the plate in controlling plate current.

$$\mu = \Delta e_b / \Delta e_c \qquad \text{for } \Delta i_b = 0$$

The amplification factor is a dimensionless quantity.

It should be noted that the three parameters are not independent but are related by $\mu = r_p / g_m$.

Because tube characteristics are nonlinear, either solutions to circuit problems must be graphical using the tube characteristic curves or for small signals equivalent linear circuits may be constructed. These equivalent circuits are found for both tubes and transistors in any up-to-date general engineering handbook. These circuits portray only the a-c portions; the d-c portions have no effect on the signal. These circuits are dependent on the manner in which the tube or transistor is to be used. For example, any of the three electrodes of the tube may be used as a reference for signal voltages. The circuits are called *grounded cathode, grounded grid,* and *grounded anode* or *plate*. The latter is also termed a cathode-follower circuit, the output signal existing between the cathode and ground. Typical of the techniques in using the equivalent circuits such as will be used in Problem 7-26 are the grounded cathode, as shown in Fig. 7-32, and the equivalent circuit, as shown in Fig. 7-33.

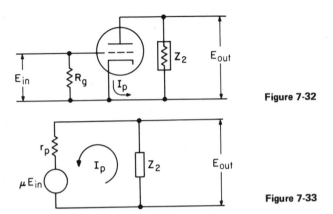

Figure 7-32

Figure 7-33

In the equivalent circuit the output voltage is $I_p Z_2$. The current I_p can be determined from the equivalent circuit.

$$I_p = \frac{\mu E_{in}}{r_p + Z_2}$$

Then $E_{out} = \dfrac{\mu E_{in} Z_2}{r_p + Z_2}$

The amplification factor or voltage gain is given by the symbol A, i.e., $A = E_{out}/E_{in}$. Therefore

$$A = \frac{\mu Z_2}{r_p + Z_2}$$

The last formula is typical of all formulas for tube and transistor circuits as found in texts and handbooks.

Problem 7-26 Vacuum-tube amplifier circuit

In the simple amplifier circuit shown in Fig. 7-34, a d-c voltmeter connected across the tube reads 200 V (E_b) and the d-c milliammeter reads 5.0 mA.
(a) What is the value of the total resistance R_L?
(b) What is the peak value of the signal voltage (E_{out}) at the output? (Assume X_C is relatively small at signal frequency.)

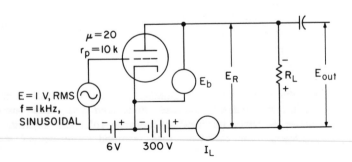

Figure 7-34

(c) What is the power being dissipated at plate of tube?

(d) Sketch as a function of time, the instantaneous voltage appearing across R_L (E_R).

Solution:

(a) The value of the resistance R_L is determined by using Ohm's law, $R = V/I$, where

$$V = E_{bb} - E_b$$
$$= 300 - 200 = 100 \text{ volts}$$

E_{bb} = plate battery voltage

$$R_L = 100/5 \, (10^{-3}) = 20 \, (10^3) = 20 \text{ k} \qquad Answer$$

(b) The peak value of output signal voltage (E_{out}) depends only on the amplification factor of the tube and the peak input value. Because the input value is an rms value, its peak value is calculated first.

$$(E_{in})_{peak} = 1 \times 1.414$$
$$= 1.414 \text{ V}$$

$$(E_{out})_{peak} = 1.414 \times A$$
$$= 1.414 \times \frac{\mu R_L}{r_p + R_L}$$
$$= \frac{1.414 \times 20 \times 20 \text{ k}}{10 \text{ k} + 20 \text{ k}} = 1.414 \times \left(\frac{40}{3}\right)$$
$$= 18.9 \text{ V} \qquad Answer$$

(c) Power dissipation at the plate is the difference of the total power input to the tube and the power dissipated in the load. Power input is purely the d-c power input, a-c power being zero. Power dissipated in the load consists of the power lost both due to d-c and a-c currents.

Power dissipated at plate = $P_{in} - P_{out}$ at load

$$P_{in} = 300 \times 5.0 \, (10)^{-3}$$
$$= 1.5 \text{ W}$$

$$P_{out} = I^2 R_L + i^2 R_L$$

$$= (5 \times 10^{-3})^2 (20,000) + (E/R_L)^2 \, (R_L)$$
$$= 500 \times 10^{-3} + \frac{(40/3)^2}{20,000}$$
$$= 0.509 \text{ W}$$

Note that the output power due to a-c current must be based on the effective or rms value of the current or voltage, not on peak value. Thus,

Power dissipated at plate = $P_{in} - P_{out}$

$$= 1.5 - 0.509 = 0.991 \text{ W} \qquad Answer$$

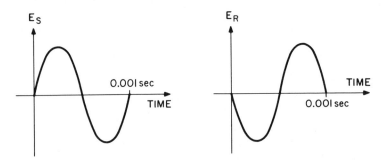

Figure 7-35

(d) The instantaneous voltage across R_L is 180° out of phase with the signal voltage E_S and of greater amplitude. The phase shift is due to the grounded cathode connection that causes phase inversion. (See Fig. 7-35.)

Problem 7-27 Vacuum-tube cathode-follower
A cathode-follower amplifier has a load that is essentially a pure resistance of 2500 ohms. The plate voltage is 200 V and the plate current is 4 mA. The tube constants are $\mu = 20$, $r_p = 10,000$, $g_m = 2000$ μmhos. Compute (a) the grid bias, (b) the plate supply voltage, and (c) the output power for a 10-V input signal. Assume that the plate current flows thru the 2500 ohms.

Solution:
In the cathode-follower circuit, the output is placed across the cathode terminal. A sketch for the amplifier circuit is shown in Fig. 7-36. Since the plate voltage is 200 V and the drop across the load is $2500 \times 4 (10)^{-3}$ or 10 V, the plate supply voltage

$$V_{\text{plate supply}} = 200 + 10$$
$$= 210 \text{ V} \qquad Answer, \text{ part (b)}$$

The grid bias is the d-c value of the negative potential of the grid with respect to the cathode. The grid is at ground or zero potential as may be seen from the circuit diagram if the E_S value, which is time dependent, is dis-

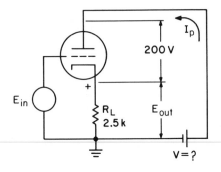

$V = ?$ **Figure 7-36**

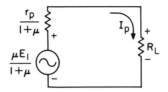

Figure 7-37

regarded. Since the potential difference across R_L is 10 V, the cathode must be 10 V above the grid. The grid bias is thus 10 V, *answer*, part (a).

The power output involves *only* the a-c component of plate current, P_{out} = $I_p^2 R_L$. Using an equivalent cathode-follower circuit, as shown in Fig. 7-37, the current may be determined as

$$I_p = \frac{\dfrac{\mu E_1}{1+\mu}}{\dfrac{r_p}{1+\mu} + R_L}$$

where $\mu = 20$, $E_1 = 10$ V input, $r_p = 10,000 \ \Omega$, $R_L = 2500 \ \Omega$.

$$I_p = 3.22 \ \text{mA}$$
$$\text{Power output} = (3.22 \times 10^{-3})^2 \ (2500)$$
$$= 0.026 \ \text{W} \qquad \textit{Answer}, \text{ part (c)}$$

The network involving the black box concept is demonstrated in Fig. 7-38. A corresponding or equivalent circuit is one in which all elements must be considered to be linear so that a change in the input voltage v_1 produces a proportional change in the output voltage v_2. In the network shown in Fig. 7-39, another symbolization is shown, the first letter subscript corresponding to the two numbers previously used, thus

$$h_{11} = h_i$$
$$h_{12} = h_r$$
$$h_{21} = h_f$$
$$h_{22} = h_o$$

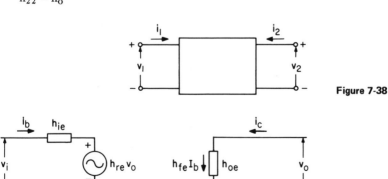

Figure 7-38

Figure 7-39

The second subscript indicates one of three modes of connecting the transistor. In the case shown, "e" refers to the common-emitter configuration.

Transistor circuit analysis is very similar to tube circuit analysis if the terminated active two-port network is used. In such network the transistor is represented as sealed device or "black box" with four a-c variables v_1, v_2, i_1, i_2, having the following relation

$$v_1 = h_{11}i_1 + h_{12}v_2$$
$$i_2 = h_{21}i_1 + h_{22}v_2$$

The symbol h stands for hybrid parameters, which are the commonly used manufacturer's specifications. The definition of these parameters follows:

$$h_{11} = \frac{v_1}{i_1}\bigg|_{v_2 = 0} = \text{input impedance for output short-circuited}$$

$$h_{12} = \frac{v_1}{v_2}\bigg|_{i_1 = 0} = \text{reverse open-circuit voltage gain}$$

$$h_{21} = \frac{i_2}{i_1}\bigg|_{v_2 = 0} = \text{forward current gain with output short-circuited}$$

$$h_{22} = \frac{i_2}{v_2}\bigg|_{i_1 = 0} = \text{output admittance with input open-circuited}$$

Here the term "short circuit" refers only to an a-c circuit, the d-c biasing voltages remaining unaffected.

As manufacturers usually give hybrid parameters for common-base configuration, conversions are necessary to the configuration used if it is not common base. These are to be found in the usual reference books. Once the parameters and the equivalent circuit are established, circuit analysis proceeds as with tubes.

chapter 8
CHEMISTRY

The questions and problems that are typically found under the heading of chemistry in most EIT examinations are usually based on an understanding of the quantitative approach to reactions. Therefore, a review is presented of basic definitions and concepts leading to the balancing of equations, stoichiometric determinations, volume-weight relations, and electrolysis.

8-1 ATOMS, MOLECULES, AND COMPOUNDS

Basic to this discussion are two classes of substances: elements and compounds. *Elements* are substances that cannot be further broken down and analyzed by chemical means. A *compound* consists of atoms of two or more kinds. An important concept is that in a particular kind of compound the weight ratio of the combining elements is invariable. Compounds are represented by formulas that use symbols for the elements comprising the compounds. The formula NaCl for salt indicates that the atoms of the elements sodium Na and chlorine Cl are combined in the ratio of one to one. When the ratio is not 1:1, then numbered subscripts indicate the ratio of the atoms, ions, or other particles. Water, represented by the formula H_2O, is composed of two hydrogen atoms for every oxygen atom.

8-2 ATOMIC WEIGHTS AND AVOGADRO'S NUMBER

The *atomic weight* of an element is its relative weight as compared to an arbitrarily chosen standard. This standard has been at various times hydrogen and oxygen. At present carbon is used. Its assigned weight is 12.

A *mole* is defined as the quantity of an element having a mass in grams equal to the atomic weight. Thus a mole of carbon represents 12 grams of carbon. Every mole of a molecular substance contains 6.023×10^{23} molecules of the substance. This number is called *Avogadro's number*.

Related to this is Avogadro's hypothesis that equal volumes of gases under the same conditions of temperature and pressure contain the same number of molecules. A *molecule* is the smallest unit in which the properties of a substance can be retained. Thus, a molecule of chlorine gas consists of just two atoms of chlorine. This molecule has the identical properties as any larger mass of chlorine.

It was noted earlier that in a given compound the ratio of the combining weights for the various elements is invariant. Further early studies in chemistry showed that two elements such as oxygen and nitrogen, or carbon and oxygen (CO and CO_2), may combine to form a series of compounds so that the weight ratio of the combining element occurs only in small whole numbers such as 2, 3, 4.

A large number of elements may combine with one particular element to form compounds. The weights of any two elements that combine with a fixed weight of a third element are known as *combining weights* or *equivalent weights*. In a practical sense this equals the atomic weight (expressed in grams or pounds) of an element divided by its valence. Many substances are multivalent. They therefore have various equivalent weights. In the case of radicals, the equivalent weight is the formula weight divided by the valence. The definition can be extended to read that a gram equivalent weight is that required weight that supplies or accepts a hydrogen H^+ or hydroxide OH^- ion. For example, the equivalent weight of $Ca(OH)_2$ is one-half of its formula weight.

Problem 8-1 Combining weights of chemical elements

A piece of zinc was placed in a solution containing 1.8961 g of $SnCl_2$. After the reaction has gone to completion, it was found that 1.1870 g of tin had been precipitated, while the zinc had lost 0.6538 g. The combining weight of zinc is 32.69. Calculate the combining weight of tin and chlorine.

Solution:

From the fact that only a part of the zinc was used up it is clear that all of the $SnCl_2$ was used. From this information the weight of the chlorine taking part in the reaction may be calculated:

Weight of $SnCl_2$	1.8961 g
Total weight of tin precipitated	1.1870 g
Weight of chlorine	0.7091 g

Now the combining weights are in the ratio as the weights of the elements taking part in the reaction. If x is the combining weight of tin, then

$$\frac{x}{32.69} = \frac{1.1870}{0.6538} = \frac{\text{tin precipitated}}{\text{zinc lost}}$$

$$= 59.4 \qquad Answer$$

Identical reasoning allows the calculation of the combining weight of chlorine. Let y be the combining weight of chlorine. Then

$$\frac{y}{32.69} = \frac{0.7091}{0.6538} = \frac{\text{chlorine in reaction}}{\text{zinc in reaction}}$$

$$y = 35.50 \qquad Answer$$

8-3 GAS LAWS AS APPLIED IN CHEMISTRY

The gas laws as applied in chemistry are, of course, the same as those used in thermodynamics. They are repeated here and augmented here to suit the needs of chemistry problems.

A mole of gas at standard conditions of temperature and pressure ($0°C$ and 760 mm) occupies 22.4 liters and contains 6.023×10^{23} molecules. Its weight in grams is, as before, equal to the number of atomic weight units.

Molecular weight of gas = density $\times$ 22.4 liters

The density in the above expression must be expressed in grams per liter at standard conditions.

The relation between the volume, pressure, and temperature for ideal gases and most real ones is expressed by $pV = nRT$, where n is the number of moles, V the total volume, and T the absolute temperature. R is the molar gas constant.

$$R = 0.08205 \text{ liter-atm-deg}^{-1}\text{-mol}^{-1}$$

For nearly all gases, the volume of a gas at a constant temperature is inversely proportional to the pressure. Also assumed constant is the quantity of gas or the number of moles, i.e., $pV = C$.

Volume-Temperature Relation

The volume of gas is directly proportional to the *absolute* temperature. Here the gas pressure and the number of moles of the gas are assumed constant.

Volume-Molecule Relation

Based on Gay-Lussac experiments, it was seen that the volumes of gas that take part or are produced by a chemical reaction are in the ratios of small integers, such as 1:1 or 2:3. Avogadro's law, based on the foregoing relation, is the following important statement:

Equal volumes of all gases under the same conditions of pressure and temperature contain the same number of molecules.

Gas Mixtures—Partial Pressures

When gases are mixed, the total pressure is the sum of the partial pressure independently exerted by each gas. This partial pressure is equal to the pressure the molecules of each gas would exert if they only were present. For example, if a mixture of nitrogen, oxygen, and carbon dioxide is contained in a closed container at a pressure of say 15 psia, then the nitrogen might contribute say 12 psia of the total pressure, the oxygen 2.5, and the carbon dioxide 0.5 psia. If the same quantity of nitrogen were confined by itself in the same container, its total pressure would be 12 psia.

Density Calculation for Gases

Knowing the molecular weight of a gas, its density may be calculated by dividing the molecular weight, say 32 g for oxygen, by the volume occupied by 1 mol of any gas at standard conditions, i.e., 22.4 liters. The density of oxygen is 32/22.4 = 1.43 g/l. Similarly for nitrogen, 28/22.4 = 1.25 g/l.

8-4   CHEMICAL REACTIONS AND THEIR EQUATIONS

A chemical reaction is the process of converting substances by the re-arrangement of atoms. Chemical reactions are described by appropriate equations. An equation represents the number of atoms of the various elements that caused the reaction. Based on the conservation of matter, both sides of an equation must balance; the number of atoms of a particular element (and therefore the weights of all substances) must always be the same on both sides of the equation.

A typical reaction describing the conservation of matter is that wherein hydrogen and oxygen combine to form water. It is described by the equation $2H_2 + O_2 \rightarrow 2H_2O$. The arrow is used in place of the equal sign to show the direction in which the reaction proceeds most readily. The equation shows four atoms of hydrogen on both sides of the equation as well as two atoms of oxygen. Of the many chemical reactions known, the most commonly used is the oxidation-reduction reaction.

A familiar example of an oxidation-reduction reaction is the "burning" of red hot iron in oxygen to form iron oxide

$$4Fe + 3O_2 \rightarrow 2Fe_2O_3$$

The burning of carbon in fluorine represents the same type of reaction

$$C + 2F_2 \rightarrow CF_4$$

These reactions are characterized by the removal of electrons from an atom or a group of atoms—the oxidation process—and by the addition of electrons — the reduction process. Correspondingly, an oxidizing agent removes and takes up electrons, a reducing agent loses electrons. In the preceding reaction, carbon is the reducing agent giving up four electrons

$$C \rightarrow C^{+4} + 4e^-$$

In the iron ore reduction reaction $2Fe_2O_3 \rightarrow 4Fe + 3O_2$, electrons are returned to the iron, producing pure iron.

$$4Fe^{+3} + 12e^- \rightarrow 4Fe$$

Akin to this thinking is the use of the term "oxidizing agent" meaning an atom, molecule, or ion that takes up electrons. Conversely, reducing agents give up electrons.

Problem 8-2 Balancing chemical equations

Balance the following equations:

(a) _____ NH_3 + _____ O_2 → _____ N_2 + _____ H_2O

(b) _____ $Ba(ClO_3)_2$ + _____ H_2SO_4 → _____ $BaSO_4$ + _____ $HClO_3$

(c) _____ CO_2 + _____ $NaOH$ → _____ Na_2CO_3 + _____ H_2O

(d) _____ FeS_2 + _____ O_2 → _____ Fe_2O_3 + _____ SO_2

(e) _____ Hg + _____ HNO_3 → $Hg(NO_3)_2$ + _____ NO + _____ H_2O

Solution:

In each case, the solution is obtained by inspection and by trial and error until the atoms of all elements are balanced on both sides of the equations. Integers are used as the coefficients for each molecular compound.

(a) Start by assuming the equation to need two molecules of NH_3 to balance the N_2 on the right side of the equation

$$2NH_3 + \underline{\quad} O_2 → N_2 + \underline{\quad} H_2O$$

This supplies six atoms of hydrogen. To balance these write

$$2NH_3 + \underline{\quad} O_2 → N_2 + 3H_2O$$

We now need three oxygen atoms on the left side. To get that we would need a coefficient of 1.5 for the oxygen:

$$2NH_3 + 1.5O_2 → N_2 + 3H_2O$$

It is preferable to use integers as coefficients throughout. Multiplying the entire equation by 2 provides this solution:

$$4NH_3 + 3O_2 → 2N_2 + 6H_2O \qquad Answer$$

The other parts of this example are done in a like manner.

(b) $Ba(ClO_3)_2 + H_2SO_4 → BaSO_4 + 2HClO_3$

(c) $CO_2 + 2NaOH → Na_2CO_3 + H_2O$

(d) $4FeS_2 + 11O_2 → 2Fe_2O_3 + 8SO_2$ $\qquad$ *Answer*

(e) $3Hg + 8HNO_3 → 3Hg(NO_3)_2 + 2NO + 4H_2O$

8-5 STOICHIOMETRY

The weights of substances involved in chemical reactions are determined primarily from the balanced chemical equation that describes the reaction. Once the atomic weight of each atom that takes part in the reaction is known, the corresponding weights in grams can be determined. This is done by expressing the atomic weight in weight units such as grams or pounds and multiplying these weights by the number of atoms taking place in the reaction. These types of calculations are called *stoichiometric calculations*.

Problem 8-3 Weight of nitrogen dioxide produced from lead nitrate

Calculate the weight in pounds of nitrogen dioxide that is produced from 50 lb of lead nitrate according to the following formula:

$$2Pb(NO_3)_2 → 2PbO + 4NO_2 + O_2$$

Solution:

The atomic weights are determined from tables:

Lead: 207.19
Nitrogen: 14.01
Oxygen: 16.00

Formula weight of lead nitrate: $2[207.19 + 2(14.01 + 3 \times 16.00)] = 662.42$
Formula weight of nitrogen dioxide: $4(14.01 + 2 \times 16.00) = 184.04$

Forming a ratio of the weights in pounds to the formula weights results in

$$\frac{x \text{ lb of nitrogen dioxide}}{50 \text{ lb of lead nitrate}} = \frac{184.04}{662.42}$$

$$x = 50 \times \frac{184.04}{662.42} = 13.90 \text{ lb} \qquad Answer$$

Problem 8-4 Weight of calcium carbonate in limestone

Seventy-five pounds of lime (CaO) are produced by heating 180 lb of limestone ($CaCO_3$). Find the percentage (weight) of pure calcium carbonate contained in the limestone.

Solution:

$$CaCO_3 \xrightarrow{\text{heat}} CaO + CO_2$$

The atomic weights are

Calcium: 40.08
Carbon: 12.01
Oxygen: 16.00

Formula weights:

CaO: $40.08 + 16.00 = 56.08$
$CaCO_3$: $40.08 + 12.01 + 48.00 = 100.09$

Weight ratios:

$$56.08/100.09 = 75/x$$
$$x = 75 \times \frac{100.09}{56.08} = 134 \text{ lb}$$

In other words, 134 lb of pure $CaCO_3$ are required to produce 75 lb of CaO. Percentage of pure calcium carbonate in limestone is

$$134/180 \times 100 = 74.4\% \qquad Answer$$

Problem 8-5 Production of nitric acid from ammonia

In one of the main steps in the Ostwald Process for the production of nitric acid, ammonia is oxidized to yield nitrogen monoxide and heat according to the chemical equation

$$4NH_3 + 5O_2 \rightarrow 4NO + 6H_2O + 215 \text{ kCal}$$

(a) If 510 lb of NH_3 are treated correctly with 960 lb of oxygen, and the reaction proceeds as completely as possible, how many pounds of NO are produced?

(b) How many kCal of heat are evolved during the simultaneous production of 1 kg of NO?

Solution:

(a) Find the atomic weights of the compounds using tables.

Nitrogen: 14.01
Hydrogen: 1.01
Oxygen: 16.00
Weight of $4NH_3 = 4[14.01 + 3(1.01)] = 68.16$
Weight of $5O_2 = 10(16.00) = 160.00$
Weight of $4NO = 4(14.01 + 16.00) = 120.04$

From the given weights of ammonia and hydrogen, it is not possible to determine if the reaction will use up all the ammonia. Check to see if sufficient oxygen is introduced to complete the reaction. Weight of oxygen (x) required based on 510 lb of NH_3 is

$$\frac{x}{510} = \frac{160}{68.16} \qquad \therefore x = 1198 \text{ lb}$$

Since more oxygen is required than is available to complete the reaction for all the ammonia, the production of NO depends on the amount of oxygen available. Let y = quantity of NO produced. Then

$$\frac{y}{960} = \frac{120.04}{160}$$

$$y = 960 \times \frac{120.04}{160} = 720.24 \text{ lb of NO} \qquad Answer$$

(b) The heat liberated during a reaction is given as 215 kCal for every 4 mol of NO. By forming a ratio between the heat evolved for the two available weights and a corresponding ratio for the weights of NO, the heat evolved can be determined.

Formula weight in grams of $4NO = 4(14.01 + 16.00) = 120.04$ g

$$\frac{\text{Heat evolved}}{215 \text{ kCal}} = \frac{1000 \text{ g}}{120.04 \text{ g}}$$

Heat evolved = 1792 kCal   *Answer*

Problem 8-6 Production of chlorine from hydrochloric acid and manganese dioxide

Chlorine may be prepared by oxidizing hydrochloric acid with manganese dioxide MnO_2. The byproducts are water and manganous ion Mn^{+2}.

What weight of MnO_2 will be required to produce 10 liters of chlorine, measured at standard temperature and pressure? It is understood that excess hydrochloric acid is present.

Solution:

First establish the number of moles of MnO_2 required to produce 1 mol of Cl_2. The basic equation contains these terms:

$$MnO_2 + HCl \rightarrow Mn^{+2} + Cl_2 + H_2O$$

Balancing first the oxygen and then the hydrogen requirement results in

$$MnO_2 + 4HCl \rightarrow Mn^{+2} + Cl_2 + 2H_2O$$

The manganese goes from Mn^{+4} to Mn^{+2} indicating a gain of two electrons; it is thus the oxidizing agent or the valence loser. The gain in electrons must be balanced by a corresponding loss of electrons. Chlorine goes from Cl^- to Cl^0, losing 1 electron per atom. Balancing the chlorine, two of the atoms make up the chlorine gas Cl_2; the other two combine with manganese to yield

$$MnO_2 + 4HCl \rightarrow MnCl_2 + Cl_2 + 2H_2O$$

The atomic weights are

Mn = 55
O = 16
H = 1
Cl = 35

Let x = grams of MnO_2, and w = weight of 10 liters of Cl_2. Then the gram-molecular weight of Cl_2 = (2)(35) = 70. Therefore,

$$\frac{10 \text{ liters of } Cl_2}{w} = \frac{22.4 \text{ liters}}{70}$$

(For ideal gas at standard conditions, one gram-molecular weight = 22.4 liters.)

$$w = \frac{10}{22.4} (70) = 31.2 \text{ g}$$

$$\frac{31.2 \text{ g of } Cl_2}{70 \text{ g-mol}} = \frac{x \text{ g of } MnO_2}{87 \text{ g-mol}}$$

$$x = \frac{87}{70} (31.2) = 38.8 \text{ g} \qquad Answer$$

8-6   THE NORMAL SOLUTION

A normal solution is defined as one containing 1 g equivalent weight of a solute per liter of solution. The gram equivalent weight equals the formula weight divided by the moles of hydrogen ions (H^+) that take part in the reaction.

Problem 8-7 Quantity of nitric acid in one liter of normal solution

Determine the quantity in grams of nitric acid required to prepare 1 liter of a 0.05N solution.

Solution:

The equivalent weight of HNO_3 is its formula weight

H =	1.008
N =	14.007
O = 16.000 3O =	48.000
Equivalent weight =	63.015
Gram equivalent weight =	63.015 g
Quantity required =	1 g equivalent weight × N
=	63.015 × 0.05
=	3.151 g *Answer*

Problem 8-8 Sodium hydroxide reaction with sulfuric acid

Determine the weight of sodium hydroxide that will fully react with 1 liter of a 0.5N solution of sulfuric acid in the following reaction:

$$2NaOH + H_2SO_4 \rightarrow Na_2SO_4 + 2H_2O$$

Solution:

Since both hydrogen ions enter into the reaction, the gram equivalent weight of a 1N solution is one-half the formula weight. The formula weight of H_2SO_4 is

$$2H = 2.02$$
$$S = 32.06$$
$$4O = \underline{64.00}$$
$$H_2SO_4 = 98.08$$

Gram equivalent weight = ½ formula weight = 49.04 g.

A 0.5N solution will contain 0.5 × 49.04 = 24.52 g. The formula weight of sodium hydroxide is

$$Na = 22.99$$
$$O = 16.00$$
$$H = \underline{1.01}$$
$$NaOH = 40.00 \text{ g}$$
$$2NaOH = 80.00 \text{ g}$$

Finally,

$$\frac{\text{Weight of NaOH}}{\text{Weight of } H_2SO_4} = \frac{80.00}{98.08}$$

$$\frac{\text{NaOH}}{24.52} = \frac{80.00}{98.08}$$

Required weight of NaOH = $24.52 + \dfrac{80.00}{98.08}$ = 20.00 g   *Answer*

Problem 8-9 Sulfur dioxide produced from zinc sulfide and oxygen

How many cu ft of SO_2, measured at 760 mmHg and 500°F, can be made by roasting 2000 lb of ZnS with oxygen?

Solution:

First establish the reaction $ZnS + O_2 \rightarrow SO_2 + Zn$. Next, look up atomic weights of zinc, sulfur, and oxygen to determine formula weights of ZnS and SO_2. Use these to find actual weight of SO_2 produced.

Oxygen: 16.00
Sulfur: 32.07
Zinc: 65.38
Weight of ZnS = 65.38 + 32.07 = 97.45
Weight of SO_2 = 32.07 + 2(16) = 64.07

Let x = weight of SO_2 produced.

$$x/2000 \text{ lb} = 64.07/97.45$$

$$x = 1316 \text{ lb}$$

$$\text{Number of moles} = \frac{\text{total weight}}{\text{molecular weight}}$$

$$= 1316/64.07 = 20.5$$

One mole equals 22.4 liters at standard conditions of temperature $(0^\circ$ C) and pressure (760 mm). Therefore, the volume at standard conditions is $20.5 \times 22.4 = 458$ liters. Use of the ideal gas equation, $pV = nRT$, allows determination of volume V_2 at $500^\circ F$:

$$V_2/V_1 = T_2/T_1$$

$$V_2 = 458 \frac{(460 + 500)}{(460 + 32)}$$

$$= 895 \text{ liters}$$

$$V_2 = \frac{895 \text{ liters}}{28.32 \text{ liters/cu ft}}$$

$$= 31.6 \text{ cu ft} \qquad Answer$$

Problem 8-10 Combining normal solutions

What volumes of 2N H_2CO_3 and 6N H_2CO_3 must be mixed to yield 700 ml of a 3N H_2CO_3 solution? Assume all volumes are additive.

Solution:

Since all volumes are additive, if there are x ml of 2N H_2CO_3, there must be $(700 - x)$ ml of 6N H_2CO_3. Referring to the definition of normality, a 2N or 6N solution is an expression of the weight of solute in the solvent. Obviously the weight of the constituent solutes in the 2N and 6N solution must equal the weight of the solute in the solution to be mixed. Let G.E.W. stand for gram equivalent weight

$$G.E.W._{2N} + G.E.W._{6N} = G.E.W._{3N}$$
$$2Nx + (700 - x)6N = 700(3N)$$

Quantity of 2N H_2CO_3 required = x = 525 ml

Quantity of 6N H_2CO_3 required = 700 − x = 175 ml

Answer

8-7 ACIDS, BASES, SALTS, AND pH

Electrolytes are substances that in the molten state or in solution conduct electricity by transfer of ions. Particularly effective electrolytes are solutions of acids, bases, and salts. An *acid* is a substance that furnishes hydrogen ions on solution in water; a *base* is a substance that furnishes the hydroxyl ion (OH⁻) in water solution. *Salts* are systems built from oppositely charged ions that do not neutralize each other.

The acidity or concentration of hydrogen ions in a solution is given by the *pH* of the solution, where the pH is defined as the negative common logarithm of the hydrogen ion concentration. The pH of pure water is 7, because pure water dissociates very slightly, specifically 1 mol of hydrogen ion per 10^7 liters of water. The concentration of $H^+ = 1/10^7 = 10^{-7}$ mol/liter.

If the pH is less than 7, the solution is acid; if more than 7, basic. For example, if a solution has a H^+ concentration of 4×10^{-6}, the pH is minus the log of 4×10^{-6}

$$pH = -(\log 4 \times 10^{-6}) = -(\log 4 + \log 10^{-6}) = -(0.602 - 6)$$
$$= 5.398$$

The solution is acidic.

chapter 9
PHYSICS

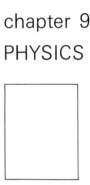

Most physics topics are directly applicable to broad areas of engineering and are discussed within their engineering discipline. Typical examples are topics in statics, dynamics, fluid mechanics, thermodynamics, and electricity. Several other physics areas are not usually found in standard engineering courses. These are the areas usually asked about in the EIT examinations under the heading of physics. Light, sound, and atomic physics are the most prominent of these areas.

9-1 LIGHT

Light is a form of electromagnetic radiation. Its speed of propagation in empty space is approximately 3×10^{10} cm/sec. This speed is reduced when light passes through matter thereby giving rise to the phenomenon called *refraction*. The ratio of the speed of light in empty space to its speed in a particular substance is known as the *index of refraction*.

$$\mu = \frac{\text{speed in empty space}}{\text{speed in substance}}$$

The wave motion of light coupled with the change in speed as light passes through different substances causes refraction, reflection, and dispersion.

In the case of reflection, the following law holds true:

Angle of incidence = angle of reflection

The angle of incidence is the angle between the normal to the surface from which the light is reflected and the direction of travel before the light reaches the surface. The angle of reflection is between the normal and the direction of the reflected light, as shown in Fig. 9-1. The image produced by a plane mirror appears as far in back of the mirror as the object is in front of the mirror. As no light penetrates through the mirror, the image is said to be virtual, i.e., not real; the image is also erect or right side up.

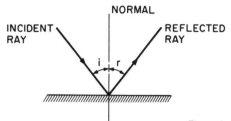

Figure 9-1

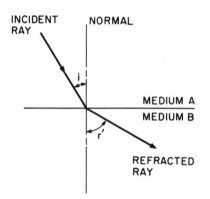

Figure 9-2. Medium A is denser than medium B; i = angle of incidence; r′ = angle of refraction.

For refraction (see Fig. 9-2) the following holds true:

$$\frac{\sin i}{\sin r'} = \frac{\text{index of refraction of medium B}}{\text{index of refraction of medium A}} = \frac{\mu_B}{\mu_A}$$

where i = angle between direction of light's ray in medium A and the normal to the interface between mediums A and B

   r′ = angle between direction of light's ray in medium B and the normal to the interface between mediums A and B

The index of refraction of a vacuum is exactly 1; that of air is also assumed to be one.

To find the index of refraction of any other material or medium, the angles of incidence and refraction at the interface between the material and air must be known or measured and the refractive equation, above, applied.

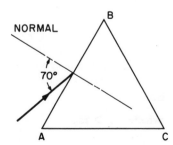

Figure 9-3

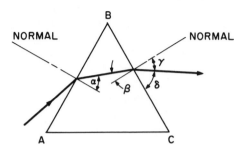

Figure 9-4

Problem 9-1 Refraction of light through glass prism

A ray of light strikes the middle of one side of an equilateral glass prism ABC, as shown in Fig. 9-3. The index of refraction of the glass is 1.5. Find and illustrate the angle of the emerging light with respect to side CB.

Solution:

Redraw the illustration and add the refracted beam within and outside the prism. Then apply the refraction equation to the entering side. (See Fig. 9-4.)

$$\sin 70° / \sin \alpha = 1.5/1$$
$$\sin \alpha = (\sin 70°)/1.5 = 0.626$$
$$\alpha = 38.8°$$

This is equal to an angle of $8.8°$ with respect to side AC; with respect to the normal to side BC, angle $\beta = 21.2°$. Now using the law of refraction again

$$\sin \gamma / \sin \beta = 1.5/1$$
$$\sin \gamma = 1.5 \sin 21.2° = 0.545$$
$$\gamma = 33°$$
$$\delta = 90 - \gamma = 57° \qquad Answer$$

Note that as the light passes from dense to a less dense medium as from glass to air, the angle between the light beam and the normal becomes larger. (See Fig. 9-2.)

9-2   TOTAL REFLECTION

A critical angle of incidence is reached when the angle of refraction reaches $90°$. At this point no light emerges from the surface. Hence total reflection occurs. The critical angle of incidence for any substance may be found by setting the angle of refraction of the less dense substance equal to $90°$ or $\pi/2$ and solving for the critical angle A_c from

$$\sin A_c = \mu_B/\mu_A \qquad \text{where } \mu_A > \mu_B$$

9-3 LENSES AND MAGNIFICATION

Because of the refracting effect as light passes from air to a denser medium, glass that is denser than air and has a high transmitivity is frequently used in lens systems. Typical lens problems deal either with convex or concave lenses and their magnifying power. The basic thin lens relation is used to determine lens effects. Schematic pictures of light rays passing through the lens tend to clarify the concepts. The basic relation to be used is

$$1/V = 1/u + 1/f$$

where V = image distance, u = object distance, and f = focal distance. The image and object distances are the distances from the image and object to the lens. Both are considered positive if they lie on opposite sides of a lens. The focal distance is the distance from the lens to the point where a parallel beam incident on the lens and parallel with its principal axis converges. The focal length is positive for convex lenses, negative for concave lenses. Magnification is defined as the ratio of the image height i to the object height S, thus:

Magnification = $i/S = |V| / |u|$

The quantity l/f is called the focusing power of the lens. If the focal length f is expressed in meters, the focusing power is expressed in diopters; the unit of diopters is $1/m$.

Problem 9-2 Converging lens image distance

A thin converging lens has a focal length of 8 in. A 2X magnification is desired of an object. (a) How far should the object be placed from the lens? (b) How far will the image be from the lens?

Solution:

The magnification gives the ratio of the image to the object distance.

$$|V|/ |u| = 2$$
$$V = 2u$$

Substituting,

$$1/V = 1/u + 1/f$$
$$1/2u = 1/u + 1/8$$
$$8 = 16 + 2u$$
$$u = -4 \text{ in.}$$
$$V = -8 \text{ in.}$$

The object should be placed 4 in. from the lens; the image will be on the same side of the lens, 8 in. away from it, as Fig. 9-5. The image will be magnified 2X, erect, and virtual since the rays do *not* meet *at the image.*

Note: Simple diagrams help in establishing thin lens relations. Refraction is assumed to take place at the central plane of the lens. Typical solution steps consist of:

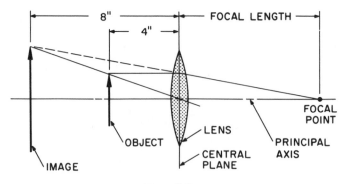

Figure 9-5

1. Drawing the lens and its central plane.
2. Drawing the principal axis, i.e., the axis through the center of the lens and at right angles to the central plane.
3. Locating the focal point(s).
4. Erecting object or image, whichever is given. These are easily represented as arrows.
5. Drawing a ray from the object or image through the center of the lens. This ray is not refracted.
6. Drawing a ray from the object parallel to the principal axis until it meets the central lens plane. Here it is refracted and passes through the focal point.
7. The intersection of the refracted ray and the ray through the lens' center locates the real image.
8. If the actual rays do not meet, then the rays are projected backward and the virtual image is established. For a convex lens this happens whenever the object distance to the lens is less than the focal length.

Optical magnification and reduction may also be produced by curved mirrors using the same equation as the thin lens equation. The following information should be noted:

1. For concave (dished inward) mirrors the focal length is positive; for convex mirrors, it is negative.
2. The focal length of a spherical mirror is one-half its radius of curvature.
3. Light rays are reflected from the surface of the mirror. Rays parallel to the mirror's principal axis will be reflected through the focal point in concave mirrors and will *appear* to come from the focal point in convex mirrors if the refracted beam is drawn through the mirror. Rays through the center of curvature of spherical mirrors are reflected along themselves.

9-4   ILLUMINATION

The amount of light striking a unit area is known as the *illumination*. This may be determined from the formula

$$\text{Illumination} = I/r^2$$

where I = intensity of the light source expressed in candles or candlepower and r = the distance from the source to the illuminated area; typically, r is given in feet, and illumination is expressed in foot-candles. It should be noted, however, that the actual units are candlepower per square foot. Light intensity is also expressed in lumens. The relation between lumens and foot-candles is

1 lm/sq ft = 1 ft-c

The concept of candlepower refers to the light intensity of the source whereas lumens actually indicate the brightness on a surface.

Another concept involves the total luminous flux emitted by a source. If a point source is assumed to be at the center of a sphere, the inside of the sphere will be evenly illuminated. The interior surface area of the sphere is $4\pi r^2$. This will receive *all* of the flux emitted by the source; this is determined as the product of the illumination and the surface area.

$$(I/r^2)(4\pi r^2) = 4\pi I \ \text{lm}$$

Thus a point source having an intensity of 200 cp will radiate 800π lm.

Problem 9-3 Grease spot photometer lamp distances

A 100-cp lamp is placed 6 ft from a grease spot photometer. How far should a 50-cp lamp be placed on the other side of the photometer to cause equal illumination on both sides of the photometer screen?

Solution:
Since the intensity of illumination must be the same on both sides of the screen:

$$I_1/r_1{}^2 = I_2/r_2{}^2$$

where I_1, I_2 = light intensity of both lamps in candlepower and r_1, r_2 = distance from lamp to screen.

$$r_2{}^2 = (I_2/I_1)r_1{}^2$$
$$r_2 = \sqrt{(50 \ \text{cp}/100 \ \text{cp})\ 6^2 \ \text{ft}^2}$$
$$= (6/\sqrt{2}) \ \text{ft} = 4.25 \ \text{ft} \qquad Answer$$

Note: In the preceding problem it has been assumed that the lights strike the surface of the screen normally, or in other words that the plane of the screen is perpendicular to a line drawn between the light sources.

If the surface is not normal to the rays, then its illumination is given by

Illumination = $(I/r_2)\cos\theta$

where θ is the angle between the light rays and the normal to the surface.

9-5 SOUND-WAVE PROPAGATION

Sound waves are longitudinal waves that cause the alternate bunching up and spreading out of the molecules that carry the wave. Sound cannot be propagated through a vacuum. Sound may be produced by causing a transverse wave to be set up in a tension member such as a string on a violin or by causing a longitudinal wave through either a solid or a fluid as for example the air in an organ pipe.

For either wave the speed of sound propagation depends strictly on the medium in which the sound has to travel. In a solid this speed is given by

$$C = \sqrt{M/\rho}$$

where M = shear modulus for transverse waves or the elastic (Young's) modulus for longitudinal waves

ρ = density of the solid

For gases the speed is

$$C = \sqrt{kp/\rho}$$

where k = ratio of specific heats (for air k = 1.4)

p = pressure

It might be noted that since the density of a gas is directly proportional to the pressure, the speed of sound in a gas is not affected by pressure.

When a string is plucked the wave form is easily observable. The relation between the speed and the wavelength is given by $C = f\lambda$ where f is the frequency or number of vibrations per second and λ is the wavelength, i.e., the distance between two consecutive identically displaced particles.

The speed of sound in air is usually taken as 1100 ft/sec. The speed of a transverse wave in a tension member is given by

$$C = \sqrt{FL/m}$$

where F is the force or tension in member, L is the length of tension member, and m is the mass of tension member.

If a string or other tension member vibrates as a whole, it produces its fundamental tone. This is also called its first harmonic. Strings may vibrate in equal length segments. The number of segments is equal to the number of the harmonic; thus a string vibrating in two segments produces the second harmonic or its *first* overtone. Now when a string produces its fundamental tone, the string vibrates as a whole. In this mode, the string represents half a wavelength. The general relation between string length L, wavelength λ, and the number of the harmonic n is $\lambda = 2L/n$. Note the number of the harmonic also equals the number of segments in which the string vibrates. (See Fig. 9-6 and Fig. 9-7.)

Problem 9-4 Vibration of tension member attached to the support of an eccentric

A 30-in., 2-lb tension member is attached to the support of an eccentric. As the eccentric is brought up to 3000 rpm, the tension member begins to vibrate noticeably. Determine the tensile force in the member.

Solution:

Since the problem states that the member only *starts* to vibrate noticeably when the eccentric reaches 3000 rpm, it may be safely assumed that the fundamental mode of vibration has been reached.

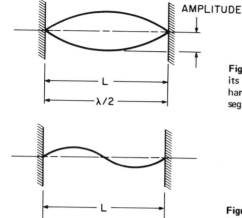

AMPLITUDE

Figure 9-6. String producing its fundamental tone or first harmonic by vibrating as one segment.

Figure 9-7. String vibrations in two segments producing first overtone or second harmonic.

$$\text{Frequency of vibration} = \frac{3000 \text{ rev}}{\text{min}} \times \frac{\text{min}}{60 \text{ sec}} \times \frac{\text{cycle}}{\text{rev}}$$

$$= 50 \text{ cycles/sec}$$

The two equations for the speed of the wave may be combined to produce

$$f\lambda = \sqrt{FL/m}$$

but $\lambda = 2L/n = (2)(30 \text{ in.})/1 = 60 \text{ in.}$

$$F = \frac{f^2\lambda^2 m}{L} = \frac{f^2\lambda^2 w}{Lg}$$

$$= \frac{50^2(\text{cycles/sec})^2 \times 60^2 \text{ in.}^2 \times 2 \text{ lb}}{30 \text{ in.} \times 32.2 \text{ ft/sec}^2 \times 12 \text{ in./ft}}$$

$$= 1550 \text{ lb} \qquad Answer$$

Similar relations exist between the wavelength and the length of either open or closed pipes. In an open pipe, i.e., a pipe open at both ends,

$$\lambda = 2L/m \qquad \text{where m = any integer}$$

In a closed pipe, i.e., a pipe closed at one end,

$$\lambda = 4L/(2n + 1) \qquad \text{where n = any integer or zero}$$

9-6   SPECIAL ACOUSTICAL PHENOMENA

Beats occur when two closely tuned instruments produce sounds whose frequency only differs by a small amount. These differences will cause successive cancellations as well as intensification of the sound produced. Intensification will occur when the two instruments are exactly in phase, cancellation when they are 90° out of phase.

The beat frequency is the difference of the producing frequency

$$f_b = f_1 - f_2$$

where f_b = number of beats per second (beat frequency)

f_1 = frequency of first instrument

f_2 = frequency of second instrument

Another important phenomenon is called the *Doppler effect*. It is the change of pitch produced by a sound source moving relative to a receiver or listener. If the receiver is stationary and the source is moving toward him, more waves are received per unit time than are sent by the source. An increase in pitch is produced. When the source recedes, fewer and fewer waves reach the receiver and the pitch decreases.

These statements may be summarized by

$$f' = f\left(\frac{v}{v \mp v'}\right)$$

if no wind velocity exists or, if wind velocity does exist,

$$f' = f\left(\frac{v + w}{v \mp v' + w}\right)$$

where f' = observed frequency at the receiver

v = velocity of sound

v' = source velocity (use $(-)$ for an approaching source or $(+)$ for a receding source)

w = wind velocity

Finally, if the receiver or observer is moving relative to the source, it has the effect of an increase $(+)$ in the sound velocity if the receiver is moving toward the source, or a decrease $(-)$ if the observer moves away from the source.

$$f' = f\left(\frac{v \pm v_R + w}{v \mp v' + w}\right)$$

where v_R = receiver velocity

Problem 9-5 Whistle frequency of moving train

At what frequency is a train whistle vibrating if a man standing still hears a pitch of 330 vibrations/sec as the train approaches at 100 ft/sec? Assume the speed of sound in air is 1100 ft/sec. At what frequency is a whistle vibrating if a man on a train (approaching a stationary whistle at 100 ft/sec) hears a pitch of 330 vibrations/sec?

Solution:

(a) With the man acting as stationary receiver, use

$$f' = f\left(\frac{v}{v - v'}\right)$$

$$\frac{330 \text{ vibrations}}{\text{sec}} = f\left(\frac{1100}{1100 - 100}\right)$$

$$f = 330(1000/1100) = 300 \text{ vibrations/sec} \qquad \textit{Answer}$$

(b) When the man is on the train, the receiver (the man) is approaching the stationary source.

$$f' = f\left(\frac{v + v_R}{v}\right)$$

$$\frac{330 \text{ vibrations}}{\text{sec}} = f\left(\frac{1100 + 100}{1100}\right)$$

$$f = 330(1100/1200) = 302 \text{ vibrations/sec} \qquad \textit{Answer}$$

The pitch of the stationary whistle is then 302 vibrations/sec. It may be noted that the effect produced on an observer is almost—though not quite—the same whether the observer is moving toward the source or the latter is moving toward the observer.

chapter 10
ENGINEERING ECONOMY

10-1 PRESENT ECONOMY

The term "present" or "immediate" economy indicates that the time value of money is not to be taken into consideration. It also indicates that a proposal can be evaluated solely on its immediate costs.

Problem 10-1 Present economy cost per piece output

Operator A produces 120 spindles/hr on a lathe. His hourly rate is $1.80. Operator B, using an identical lathe, is able to produce 150 identical units/hr. The overhead charge for a lathe is fixed at $2.50/hr. Determine operator B's hourly rate so that his cost per piece is identical to A's.

Solution:

This is an obvious example of a present economy problem—only the immediate costs of producing need be compared.

Cost per unit for operator A $= \dfrac{1.80 + 2.50}{120} = \$0.0358$

Let x = hourly rate of operator B. Then

$$\frac{x + 2.50}{150} = \$0.0358$$

$$x = \$2.88 \quad Answer$$

10-2 SIMPLE AND COMPOUND INTEREST

The term "interest" is a way of expressing the rental cost of a sum of money called the "principal" P. Usually interest i is charged for the use of the principal. Interest is charged for specified periods. An interest rate of 6% per annum equals 6% per year. For simple interest, this is then prorated for longer or shorter periods. For example, $200 borrowed at 6% per annum and actually repaid at the end of a year and a half will cost $200 $\times$ 0.06 $\times$ 1.5 = $18. This is expressed by the formula $S = P(1 + ni)$, where S is the sum due at the end of a year and a half ($218) and n is the interest period (1.5). Correspondingly the present value of a sum of $218 at 6% due one and one-half years from now is $200 as expressed by $P = S/(1 + ni)$.

In compound interest, interest is due on a sum of money at the end of every interest period. More than one interest period is normally involved before the principal must be fully repaid. The term "compounding" refers to the fact that the interest due at the end of a second period is due on the sum of the principal and the interest which was due but not paid at the end of the first period.

Indicative of this method of payment is Table 10-1, where S is the sum of money due at the end of an interest period, i the interest per period, and P the principal borrowed.

Table 10-1

No. of Period	Sum Due at End of Period
1st	$S = P + Pi = P(1 + i)$
2nd	$S = P + (P + Pi) i = P(1 + i + i^2)$
3rd	$S = P + (P + Pi + Pi^2)i$
	$S = P(1 + i + i^2 + i^3)$
	$S = P(1 + i)^3$
nth	$S = P(1 + i)^n$

Often the interest rate i is an annual one but interest is actually paid or due at stated intervals during the year. This is accounted for by computing the interest per interval and determining the total value for all intervals. Thus,

$$S = P\left(1 + \frac{i}{f}\right)^{nf}$$

where f is the number of intervals per year and n is the number of years. If the interest is compounded quarterly, $f = 4$.

To determine the present value P of a payment to be made in the future, the equation is solved for P.

$$P = \frac{S}{\left(1 + \frac{i}{f}\right)^{nf}}$$

When interest is compounded more than once per year, the effective annual interest rate is higher than the nominal annual interest that is usually given. The effective annual interest rate i amounts to

$$i' = \left(1 + \frac{i}{f}\right)^{f} - 1$$

10-3   CAPITAL RECOVERY SCHEDULES

Many capital recovery schedules call for equal payments R over the length of time allowed for capital recovery. Each payment R accumulates interest upon being paid so that the sum of payments, each of equal value R, plus annually compounded interest i may be represented by

$$S = R(1 + i)^n + R(1 + i)^{n-1} + \cdots + R$$

or $S = R \left[\dfrac{(1 + i)^n - 1}{i} \right]$

Thus, the amount R required to meet a specified sum at a future time is expressed by

$$R = S \left[\frac{i}{(1 + i)^n - 1} \right]$$

Another interesting application results from substituting $S = P(1 + i)^n$ in the preceding equation.

$$R = P \left[\frac{i(1 + i)^n}{(1 + i)^n - 1} \right]$$

Here R represents a series of equal payments to be obtained in the future for a present investment P. For example, let us determine the equal (year-end) payments that will be available for the next four years if we invest $4000 at 6%.

$$R = \$4000 \left[\frac{0.06(1 + 0.06)^4}{(1 + 0.06)^4 - 1} \right] = \$4000(0.28859)$$

$$= \$1154.36$$

10-4   THE USE OF INTEREST FACTOR TABLES

Most books on engineering economy as well as most handbooks have a set of tables that simplify the evaluation of interest by giving a set of values for each interest rate for all methods of payments so far discussed. For the preceding example, the term $[i(1 + i)^n] / [(1 + i)^n - 1]$ is the "capital recovery factor" in the equal payment series. Its value 0.28859 can be found by direct consultation of the 6% interest table.

Interpolation

If values of interest such as $4\frac{1}{2}$% or $5\frac{1}{4}$% occur, the interest factors may be determined by straight-line interpolation between the 4% and 5% values for the $4\frac{1}{2}$% interest rate, i.e., the factor will lie half way between the values given for the 4% and 5% factors, respectively. Similarly, for $5\frac{1}{4}$% the factor will lie a quarter of the way between the 5% and 6% factors.

The following tables are usually found in handbooks such as the C.R.C. Standard Mathematical Tables or books on engineering economy.

1. Amount at compound interest, $(1 + i)^n$. Also called the compound amount factor, single payment. Used to find S given P.
2. Present value, $1/(1 + i)^n$. Also called present worth factor, single payment. Used to find P given S.
3. Amount of annuity, $[(1 + i)^n - 1]/i$. Also called compound amount factor, equal payment series. Used to find S given R.
4. Sinking fund factor, $i/[(1 + i)^n - 1]$. Used to find R given S.
5. Present value of annuity, $[(1 + i)^n - 1]/i(1 + i)^n$. Also called present worth factor equal payment series. Used to find P given R.
6. Annuity whose present value is 1, $i(1 + i)^n[(1 + i)^n - 1]$. Also called capital recovery factor. Used to find R given P.

Problem 10-2 Present cost of alternative construction

In determining which type warehouse to build the following costs are to be taken into account.

In a type I warehouse, initial cost will be $24,000. This warehouse has adequate capacity for the near future, but 12 years from now an addition will be required that costs $15,000.

A type II warehouse costs $34,000. This type has the same capacity as the type I warehouse with its addition.

Which of these warehouses should be built, assuming that depreciation is negligible and that the interest rate is 7%?

Solution:

Assuming that money is available, let us compare the present cost of the type I warehouse with addition to that of type II, namely $34,000.

The present cost of $15,000 is determined from the present worth factor using i = 7%, n = 12:

$$P = S/(1 + i)^n$$
$$= 15,000 \times 0.444 = \$6660$$

The present cost of type I is seen to be $24,000 + 6660 = \$30,660$. Since this is a smaller sum than required for the type II building, type I building should be put up.

10-5 DEPRECIATION

Depreciation is defined as the decrease in the value of assets due to aging (i.e., the reverse of the economic process for quality wines). Depreciation prediction or forecasting must usually be based on past experience in which first cost and final salvage or resale values are known. In addition to this, it is desirable but not usually possible to obtain the year by year value of an asset. In forecasting the depreciation of an asset, three trend curves are in common use, classifiable as follows:

1. straight-line depreciation,
2. sinking fund depreciation, and
3. fixed percentage on diminishing balance depreciation.

Straight-line depreciation assumes a constant rate of depreciation and the annual depreciation is computed by

$$\text{Depreciation} = \frac{\text{first cost} - \text{final value}}{\text{life (in years)}}$$

$$= (P - L)/n$$

The capital could earn interest if it were not invested in an asset. The unearned interest equals the investment in the asset per year times the interest rate. Thus, unearned interest amounts to the following:

During first year: Pi

During second year: $\left[P - \frac{(2 - 1)(P - L)}{n}\right]i$

During nth year: $\left[P - \frac{(n - 1)(P - L)}{n}\right]i = Li + \frac{(P - L)}{n}i$

The average unearned interest per year is based on the first and last year:

$$\frac{i}{2}\left[P + L + \frac{P - L}{n}\right]$$

Problem 10-3 Investment choice influenced by efficiency of new equipment

A new snow removal machine costs $50,000. The new machine will operate at a reputed savings of $400 per day over the present equipment in terms of time and efficiency. If interest is at 5% and the machine's life is assumed to be 10 years with zero salvage, how many days per year must the machine be used to make the investment economical?

Solution:

Assume straight-line depreciation and no salvage value.

$$\text{Annual depreciation} = \frac{50,000 - 0}{10} = \$5000$$

$$\text{Average annual unearned interest} = \frac{1}{2}\left[50,000 \times 0.05 + \frac{50,000\,(0.05)}{10}\right] = \$1375$$

Annual cost = $6375

To invest in this machine, the yearly savings must at least equal $6375. The number of days m the machine must be used is therefore

m = 6375/400 = 15.9 days *or* 16 days   *Answer*

In the sinking fund method, equal valued periodic deposits (usually annual payments) are made over the predetermined life span of the asset. At the end of this life span, the sum of the deposits plus accumulated interest equals the asset's depreciation.

In essence, the difference between the first cost and the estimated salvage value must be computed. Then, this difference is the sum S which must be accumulated by periodic payments R over the life of the depreciating asset. Use the "sinking fund factor" table.

Problem 10-4 Accumulation of sinking fund

Based on the sinking fund method and using the values of the previous example, what number of days must the machine be used if the amount to be accumulated in 10 years is $50,000?

Solution:

$R = S\, i/[(1 + i)^n - 1]$

for $i = 5\%$ and $n = 10$, the sinking fund factor.

$i/[(1 + i)^n - 1] = 0.0795$

Therefore, $R = 50,000 \times 0.0795 = \$3975$. To invest in the machine using the sinking fund, the yearly savings must be at least $3975. The number of days the machine must be used is therefore $m = 3975/400 = 9.9$ days or 10 days.

Note: If tables for sinking fund factors are not available, the value may be determined from the amount of annuity interest table since amount of annuity = 1/(sinking fund factor).

A third method of depreciation, more conservative than the first two methods, is called the "method of fixed percentage on diminishing returns." This method features high initial depreciation and progressively smaller depreciation. This method will cause the depreciation to follow a pattern similar to that experienced for the depreciation of automobiles. If D is the rate of depreciation, then the undepreciated balance at the end of the first, second, and nth year will be, respectively, $P(1 - D)$, $P(1 - D)^2$, $P(1 - D)^n$. The generalized formula for D is

$D = 1 - (L/P)^{1/n}$

where L is the salvage value of the asset. Note that this method does not allow the salvage value of the asset to be zero.

Problem 10-5 Establishment of fund for future fixed income

A consulting engineer decides to set up an educational fund for his son that will provide $3000 per year for 6 years starting in 16 years. The best interest rate he expects to get is 5% compounded quarterly. He wants to accumulate the necessary capital by making quarterly deposits until his son starts college.

Solution:

The problem is best handled by first determining the amount needed in 16 years. Since no additional funds are to be paid in, the amount needed at the beginning of the 16th year can be determined from the equal payment series, present worth factor. Since interest is compounded quarterly, the effective annual interest is first determined.

$$i' = \left(1 + \frac{0.05}{4}\right)^4 - 1$$

$$= 0.051$$

Six equal payments of $3000 are required; their worth at the beginning of the 16th year is

$$P = R[(1 + i)^n - 1]/i(1 + i)^n$$
$$= 3000[(1 + 0.051)^6 - 1]/0.051(1 + 0.051)^6$$
$$= 3000[1.348 - 1]/0.051(1.348)$$
$$= \$15,210$$

The engineer has 15 years to accumulate this fund. His quarterly deposits are determined by using the sinking fund factor. There are 15 X 4 or 60 interest payments to be made at a quarterly interest rate of 0.0125.

$$R = Si/[(1 + i)^n - 1]$$

Using $n = 60$,

$$R = \$15,210(1/88.5745) = \$172.00 \qquad Answer$$

Thus his quarterly deposit is $172.00, where 88.5745 represents the amount of annuity.

Problem 10-6 Investment choice influenced by quality

A low carbon steel machine part, costing $350 installed, lasts 6 years when operating in a corrosive atmosphere.

An identically shaped part, but treated for corrosion resistance, would cost $650 installed.

How long would the corrosion resistance part have to last to be at least as good an investment as the untreated part? Assume money is worth 7%.

Solution:

Since the life of the treated part is not known, the comparison is best made on the basis of the annual cost. Subsequently, the life of the treated part can be determined. Assuming no salvage value on the $350 part, i.e., the depreciation equals $350, this amount as well as interest on the $350 must be accumulated in 6 years. Using the capital recovery factor,

$$R = P\left(\frac{i(1 + i)^n}{(1 + i)^n - 1}\right)$$

$$= 350 \times 0.2098$$

$$= \$73.50 \text{ per year required}$$

This amount must be equal to or greater than the annual cost of the treated part.

Similarly the treated part has no salvage value. Its annual cost must equal $73.50 to be competitive. Then, using the capital recovery factor c.r.f. with n unknown,

$73.50 = $650 \times$ c.r.f.

c.r.f. $= 73.50/650.00 = 0.113$

for   n = 14   c.r.f. = 0.114   . . .

n = x   . . .   c.r.f. = 0.113

n = 15   c.r.f. = 0.109   c.r.f. = 0.109

Difference = 15 − 14 = 1.00   difference = 0.005   = 0.004

$0.004/0.005 = (15 − x)/1.00$

x = 14.20

Therefore, the treated part must last at least 14.20 years or nearly 14 years 2½ months.   *Answer*

10-6   BOOK VALUE

The book value is a fictitious value based on the estimated depreciation. The book value may be calculated as the difference between an asset's first cost and the amount in the sinking fund.

The book value may be higher, lower, or the same as the actual or market value of the asset.

Problem 10-7 Determination of depreciation and book value using the sinking fund method

A tractor-trailer has a first cost of $32,000, an estimated life of 8 years, and an estimated salvage value of $7000. Using the sinking fund method with a 6% interest rate, find (a) the depreciation charge in the first year, (b) the depreciation charge in the fourth year, and (c) the book value at the end of 5 years.

Solution

A series of equal payments or annual deposits are made, each of which earns 6% interest per year. The depreciation charge is the total depreciation of the asset during the year. This is equal to the annual deposit plus the interest during the year on the sum of the previous deposits. Annual payment is calculated on the basis of eight yearly deposits at a 6% interest rate. Use the sinking fund factor, given S to find R,

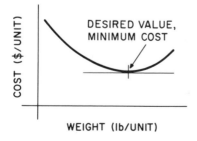

WEIGHT (lb/UNIT)   **Figure 10-1**

Annual payment = $(32{,}000 - 7000)(0.101)$

= $2525

With the annual payment available a table can be constructed to determine the depreciation charge during any year and the book value.

1 Year No.	2 Annual Deposit	3 Interest on Sum of Deposits	4 Sum of (2) and (3)	5 Sum of Deposits and Interest	6 Book Value
0	—	—	—	—	$32,000
1	$2525	0	$2525	$2525	29,475
2	2525	6% X 2525 = $152	2677	5202	26,798
3	2525	6% X 5202 = 312	2837	8041	23,959
4	2525	484	3009	11,050	20,950
5	2525	664	3189	14,239	17,761
.	.				.
.	.				.
.	.				.
8	2525				7000

Column 4 in the table represents the amount of the annual depreciation, i.e., the depreciation charge. Column 5 is the accumulated depreciation charge.

(a) The depreciation charge in the first year is $2525   *Answer*
(b) The depreciation charge in the fourth year is $3009   *Answer*
(c) The book value at the end of the fifth year is $17,761   *Answer*

Problem 10-8 Determination of minimum value

The total cost of a cast product consists of (1) the raw material cost that is directly proportional to the weight of the casting, (2) the machining cost that varies inversely as the weight, and (3) the overhead cost that remains constant per unit produced regardless of weight. (a) Find the weight giving the minimum total cost per casting. (b) Find the minimum total cost per casting.

Solution:

This problem is primarily concerned with minimum values; therefore, it is essentially a calculus problem. Use the following symbols to set up a cost equation:

C_T = total cost

C_W = cost based on weight

C_M = machining cost

C_O = overhead unit cost

W = weight

$C_W = k_1 W$ (direct proportion of raw material cost to weight)

$C_M = k_2/W$ (inverse proportion of machining cost to weight)

$C_O = C_O$ (constant value)

$C_T = k_1 W + k_2/W + C_O$

A plot of total cost with respect to weight would plot essentially, as shown in Fig. 10-1. The minimum cost can be determined by differentiating cost with respect to weight.

$dC_T/dW = k_1 - k_2/W^2$

The minimum cost can be ascertained by equating the right-hand side of the above equation to zero, i.e., find the low point of the curve where its tangent is horizontal.

$k_1 - k_2/W^2 = 0$

$$W = (k_2/k_1)^{\frac{1}{2}}$$

A check on units at this point is suggested. The units for k_1 and k_2 are

$k_1 = \$/lb$ and $k_2 = \$ \times lb$

Therefore, $W = \left(\dfrac{\$ \times lb}{\$/lb} \right)^{\frac{1}{2}} = (lb^2)^{\frac{1}{2}} = lb$

The minimum cost occurs when

$$W = (k_2/k_1)^{\frac{1}{2}} \ lb \qquad \textit{Answer}, \text{ part (a)}$$

The minimum total cost is

$$C_T = [k_1(k_2/k_1)^{\frac{1}{2}} + k_2(k_1/k_2)^{\frac{1}{2}} + C_O] \text{ dollars} \qquad \textit{Answer}, \text{ part (b)}$$

chapter 11
STRESS

11-1 TENSILE AND COMPRESSIVE STRESS

An external load applied to a member along its longitudinal axis induces a substantially uniform stress distribution on every cross section of the member perpendicular to that axis and whose centroid is coincident with that axis. A load so applied is commonly called an axial load. The stress produced is tensile or compressive depending upon whether the force applied to the member tends to stretch or to crush it. The axial force P in Fig. 11-1 tends to compress the member. Stress or stress intensity is defined as the force per unit of area and is given by

$$f_a = P/A \qquad\qquad (11\text{-}1)$$

where P is the load applied to the member and A the area of the selected cross section.

Problem 11-1 Axial stress
In Fig. 11-2, two bars are shown supporting a load of 10,000 lb. The cross-sectional area of bar AB is 1.0 in.^{2}, and the area of bar BC is 0.75 in.^{2} Compute the stress in AB and BC.

Solution:
The bars are not subjected to any lateral loading between their end connections. Therefore, the force that each bar experiences is directed along its longitudinal axis and Eq. (11-1) may be used. Apply the method of joints to connection B. (See Fig. 11-3.)

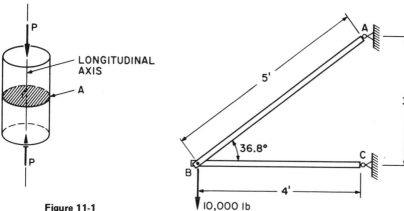

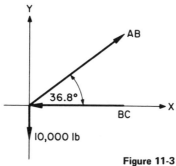

Figure 11-1

Figure 11-2

Figure 11-3

$\Sigma F_Y = 0$ AB sin $36.8° - 10,000 = 0$

AB = 16,670 lb

$\Sigma P_X = 0$ AB cos $36.8° - BC = 0$

BC = 13,330 lb

Positive values for the forces were obtained indicating that their directions were assumed correctly. The origin of the reference axes coincides with pin connection B and the direction of force AB shows that pin B is pulling at member AB, thereby inducing tensile stress, whereas pin connection B pulls at member AB—it pushes against member BC inducing compressive strain.

Stress in member AB:

$f_a = P/A$ $(f_a)_{AB} = P/A = 16,670/1$

= 16,670 psi   *Answer*

Stress in member BC:

$f_a = P/A$ $(f_a)_{BC} = P/A = 13,330/0.75$

= 17,800 psi   *Answer*

11-2   SHEAR STRESS

In Sec. 11-1 the stress produced by an external load applied perpendicular to the selected cross section was examined.

The situation is now considered wherein stress is produced by forces acting parallel to the selected cross section. These parallel forces have action lines separated by a small distance and act upon the same member in opposite directions. Figure 11-4 shows two pull bars connected by a pin. The forces P tend to shear the pin across the face of section a-b, which section lies in a plane parallel to the applied force action lines and perpendicular to the longitudinal axis of the pin. To counter this shear tendency, the pin develops an internal shear stress given by

$$f_v = P/A \tag{11-2}$$

where P is the applied load and A is the total area resisting shear.

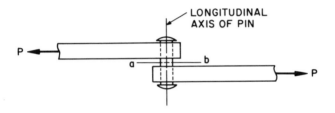

LONGITUDINAL
AXIS OF PIN

Figure 11-4

Problem 11-2 Shear stress in the pin of a pin-connected joint

Figure 11-5 shows a pin-connected joint. Determine the cross-sectional diameter of the pin required to carry the 20,000-lb load. The allowable shear stress is 10,000 psi.

Solution:

The 20,000-lb load tends to shear the pin across both cross sections a-b and c-d. Therefore, a shear stress is developed across a total area of twice the pin cross-sectional area A_{pin}

$$f_v = P/A \qquad 2A_{pin} = P/s_s = 20,000/10,000 = 2$$
$$A_{pin} = \pi d^2/4 = 1$$
$$d = 1.13 \text{ in.} \qquad Answer$$

11-3   STRAIN

When a member is subjected to an axial load, the member material sustains both longitudinal and lateral deformation. The longitudinal deformation is expressed in terms of strain ϵ, which for a member of constant cross section and homogeneous material is given by

$$\epsilon = \frac{\Delta L}{L} \tag{11-3}$$

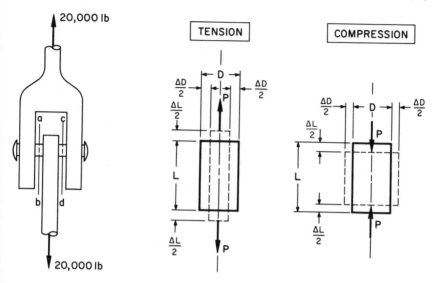

Figure 11-5

Figure 11-6

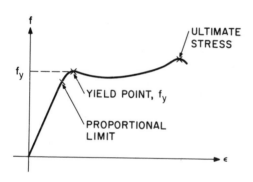

Figure 11-7

where L is the length and ΔL is the deformation experienced by the length L. The longitudinal and lateral deformations for members in tension and compression are shown in Fig. 11-6. The axial tension load causes the member to elongate a distance ΔL in the longitudinal direction, and narrow a distance ΔD in the lateral direction, whereas the axial compression load causes a contraction ΔL and an expansion ΔD, respectively. The lateral strain is given by

$$\epsilon_D = \frac{\Delta D}{D} \tag{11-4}$$

Longitudinal and lateral strain bear a relationship to one another given by Poisson's ratio ρ, which is the lateral strain divided by the longitudinal strain. Steel has a value for ρ of about 0.25.

$$\rho = \epsilon_D/\epsilon \tag{11-5}$$

The stress and longitudinal strain produced by an axial load are related by the equation

$$f = E\epsilon \qquad (11\text{-}6)$$

where E is the modulus of elasticity and constant of proportionality. Steel has a modulus of elasticity $E_s = 30 \times 10^6$ psi. For structural steel, a graphical representation of Eq. (11-6) would appear as shown in Fig. 11-7. Equation (11-6) is valid so long as the member material is not stressed beyond its proportional limit. The problems in this book presuppose that the proportional limit is not exceeded. The yield point f_y occurs when there is a substantial increase in strain with no corresponding change in stress. It should not be confused with the ultimate stress that is the maximum stress that the material can sustain. The yield point f_y serves as a convenient reference for calculating allowable stress. The allowable stress is always some fraction of f_y.

The longitudinal deformation ΔL may be explicitly related to the external axial load by combining Eqs. (11-1), (11-3), and (11-6)

$$\Delta L = fL/E = PL/AE \qquad (11\text{-}7)$$

Problem 11-3 Stress-strain relation applied to a dual material short compression member

A short compression member is to be made from a steel pipe of 4 in. O.D. filled with concrete and axially loaded. The maximum allowable compressive stress in the steel is 18,000 psi and in the concrete, 1250 psi. The member supports a load of 100,000 lb. Determine the maximum inside diameter of the pipe.

Steel: $E_s = 30 \times 10^6$ psi

Concrete: $E_c = 2.5 \times 10^6$ psi

Solution:

From the statement of the problem, the schematic is drawn in Fig. 11-8, where the load is assumed to act over the entire top cross section of the member. It is required to find the least area of steel cross section that may be used compatible

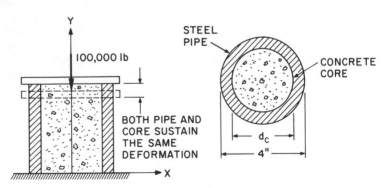

Figure 11-8

with the 4-in. O.D. restriction. The minimum steel cross section is required when the concrete core supports so much of the 100,000-lb load that it develops its 1250 psi allowable stress. The concrete core carries a load P_c equal to the product of its area A_c and the maximum allowable compressive stress f_c.

$$P_c = A_c f_c = (\pi d_c^2/4)(1250) \tag{11-8}$$

where d_c is the concrete core diameter; this dimension is also the maximum inner diameter of the steel pipe.

The steel pipe has a cross-sectional area A_s equal to $(\pi/4)(4^2 - d_c^2)$ and supports a load P_s given by

$$P_s = A_s f_s = (\pi/4)(4^2 - d_c^2)f_s \tag{11-9}$$

A summation of forces in the Y-direction shows that the sum of P_s and P_c must equal the applied 100,000-lb load:

$$(\pi/4)d_c^2(1250) + (\pi/4)(4^2 - d_c^2)f_s = 100,000 \tag{11-10}$$

Before this equation may be solved for d_c, it is necessary to determine the stress developed in the steel pipe. This stress cannot be found by an additional equation of static equilibrium; therefore, it is necessary to examine the structure and determine a condition based on a relation between the strains produced in the member materials. The strain relation can be developed by considering the longitudinal deformations sustained by the steel pipe and concrete core.

Since the load is applied across the entire top section of the composite member, both steel and concrete sustain equal longitudinal deformations. The steel pipe and concrete core are of equal length and experience equal deformation, therefore their strains must be equivalent:

$$\epsilon_s = \epsilon_c \tag{11-12}$$

The concrete develops its allowable compressive stress and the concrete strain ϵ_c may be calculated

$$f_c = E_c \epsilon_c \qquad \epsilon_c = \frac{f_c}{E_c} = \frac{1250}{2.5 \times 10^6}$$

$$= 500 \times 10^{-6} \text{ in./in.}$$

Because of the equivalent strains,

$$f_s = E_s \epsilon_s = E_s \epsilon_c = (30 \times 10^6)(500 \times 10^{-6})$$

$$= 15,000 \text{ psi}$$

Substitute this value of f_s into Eq. (11-10) and solve for d_c:

$$d_c = 2.86 \text{ in.} \qquad Answer$$

It is very important to note that once it was established that the concrete was to develop its maximum allowable stress, it became necessary to calculate separately f_s. It would have been incorrect to use the allowable 18,000-psi stress for f_s in Eq. (11-10) because, as was shown, the equal deformations establish the relationship between f_s and f_c.

Problem 11-4 Statically indeterminate structure

The tension bars A and B in Fig. 11-9 are connected in a fixed position at the top and to a rigid bar CD at the bottom. Assume that bar CD does not bend and is weightless and D remains in a fixed position. Determine the magnitude of P necessary to produce an axial stress of 12,000 psi in bar A. For bar A the area is 3 in.^{2} and $E = 10 \times 10^6$ psi, while for bar B the area is 2 in.^{2} and $E = 25 \times 10^6$ psi.

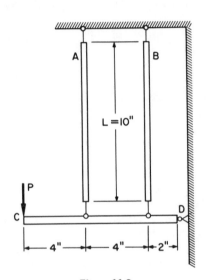

| Figure 11-9 | Figure 11-10 |

Solution:

A free-body diagram is drawn in Fig. 11-10, which shows the acting forces and deformations sustained by tension members A and B. To produce the stipulated 12,000-psi axial stress in tension bar A will require the application of force F_A:

$$f_a = P/A \qquad (f_a)_A = F_A/A_A$$

$$F_A = (f_a)_A A_A = (12,000)(3) = 36,000 \text{ lb}$$

where A_A is the cross-sectional area of member A and $(f_a)_A$ is the given 12,000-psi stress.

Take a moment summation about pin D:

$$\circlearrowleft + \Sigma M_D = 0 \qquad -P(10) + 36,000(6) + F_B(2) = 0 \tag{11-13}$$

An examination of the free-body diagram shows that additional equations of static equilibrium will not provide a solution for F_B. It is therefore necessary to determine a condition based on the longitudinal deformation of the tension members. An equation may be developed relating the strains produced in members A and B by first establishing a relation between the deformations ΔL_A and ΔL_B sustained by members A and B, respectively. From similar triangles

$$\Delta L_B/2 = \Delta L_A/6 \tag{11-14}$$

The strains are given by

$$\epsilon_A = \Delta L_A / L \tag{11-15}$$

$$\epsilon_B = \Delta L_B / L \tag{11-16}$$

Solve Eq. (11-14) for ΔL_A and substitute into Eq. (11-15).

$$\epsilon_A = 3\Delta L_B / L \tag{11-17}$$

Solve Eq. (11-16) and Eq. (11-17) separately for ΔL_B and equate the results.

$$L\epsilon_B = L\epsilon_A / 3$$

The unloaded lengths L of members A and B are equal and cancel.

$$\epsilon_B = \tfrac{1}{3} \epsilon_A \tag{11-18}$$

It has been stipulated that 12,000-psi stress be developed in member A. Equation (11-18) establishes a relation between the stress in member A and that in member B that permits the calculation of the latter.

$$\epsilon = f_a / E \qquad (f_a)_B / E_B = (f_a)_A / 3E_A$$

$$(f_a)_B = E_B (f_a)_A / 3E_A$$

$$= \frac{(25 \times 10^6)(12.000)}{3(10 \times 10^6)}$$

$$= 10{,}000 \text{ psi}$$

The axial load F_B carried by member B that produces this stress is then calculated:

$$f_a = P/A \qquad (f_a)_B = F_B / A_B$$

$$F_B = (f_a)_B A_B$$

$$= (10{,}000)(2) = 20{,}000 \text{ lb}$$

Equation (11-13) may now be solved for P.

$$P = 25{,}600 \text{ lb} \qquad \textit{Answer}$$

11-4 THERMAL STRESS

A material undergoes changes in its dimensions in response to changes in temperature. Problems dealing with the effects of changes in member length are the most often encountered. A member of initial length L whose thermal expansion is unrestricted will experience a change in length ΔL_T for a temperature change ΔT in accordance with the equation

$$\Delta L_T = \alpha L \, \Delta T \tag{11-19}$$

where α is the coefficient of linear expansion and is different for different materials.

Any restriction of the thermal expansion causes stress to develop within the material. Suppose rod AB, of length L, is placed between immovable supports as

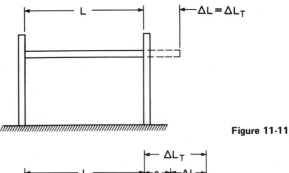

Figure 11-11

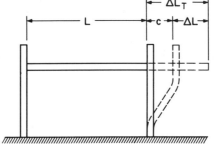

Figure 11-12

shown in Fig. 11-11 and is initially unstressed. A rise in temperature ΔT would cause the member to lengthen a distance ΔL_T, if it were not for the immovable end supports. To the heated member, the immovable supports become axial compression loads; these loads may be thought of as deforming the heated member by shortening its length the distance ΔL_T. The imposition of a restriction on linear expansion produces thermal stresses which are related to strain ϵ by the equation $f = E\epsilon$, where $\epsilon = (\Delta L)/L$. Here the end supports do not yield, therefore ΔL_T is equal to the ΔL used to calculate strain.

The ΔL used to compute the strain is not always the length ΔL_T computed from Eq. (11-19). For example, if, as shown in Fig. 11-12, a wall yields a distance c to the expanding rod, then the strain developed is computed from $\epsilon = (\Delta L_T - c)/L$ because the stress develops only in response to the deformation that is imposed upon the rod by the end reactions.

Problem 11-5 Effect of thermal stress on a steel tie rod

A $\frac{1}{2}$-in. diameter steel tie rod is joined to two rigid walls 18 ft apart in such a way that an axial tensile stress of 20,000 psi exists in the rod. Use temperature coefficient of 6.5×10^{-6} and $E = 30 \times 10^{6}$ psi.

(a) Determine the temperature change that would reduce the stress to zero.

(b) If one of the walls yields so as to widen the distance between them by 0.05 in. when the rod is heated through the temperature change determined in part (a), what is the stress that remains in the rod?

(c) If one of the walls yields so as to widen the distance between them by 0.05 in. when the rod is heated through a temperature change twice that found in part (a), what is the stress that remains in the rod?

Solution:

(a) At the initial temperature the rod is stressed in tension. Therefore, the end reactions exert an axial pull force on the rod, elongating it a distance ΔL. The longitudinal elongation is calculated

$$\Delta L = \frac{fL}{E} = \frac{20,000[(18)(12)]}{30 \times 10^6}$$

$$= 0.144 \text{ in.}$$

If the axial load were removed, the rod would assume its unstressed length, which is 18 ft less 0.144 in. Of course the length of the rod is fixed at 18 ft by the spacing between the rigid walls. It is therefore convenient to think of the rod as comprising the sum of its unstressed length and the elongation ΔL. (See Fig. 11-13.)

To increase the length of the rod 0.144 in. by thermal action requires that it be heated through a temperature change ΔT

$$\Delta L_T = \alpha L \, \Delta T$$

$$\Delta T = \frac{\Delta L_T}{\alpha L} = \frac{0.144}{(6.5 \times 10^{-6})[(18)(12)]}$$

$$= 102.6°F \qquad Answer$$

When the rod is heated, its unstressed length becomes longer and longer, taking up more and more of the elongation ΔL produced by the axial pull force. After the temperature has increased through the entire increment ΔT, no part of

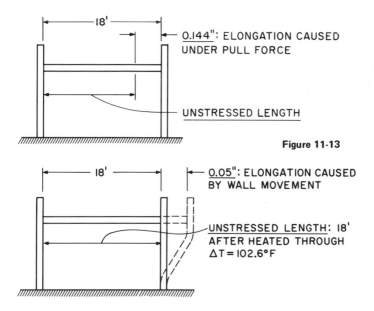

|← 18' →|

0.144": ELONGATION CAUSED UNDER PULL FORCE

UNSTRESSED LENGTH

Figure 11-13

|← 18' →|

0.05": ELONGATION CAUSED BY WALL MOVEMENT

UNSTRESSED LENGTH: 18' AFTER HEATED THROUGH $\Delta T = 102.6°F$

Figure 11-14

the total 18-ft length will comprise an axial-produced elongation. More specifically at the final temperature, the rigid walls will not have to exert any axial pull on the rod in order that it span the entire 18-ft length.

(b) In part (a), where there was no yield of the end supports, it was found that if the rod is heated through a temperature change ΔT of 102.6°F, the unstressed length of the rod would equal the 18-ft span between the walls. Therefore the wall movement causes the rod to undergo a longitudinal deformation measured entirely by this movement. Since the walls have separated a distance of 0.05 in. as shown in Fig. 11-14, the rod is elongated by that amount that corresponds to a strain of

$$\epsilon = \frac{\Delta L}{L} = \frac{0.05}{(18)(12)}$$

$$= 2.31 \times 10^{-4} \text{ in./in.}$$

The stress developed in response to this strain is

$$f = E\epsilon = (30 \times 10^6)(2.31 \times 10^{-4})$$

$$= 6930 \text{ psi, tensile stress} \qquad Answer$$

(c) Before the application of any heat, the rod is elongated 0.144 in. as calculated in part (a). Imagine the rod with its end reactions removed; it would then assume its unstressed length of 18 ft less 0.144 in. If the unconstrained rod were permitted to elongate thermally through a temperature range of 205.2°F, it would elongate an amount

$$\Delta L_T = \alpha L \, \Delta T = (6.5 \times 10^{-6})(18 \times 12)(205.2)$$

$$= 0.288 \text{ in.}$$

As the rod is heated, its length expands first taking up the elongation of 0.144 in. caused by the pull force exerted by the end reactions at the initial temperature and then through the 0.05-in. distance yielded by the moving wall. If it were not for the restriction imposed on further expansion by the walls, the rod would continue to expand another 0.094 in. (See Fig. 11-15). To the heated member, the walls now act as axial compression loads, which are thought of as

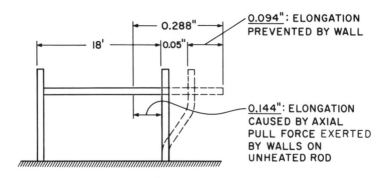

Figure 11-15

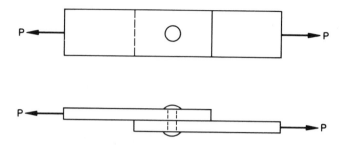

Figure 11-16.   Simple lap joint.

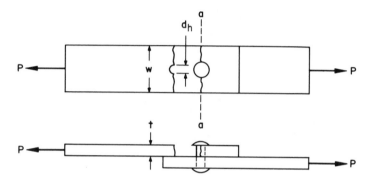

Figure 11-17.   Tension failure.

deforming the heated member by shortening its length 0.094 in. Stress develops only in response to the deformation imposed by the end reactions

$$f = E\epsilon = E\frac{\Delta L}{L} = (30 \times 10^6)\frac{0.094}{18 \times 12}$$

= 13,060 psi, compressive stress   *Answer*

11-5   STRUCTURAL RIVETED JOINTS

There are three principal modes of failure that a riveted joint may experience, namely: tension, bearing, and shear. These modes will be examined briefly in reference to the simple lap joint of Fig. 11-16. In each instance, failure analysis evolves about the simple stress equation, $f = P/A$, where f is the computed stress, P is the applied load in pounds, and A the area in square inches.

Tension failure concerns the failure of the plate itself and is shown in Fig. 11-17 to be a tearing action. Failure occurs at the section subjected to the highest tensile stress. This corresponds to the cross section of minimum area and is found at section a-a, which cuts through the plate at the rivet hole. Observe that the section is taken perpendicular to the applied force. The tensile stress is calculated from

$$f_t = \frac{P}{A} = \frac{P}{(w - d_h)t} \tag{11-20}$$

where w is the width of the plate, d_h is the rivet hole diameter, and t is the plate thickness.

The allowable tensile stress f_t is determined in accordance with AISC specification.

$$f_t = 0.60f_y \tag{11-21}$$

The more commonly used steels have a yield stress f_y of either 33,000 psi or 36,000 psi. If a problem does not specify the steel used, then it is assumed that the steel used has a yield stress of 33,000 psi.

The load applied to the plate causes the contacting surfaces of the rivet and plate to bear against each other. Bearing failure is evidenced by either a deformation of the rivet hole, a crushing of the rivet, or both. The bearing stress is calculated from

$$f_p = P/A = P/d_r t \tag{11-22}$$

where d_r is the rivet diameter and t is the plate thickness. Figure 11-18 shows a situation wherein excessive bearing pressure has crushed the material of the top plate and formed an elongated rivet hole. The denominator of Eq. (11-21) is the projected area of the rivet to plate bearing contact surface. The projected area is used in lieu of the actual contact area because the stress distribution over the latter is uneven. Use of the projected area yields a good approximation of the bearing stress. The allowable bearing stress f_p is determined in accordance with AISC specifications.

$$f_p = 1.35f_y \tag{11-23}$$

where f_y is the yield point of the steel used for the plate.

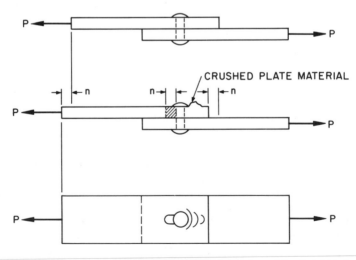

Figure 11-18.   Bearing failure. Elongation of the top plate rivet hole has caused the top plate to shift a distance n to the left.

Shear failure was considered in Sec. 11-2 and occurs when the plates of the simple lap joint of Fig. 11-16 separate as shown in Fig. 11-19. The shear stress is calculated from

$$f_v = \frac{P}{\pi d_r^2/4}$$

(11-24)

where d_r is the rivet diameter. The allowable shear stress f_v is obtained from the AISC specification. If the type of rivet is not specified in a problem, then it is assumed that the A141 hot-driven type is used with an allowable shear stress of 15,000 psi.

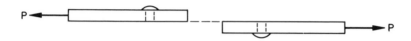

Figure 11-19. Single shear failure.

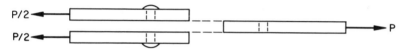

Figure 11-20. Double shear failure.

In examining the AISC specifications, the reader will notice that two types of connections are designated, namely friction type and bearing type. In the latter some slip is permissible, and in the former, slip cannot be tolerated and must be prevented by friction produced by a high clamping force. The problems encountered usually do not specify which type connection is intended; however, the bearing type is the most common and it is assumed that the connection is of the bearing type.

Shear failure of a double lap joint is shown in Fig. 11-20 where the rivet shank is sheared in two places. Equation (11-24) is extended to this double-shear condition by multiplying the denominator $\pi d_r^2/4$ by 2.

Returning a moment to bearing failure, it should be noted that the AISC commentary on the specification states that there is no difference between single-shear bearing and enclosed bearing. Therefore, the recommended allowable stress is the same for both single-shear bearing and double-shear bearing.

In addition to the three principal modes of failure just considered, tear-out failure can occur if the edge distance j in Fig. 11-21 is too small. This type of failure is unlikely if the distance between the center of a rivet hole and the edge of the plate is made equal to at least 1.5 to 2 times the diameter of the rivet hole. Even when an edge distance is not in the line of stress, i.e., in a line parallel to the load, it is good practice to maintain this distance.

The strength of a riveted joint is often compared to the strength of a solid plate. This comparison is expressed in terms of joint efficiency:

$$Eff = \frac{P_{RP}}{P_{SP}}$$

(11-25)

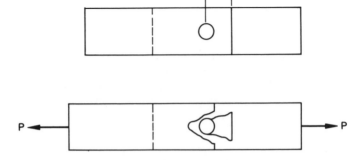

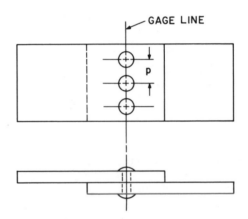

Figure 11-21.   Tear-out failure.

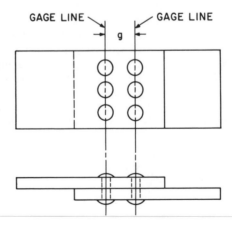

Figure 11-22.   Single-riveted lap joint.

Figure 11-23.   Double-riveted lap joint.

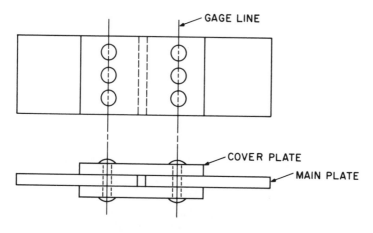

Figure 11-24.   Single-riveted butt joint.

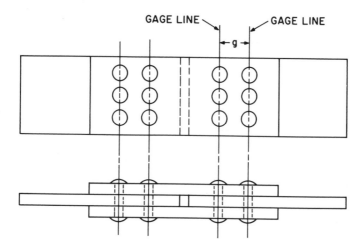

Figure 11-25.   Double-riveted butt joint.

where P_{RP} is the permissible or safe load in pounds that may be applied to the riveted plate without exceeding any of the allowable stresses and P_{SP} is the load in pounds that may be safely applied to a solid plate of the same section. Problem 11-7 will show the rivet configuration required to achieve maximum joint efficiency.

Several common multiple-riveted joints are shown in Figs. 11-22 through 11-25. The centerline through a row of rivets is the gage line and the distance between two adjacent gage lines is the transverse pitch or gage distance g. The distance between two adjacent rivets on the same gage line is known as the pitch p. When two or more rows of rivets are used, they may be arranged in either chain or stagger configuration; this is shown in Fig. 11-26 for a double-riveted lap joint. The distance p_d is the diagonal pitch between rivets in adjacent staggered rows.

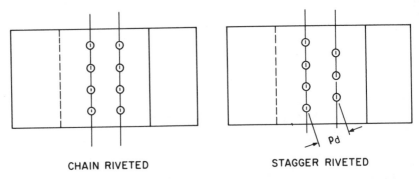

CHAIN RIVETED   STAGGER RIVETED

Figure 11-26.   Rivet configurations.

The AISC Manual requires that the minimum distance between rivet hole centers be preferably not less than three times the rivet diameter; this provision is applicable irrespective of whether the spacing in question be between two rivet holes on the same gage line or two rivet holes each on opposite gage lines. Often an examination problem will be given without an accompanying sketch. Therefore, the reader should examine Figs. 11-22 through 11-26 carefully and become thoroughly familiar with rivet nomenclature.

In most structural sections the rivet holes are punched. The punching operation weakens the plate material in the immediate vicinity of the hole perimeter, which is compensated for by taking the rivet hole diameter as $\frac{1}{8}$ in. greater than the rivet diameter.

The basic equations, Eqs. (11-20), (11-22), and (11-24), will be applied to multiple-riveted connections in the following examples. Each of these equations has an expression for the area over which the applied load acts and careful attention should be given to its calculation, especially as to how it incorporates the areas of some or all the rivets of a joint.

Problem 11-6 Stress analysis of a single lap joint

A steel hanger consists of a plate 5 in. wide by $\frac{3}{8}$ in. thick held at the top by four $\frac{7}{8}$-in. rivets in single shear, as shown in Fig. 11-27. In which way and where is the joint most likely to fail, based on the allowable unit stresses of the AISC? What is the efficiency of the joint?

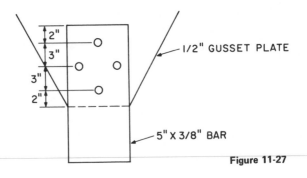

Figure 11-27

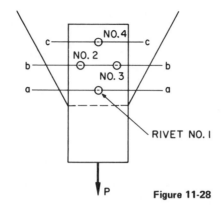

Figure 11-28

Solution:

Each of the three principle modes of failure defined by the respective Eqs. (11-20), (11-22), and (11-24) is evaluated. The three separate evaluations are made by assuming that the applicable allowable stress is developed, and calculating the corresponding load P that produced it. The lowest value of P so calculated will be the maximum allowable load that the joint will support. The failure mode corresponding to this low value of P will indicate where and how joint failure occurs. Since the steel strength is not specified, it will be assumed that the steel used has a yield strength f_y of 33,000 psi.

Tension Failure Mode: Consider first the cross section a-a at rivet No. 1, as shown in Fig. 11-28, and apply Eq. (11-20):

$$f_t = \frac{P_t}{(w - d_h)t}$$

where $f_t = 0.60f_y = 0.60(33,000) = 20,000$ psi

$w = 5$ in.

d_h = diameter of rivet plus $\frac{1}{8}$ in. = $\frac{7}{8} + \frac{1}{8} = 1$ in.

$t = \frac{3}{8}$ in.

$(P_t)_{a-a} = f_t(w - d_h)t = 20,000(5 - 1)(\frac{3}{8}) = 30,000$ lb

Consider next the possibility of tension failure at cross section b-b where the tensile force is applied across a smaller net area. The rivets all contribute equally to support the load P so that each rivet transfers to the gusset plate $\frac{1}{4}$P. Because rivet No. 1 transfers to the gusset plate $\frac{1}{4}$P, $\frac{3}{4}$P remains to tear the plate at cross section b-b.

$$\frac{3}{4}(P_t)_{b-b} = (w - 2d_h)tf_t = (5 - 2)(\frac{3}{8})(20,000) = 22,500 \text{ lb}$$
$$(P_t)_{b-b} = 30,000 \text{ lb}$$

The tension failure calculations show that a load exceeding 30,000 lb can cause the plate to tear at either a-a or b-b. It is unnecessary to consider c-c because only $\frac{1}{4}$P remains there to tear the plate at a net area equal to that at cross section a-a.

Bearing Failure Mode: The bearing forces applied by the rivets tend to crush the material of the thinner connecting member that in this example is the bar. The total effective bearing surface is equal to the number of rivets times the product of the bar thickness t and the rivet diameter d_r. Equation (11-22) is applied by assuming that the allowable bearing stress is developed and calculating the load P_p required to produce this stress.

Total effective bearing area = $4d_r t$ = $4(\frac{7}{8})(\frac{3}{8})$ = 1.312 sq in.

The allowable bearing stress on the projected area of rivets in a bearing-type connection is

$f_p = 1.35f_y = 1.35(33,000) = 44,500$ psi

$P_p = f_p$ (total effective bearing area) = 44,500 (1.312) = 58,500 lb

Shear Failure Mode: Since the rivets all contribute equally to support the load P, they all resist shear at the same time. The rivets are in single shear and the total shear area is equal to the product of the number of rivets and the area of one rivet.

Total shear area = $4[\pi d_r^2/4]$ = $4[\pi(\frac{7}{8})^2/4]$ = 2.41 sq in.

The type of rivets used is not specified in the problem. Therefore, assume that A141 hot-driven rivets are used. From the AISC Manual, the allowable shear stress f_v is 15,000 psi and applying Eq. (11-24)

$P_v = f_v$ (total shear area) = 15,000(2.41) = 36,200 lb

The maximum allowable load which the steel hanger will support is 30,000 lb and is governed by the tension failure mode. The joint is most likely to fail in tension. Since the same load, 30,000 lb, causes the allowable tensile stress to exist at both cross sections a-a and b-b, the plate can tear at either cross section.

The joint efficiency is determined by applying Eq. (11-25):

Joint efficiency = P_{RP}/P_{SP}

It was determined above that the permissible load P_{RP} that may be applied to the riveted plate without exceeding any of the allowable stresses is 30,000 lb. The load P_{SP} that may be safely applied to a solid plate of the same section is governed by the tension failure mode.

$P_{SP} = f_t A = f_t wt = (20,000)(5)(\frac{3}{8})$ = 37,500 lb

where w is the width of the bar and t is its thickness.

Joint efficiency = $(30,000/37,500) \times 100\%$ = 80%   *Answer*

Problem 11-7 Joint of maximum efficiency

Design a lap joint of maximum efficiency between two 18-in. × $\frac{1}{2}$-in. mild steel plates using $\frac{7}{8}$-in. rivets.

Solution:

A joint of maximum efficiency is designed by using one rivet in each of the two outermost rows and adding an additional rivet to each succeeding inner row to form the diamond-shaped pattern of Fig. 11-29. It is first necessary to determine

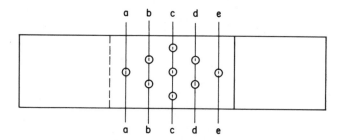

Figure 11-29

the allowable rivet shear and bearing loads. Since a specific rivet type is not indicated, the assumption is made to use the A141 hot-driven rivet. The allowable shear stress f_v is therefore 15,000 psi.

$$\text{Shear } P_v = f_v \frac{\pi d_r^2}{4} = 15,000 \frac{\pi(\frac{7}{8})^2}{4} \ 9020 \text{ lb/rivet}$$

The allowable bearing stress f_t is determined in accordance with the AISC Manual. Since the yield stress f_y of the plate steel is not specified, the assumption is made that f_y is 33,000 psi. Note that the yield stress used is that of the plate material and not that of the rivet material. It is almost always the case that it is the plate that crushes rather than the rivet.

$$f_p = 1.35 f_y = 1.35(33,000) = 44,500 \text{ psi}$$

$$\text{Bearing } P_p = f_p d_r t = 44,500(\tfrac{7}{8})(\tfrac{1}{2}) = 19,470 \text{ lb/rivet}$$

The allowable shear load of 9020 lb/rivet is smaller and will be used to determine the required number of rivets n. But before this number can be calculated, the allowable tensile load $(P_t)_{a-a}$ that the net section at row a-a can support must be calculated. Since a joint of maximum efficiency is desired, only one rivet hole will be in row a-a. The rivet hole diameter d_h is taken as the rivet diameter plus $\frac{1}{8}$ in. The allowable tensile stress f_t of the plate is determined from the AISC Manual, $f_t = 0.60 f_y = 0.60(33,000) = 20,000$ psi. Calculating the allowable tensile load at row a-a:

$$(P_t)_{a-a} = f_t(w - d_h)t = 20,000 \ [18 - (\tfrac{7}{8} + \tfrac{1}{8})] \ \tfrac{1}{2} = 170,000 \text{ lb}$$

In a structural joint all the rivets contribute equally to support the applied load provided the load passes through the centroid of the rivet pattern and the rivets are all the same size. Since each $\frac{7}{8}$-in. rivet will support only 9020 lb without shearing, a total number of at least n = 170,000/9020 = 18.5 or 20 rivets will be required. The number of rivets should be rounded off to the most convenient higher number.

Establish all edge distances j at two times the rivet hole diameter d_h, j = $2d_h$ = 2(1) = 2 in. Make the gage distance g equal to three times the rivet diameter d_r, g = $3d_r$ = 3($\frac{7}{8}$) = 2.63 in., say $2\frac{3}{4}$ in.

The rivet pitch p along the gage lines can be determined after the rivet pattern is established. It must be equal to at least three times the rivet diameter. Start positioning the rivets in a diamond pattern from left to right. The first three rows total 6 rivets; therefore, place 4 rivets in each of two center rows and complete the right-hand side of the diamond pattern with the remaining 6 rivets, as shown in Fig. 11-30. By locating the rivets at equal spaces along the gage lines of the two center rows and within the edge distance margin, a rivet pitch of $4\frac{2}{3}$ in. is obtained. The remaining rivets are also pitched at $4\frac{2}{3}$ in. along the other gage lines and positioned within the perimeter of the diamond pattern. This is greater than the minimal three rivet diameters pitch and neatly distributes the rivets transversely across the joint. If a very compact design were required, the gage distance between the staggered rows could be reduced to even less than 2.63 in. by a small fraction, i.e., the gage distance between the staggered rows could be made to correspond to a diagonal pitch of three rivet diameters.

The allowable tensile load $(P_t)_{a-a}$ for the first row a-a was calculated to be 170,000 lb. The allowable tensile loads at the other rows must also be computed and compared with the actual working load at the corresponding row. The allowable tensile loads are computed below.

Row a-a: $(P_t)_{a-a} = 170,000$ lb

Row b-b: $(P_t)_{b-b} = f_t(w - 2d_h)t = 20,000[18 - 2(1)]\frac{1}{2} = 160,000$ lb

Similarly: $(P_t)_{c-c} = 150,000$ lb

$(P_t)_{d-d} = 140,000$ lb

The allowable load $(P_t)_{a-a}$ is used as an actual working load applied to the joint. Then the load transferred by each rivet from one plate to the other is equal to the allowable load $(P_t)_{a-a}$ divided by the number of rivets.

$$\frac{(P_t)_{a-a}}{n} = \frac{170,000}{20} = 8500\text{-lb load transferred per rivet}$$

This value is less than the allowable shear load because the number of rivets was rounded off to the most convenient higher number.

The actual tensile loads p_t at the other rows are now calculated.

$(p_t)_{a-a} = (P_t)_{a-a} = 170,000$ lb

$(p_t)_{b-b} = 170,000 - 8500 = 161,500$ lb

The calculations need not be carried further, because if the allowable load $(P_t)_{a-a}$ were indeed applied to the joint, the actual load $(p_t)_{b-b}$ at row b-b would exceed the allowable load $(P_t)_{b-b}$ at that row by 1500 lb.

It is therefore necessary to lower the working load $(p_t)_{a-a}$ that may be applied to the joint. Try that value of $(p_t)_{a-a}$ that causes the working load at row b-b to equal the allowable load $(P_t)_{b-b}$. The equation that expresses this condition, and from which $(p_t)_{a-a}$ may be calculated, is

$(P_t)_{b-b} = (p_t)_{a-a} - (p_t)_{a-a}/n$

where $(p_t)_{a-a}/n$ represents the part of the working load that has been transferred from one plate to the other by the rivet in row a-a. The allowable load $(P_t)_{b-b}$ was previously calculated to be 160,000 lb. Therefore,

$160,000 = (p_t)_{a-a} - (p_t)_{a-a}/20$

$(p_t)_{a-a} = 168,400$ lb

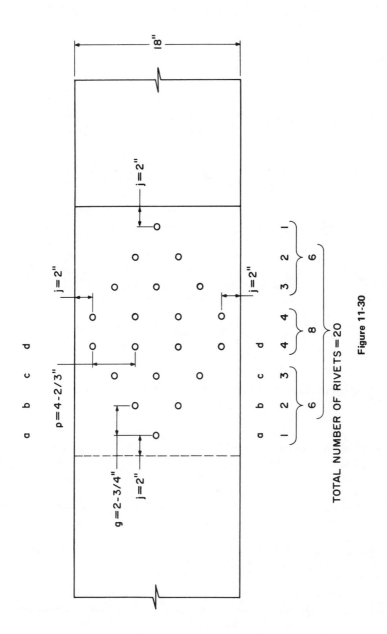

TOTAL NUMBER OF RIVETS = 20

Figure 11-30

The working load now reduced to 168,400 lb is applied to the joint and used to determine the new lower working load at the remaining rows. A comparison must again be made with the allowable loads previously calculated. Calculate the new lower actual working load at row c-c:

$$(p_t)_{c-c} = (p_t)_{a-a} - 3\left[\frac{(p_t)_{a-a}}{n}\right] = 168,400 - 3\left(\frac{168,400}{20}\right) = 143,140$$

The term $3[(p_t)_{a-a}/n]$ indicates that at row c-c the three rivets in rows a-a and b-b have transferred 25,260 lb of the applied 168,400-lb working load to the other plate. Consequently, the allowable load of 150,000 lb at row c-c is not exceeded.

The working load acting at row d-d with a load of 168,400 lb applied to the joint is

$$(p_t)_{d-d} = (p_t)_{a-a} - 6\left[\frac{(p_t)_{a-a}}{n}\right] = 168,400 - 6\left(\frac{168,400}{20}\right) = 117,880 \text{ lb}$$

At no row does the working load exceed the allowable load that the plate material can support. The 168,400 lb is the highest load that the joint can safely support. If this load were increased, tension failure would cause the plate to tear across row b-b. With 168,400 lb applied to the joint, each rivet carries 168,400/20 or 8420 lb. This is less than the load required for shear failure and far less than the load required for bearing failure.

The joint efficiency is calculated using Eq. (11-25),

$$\text{Joint efficiency} = \frac{P_{RP}}{P_{SP}} = \frac{168,400}{f_t wt} = \frac{168,400}{(20,000)(18)(\frac{1}{2})} = 0.936$$

$$= 93.6\% \quad Answer$$

11-6   RIVETED JOINTS IN PRESSURE VESSELS

The concepts considered in Sec. 11-5 for structural joints are only slightly modified when evaluating the riveted joints of pressure vessels.

Rivet holes in pressure vessels are either drilled or first punched to less than full size and then reamed to full size. These steps minimize injury to the plate material at the rivet-hole periphery and make it unnecessary to take the rivet-hole diameter as $\frac{1}{8}$ in. greater than the rivet diameter as with the punched plates used in structural joints. The rivet hole diameter is, however, made $\frac{1}{16}$ in. greater than the undriven rivet diameter and the rivet when driven is assumed to fill out the rivet hole completely. Therefore, the bearing and shear areas are both based on the rivet-hole diameter and with this provision the stress equations considered in Sec. 11-5 are applicable. The net tension area is also based on the rivet hole diameter.

The applicable allowable stresses for pressure vessels usually are included in the statement of the problem. One such set of stresses could be from the ASME Boiler Code that for unfired pressure vessels is: tension 11,000 psi, bearing 19,000 psi, and shear 8800 psi. As Problem 11-8 shows, sometimes other allowable stresses are given.

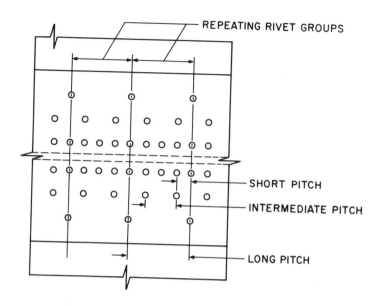

REPEATING RIVET GROUPS

SHORT PITCH

INTERMEDIATE PITCH

LONG PITCH

Figure 11-31

The triple-riveted butt joint of Fig. 11-31 is a portion of a riveted joint that joins the seam of a pressure vessel. The longest rivet pitch is known as the "long pitch" and the shortest rivet pitch as the "short pitch." A rivet pitch of length in between the longest and shortest rivet pitches is known as the "intermediate rivet pitch."

Pressure vessel joints are in the form of repeating rivet groups and a joint analysis is made by evaluating the stress conditions at one such repeating rivet group. The length of a repeating rivet group is determined by inspection in answering the question: What segment length will include a rivet configuration that is exactly the same in every particular as that included by other segments of identical length along the length of the joint, the sum of all such segment lengths being equal to the entire length of the joint? A repeating rivet group is shown for the triple-riveted butt joint of Fig. 11-31.

Problem 11-8 Stress analysis of a repeating rivet group

What maximum pressure may a 100-in.-diameter steel tank be subjected to under the following specifications; material $\frac{3}{8}$-in. thick; triple riveted lap splice made up of $\frac{5}{8}$-in. rivets, spaced 2 in. in center row and 4 in. in outer rows; allowable unit stresses, 18,000, 27,000, and 13,500 psi for tension, bearing, and shear, respectively. What is the efficiency of the joint?

Solution:

The problem states that the lap joint is triple riveted, which means that there are three rivet rows. If the problem had stated triple-riveted butt joint, then there would be three rows of rivets on each side of the joint.

The rivet pitch in the outer rows is 4 in., and 2 in. in the center row; this configuration is shown in Fig. 11-32. The edge distance is not specified and is assumed to be at least twice the rivet-hole diameter.

The joint analysis is made by evaluating the stress conditions at a repeating rivet group. The rivet configuration constituting a repeating rivet group is determined by inspection. Figure 11-32 shows that the repeating rivet group has two half rivets in each of the outer rows and one whole and two half rivets in the center row for an effective total of four rivets.

It is necessary to determine in which way the joint is most likely to fail. The tension force corresponding to the failure condition will be the maximum force that the pressure may establish in the tank walls without causing it to open at the splice.

Tension Failure Mode: Refer to Fig. 11-32.

At the outer row a-a: $P_t = f_t(w - d_h)t = 18,000(4 - {}^{11}\!/_{16})\tfrac{3}{8} = 22,400 \text{ lb}$

At the center row b-b: $\tfrac{3}{4}P_t = f_t(w - d_h)t = 18,000(4 - {}^{22}\!/_{16})\tfrac{3}{8} = 17,730 \text{ lb}$

$$P_t = 23,600 \text{ lb}$$

Here w is the length of a repeating rivet group. In pressure vessel joints the rivet hole is taken as $\tfrac{1}{16}$ in. greater than the diameter of the undriven rivet. Therefore, d_h is equal to $\tfrac{5}{8}$ in. plus $\tfrac{1}{16}$ in. Only $\tfrac{3}{4}P_t$ tears at rivet row b-b because the two half rivets in row a-a together transfer $\tfrac{1}{4}P_t$ to the other plate. A tensile force of 22,400 lb must be established in the tank shell in order to tear the joint at row a-a and a force of 23,600 lb is needed to tear the joint at row b-b. It should be remembered that these forces are applied over the length of a repeating rivet group. It is not necessary to consider rivet row c-c because there only $\tfrac{1}{4}P_t$ remains to tear the plate at a net area equal to that at rivet row a-a.

Bearing Failure Mode: The force P_p that causes bearing failure is calculated. All the rivets contribute equally to support the load and they all resist bearing at the same time. Therefore, the effective bearing area is the sum of all the rivet bearing areas.

Total bearing area = $4d_h t = 4({}^{11}\!/_{16})(\tfrac{3}{8}) = 1.031$ sq in.

$P_p = f_p(\text{total bearing area}) = (27,000)(1.031) = 27,800 \text{ lb}$

Rivets tend to crush the thinner plate material; however, here both plates of the lap splice are the same thickness and both are equally vulnerable to bearing failure. The value of t is therefore $\tfrac{3}{8}$ in. If one of the plates had been thinner, its thickness would be used to compute the bearing area.

The diameter of the rivet hole is used to compute the bearing area, because the problem involves a pressure vessel and the rivet when driven is assumed to fill out the rivet hole completely.

Shear Failure Mode: The force P_v needed to cause shear failure is calculated. The rivets are in single shear and the total shear area is equal to the sum of all the rivet shearing areas.

Total shear area = $4\left[\dfrac{\pi d_h{}^2}{4}\right] = 4\left[\dfrac{\pi({}^{11}\!/_{16})^2}{4}\right] = 1.485$ sq in.

$P_v = f_v(\text{total shear area}) = (13,500)(1.485) = 20,000 \text{ lb}$

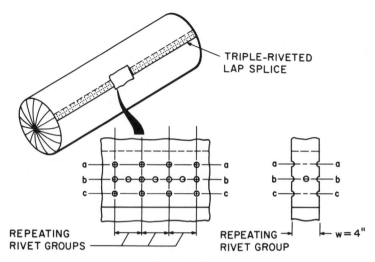

Figure 11-32

A force of 20,000 lb is the maximum force that the pressure may establish in the tank walls without causing the splice to open and is governed by the shear failure mode. The joint is most likely to fail in shear.

Figure 11-33 shows the forces acting on a tank half-section having a length equal to the length of one repeating rivet group. The pressure p is assumed to act uniformly over the entire inner surface and establishes the tensile force P. Relating pressure p to P:

$$[\tfrac{1}{2}\pi(\text{diameter of tank})] \ (\text{length of repeating rivet group})p = 2P$$

Substituting the 20,000-lb maximum allowable load that the lap joint can safely withstand,

$$[\tfrac{1}{2}\pi(100)] \ (4)p = 2(20,000)$$

$$p = 63.7 \text{ psi}$$

The efficiency of the joint is calculated using Eq. (11-25):

$$\text{Joint efficiency} = \frac{P_{RP}}{P_{SP}} = \frac{20,000}{f_y wt} = \frac{20,000}{(18,000)(4)(\tfrac{3}{8})} = 0.741$$

$$= 74.1\% \qquad Answer$$

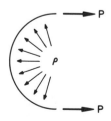

Figure 11-33

11-7   STRUCTURAL RIVETED JOINTS–ECCENTRICALLY LOADED

An eccentrically loaded rivet connection differs from those studied in Secs. 11-5 and 11-6 in that the line of action of the applied force does not pass through the rivet group centroid. This causes the load to be unevenly distributed among the rivets. Therefore, if the stress in a particular rivet is to be calculated, it is necessary to first calculate the value of the load on that rivet.

The riveted plate of Fig. 11-34 can be thought of as a beam fixed at one end and free at the other. The equilibrium equations of statics are used to determine the nature of the end reaction at the rivet group. The column is rigid and the rivets apply a reaction force to the plate that is determined by using the equation $\Sigma F_Y = 0$. The reaction R_c thus determined is equal and in a direction opposite to P and its line of action passes through the centroid of the rivet group. See Fig. 11-35. By taking a moment summation about the centroid of the rivet group, $\Sigma M_c = 0$, it is found that the rivets also apply a counterclockwise moment to the plate equal to Pd. This moment resists the tendency of the eccentrically applied load P to rotate the plate in the clockwise direction.

All the rivets of the rivet group contribute to develop the combined vertical force and moment end reactions. The total force H that each rivet must withstand is the vector sum of two component forces that are readily calculated. The first component force is in the direction of R_c and is equal to $R_c/$(number of rivets), because the line of action of R_c passes through the rivet group centroid. The second component force J resists the tendency of the eccentric load P to rotate the plate in a clockwise direction about the rivet group centroid moment center. In Fig. 11-35, notice that component force J also has the rivet group centroid as its moment center and that it is perpendicular to the moment arm j between the rivet and rivet group centroid. The product of J and j is a component moment and the sum of all such component moments is equal to the moment end reaction Pd.

$$Jj + Jj + Jj + Jj = Pd$$
$$4Jj = Pd$$
$$J = Pd/4j$$

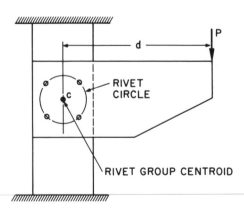

RIVET CIRCLE

RIVET GROUP CENTROID

Figure 11-34.   Eccentrically loaded riveted joint.

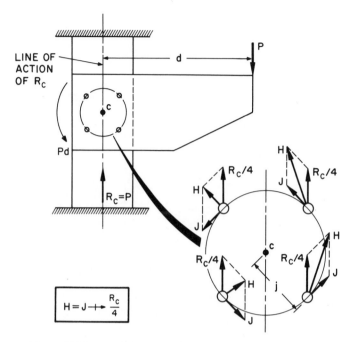

Figure 11-35. Eccentrically loaded riveted joint—end reaction.

A vector summation of the two component forces can now be made to determine the magnitude and direction of the total force H:

$$H = J \leftrightarrow \frac{R_c}{4}$$

Consider a rivet group having two concentric rivet circles as shown in Fig. 11-36. The component forces J and Q act counterclockwise to resist the tendency of the eccentric load P to rotate the plate in a clockwise direction about the rivet group centroid. Component forces J and Q are directly proportional to their distances from the rivet group centroid moment center, i.e., $J/j = Q/q$. This proportion exists because force is directly related to stress and stress is directly proportional to strain and, finally, the strain in a rivet varies in direct proportion to its distance from the moment center. Otherwise stated, the deformation of the rivets in the outer rivet circle is greater and directly proportional to the deformation of the rivets in the inner rivet circle, for a given eccentric load and if the elastic limit is not exceeded. The geometry and equations that establish the relation between J and Q are shown in Fig. 11-36. It should be noted that the proportion relates only to forces such as J and Q that contribute component moments, the sum of which equal the moment end reaction.

Failure of an eccentrically loaded rivet connection will most likely occur because of rivet shear failure. The different values of H cause correspondingly different values of shear stress to develop in the rivets. The shear stress f_v can be calculated using the basic Eq. (11-24).

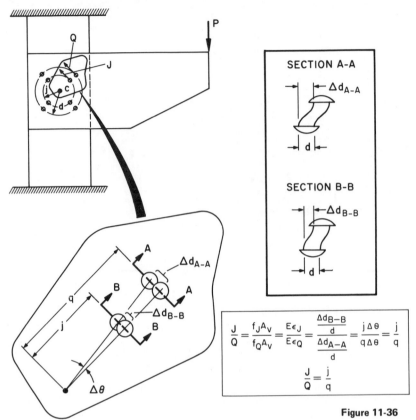

$$\frac{J}{Q} = \frac{f_J A_v}{f_Q A_v} = \frac{E \epsilon_J}{E \epsilon_Q} = \frac{\dfrac{\Delta d_{B-B}}{d}}{\dfrac{\Delta d_{A-A}}{d}} = \frac{j \Delta \theta}{q \Delta \theta} = \frac{j}{q}$$

$$\frac{J}{Q} = \frac{j}{q}$$

Figure 11-36

Sometimes it is required to determine the correct rivet size. For convenience, the rivets of a riveted connection are usually all of the same size. After having determined the total force that each rivet must sustain, the maximum value is used to calculate the rivet shank area required.

Bearing failure is possible if the bracket thickness is inadequate. If a problem gives this dimension, then a bearing failure mode analysis should be made. Assuming that the correct rivet size has been calculated, or a given rivet size has been evaluated and found to be adequate in shear, the maximum total force acting on a rivet is used in Eq. (11-22) to make the bearing failure mode analysis.

Problem 11-9 Eccentrically loaded rivet connection

Assuming all rivets the same size, determine the rivet size for the condition shown in Fig. 11-37.

Solution:

Since the 2000-lb load is eccentrically applied, the rivet group, to maintain static equilibrium, will develop a composite end reaction consisting of an upward vertical reaction force and a counterclockwise moment. The line of action of the

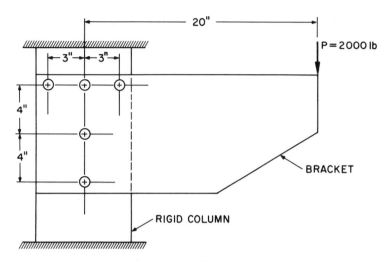

Figure 11-37

upward vertical reaction force passes through the rivet group centroid, which centroid is also the moment center of the reaction moment. The composite end reaction will be unevenly distributed among the rivets and rivet shear failure will occur unless the rivets are of sufficient cross-sectional shank area. Before the rivet size, to prevent shear failure, can be calculated, it is first necessary to calculate the total force on each rivet.

The rivet group is only symmetrical with respect to the Y-axis as shown in Fig. 11-38, which makes it necessary to calculate the y-coordinate of the rivet group centroid. This is done by considering each rivet as a unit of area and using the method of Sec. 2-6, namely:

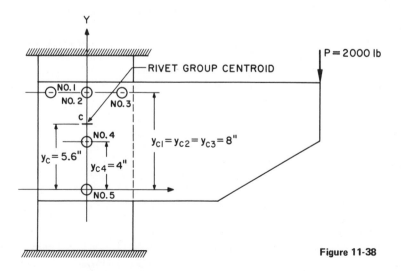

Figure 11-38

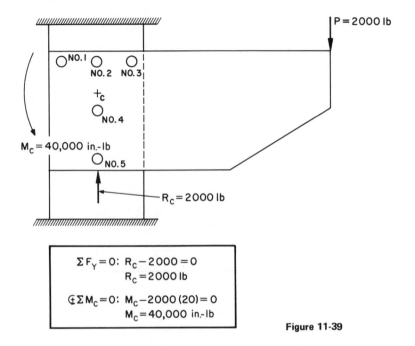

$$\Sigma F_Y = 0: \quad R_c - 2000 = 0$$
$$R_c = 2000 \text{ lb}$$

$$\mathbb{G}\Sigma M_c = 0: \quad M_c - 2000\,(20) = 0$$
$$M_c = 40,000 \text{ in.-lb}$$

Figure 11-39

$$Ay_c = \sum_{n=1}^{n=p} a_n y_{cn} \qquad (2\text{-}6)$$

$$(1 + 1 + 1 + 1 + 1)y_c = 1(0) + 1(4) + 1(8) + 1(8) + 1(8)$$

$$y_c = 5.6 \text{ in.}$$

The composite end reaction comprising the upward vertical reaction and counterclockwise moment is determined using the equilibrium equations of statics as shown in Fig. 11-39.

The total force that each rivet sustains is the vector sum of two component forces. The first component force is the proportionate share of the upward vertical reaction and the second is the rotation resisting force perpendicular to the moment arm joining the rivet and rivet group centroid moment center. Since the upward vertical reaction passes through the rivet group centroid, each rivet supports an equal share calculated as follows:

$$R_c/(\text{number of rivets}) = 2000/5 = 400 \text{ lb/rivet}$$

and shown in Fig. 11-40.

The second component force is developed by each rivet to resist the tendency of the 2000-lb load to rotate the plate in the clockwise direction. These components act in a counterclockwise direction and are shown in Fig. 11-41. The rotation resisting component forces are directly proportional to their distances from the rivet group centroid moment center; therefore,

$$Q/1.6 = J/2.4 = U/3.84 = Z/5.6$$

The fact that rivets are not positioned along the same radius extending from the moment center does not affect the proportionality between the rotation resisting

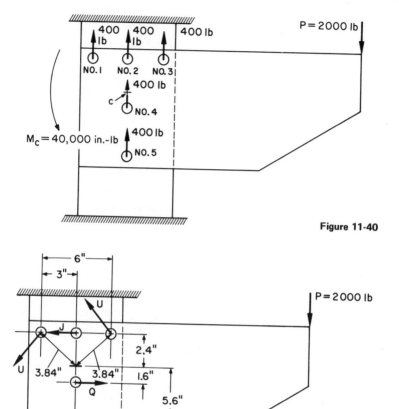

Figure 11-40

Figure 11-41

$$Q/1.6 = J/2.4 = U/3.84 = Z/5.6$$

component forces because the magnitude of these forces is independent of their position on the circumference of a rivet circle. The sum of the products of the rotation-resisting force components and their respective moment arms is equal to the moment end reaction:

$$Z(5.6) + U(3.84) + U(3.84) + J(2.4) + Q(1.6) = 40,000$$

Use the proportions between the forces and solve for Z.

$$U = 3.84(Z/5.6)$$
$$Q = 1.6(Z/5.6)$$
$$J = 2.4(Z/5.6)$$

$$Z(5.6) + 3.84(Z/5.6)(3.84) + 3.84(Z/5.6)(3.84) + 2.4(Z/5.6)(2.4)$$
$$+ 1.6(Z/5.6)(1.6) = 40,000$$
$$Z = 3240 \text{ lb}$$

Use the value of Z and solve for U, Q, and J:

$$U = 3.84(Z/5.6) = 3.84 (3240/5.6) = 2220 \text{ lb}$$
$$J = 2.4(Z/5.6) = 2.4(3240/5.6) = 1389 \text{ lb}$$
$$Q = 1.6(Z/5.6) = 1.6(3240/5.6) = 926 \text{ lb}$$

The total force H that each rivet sustains is determined by calculating the vector sum of the two component forces. These forces are shown separately in Figs. 11-40 and 11-41. They are shown again in Fig. 11-42 together with their vector summations. The maximum vector force governs the selection of the rivet size and is found to be at rivet number 5.

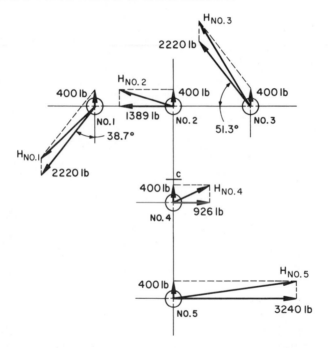

$$H = \sqrt{(\Sigma F_X)^2 + (\Sigma F_Y)^2}$$

$$H_{NO.1} = \sqrt{[-(2220)(\sin 38.7°)]^2 + [400 - (2220)(\cos 38.7°)]^2} = 1942 \text{ lb}$$

SIMILARLY, $H_{NO.2} = 1446$ lb
$H_{NO.3} = 2550$ lb
$H_{NO.4} = 1009$ lb
$H_{NO.5} = 3262$ lb

Figure 11-42

If the allowable shear stress f_v is not to be exceeded,* the shank of rivet number 5 must have a cross-sectional area of at least

$A = H_5/f_v = 3240/15,000 = 0.216$ sq in.

Since all rivets are assumed to be the same size, five rivets having a diameter of at least 0.524 in. are required. Use five 5/8-in.-diameter rivets.   *Answer*

Bearing failure was not considered because no width dimension is specified for the bracket. It is assumed that the bracket has a thickness adequate to preclude bearing failure.

11-8   STRUCTURAL WELDED JOINTS

Two common types of welds are the butt weld and fillet weld and are shown, respectively, in Figs. 11-43 and 11-44. As indicated, a butt weld is used to join two pieces at their edges. If the plates joined by a butt weld are more than $\frac{1}{4}$-in. thick, it is required that the edges be beveled to ensure a good connection. However, it is the fillet weld that is the most common in structural work. Figure 11-45 shows all the nomenclature corresponding to the fillet weld. The size dimension is also known as the leg of the weld and must be at least $\frac{3}{16}$ in. to have adequate strength for structural connections. Larger weld sizes are required if the material thickness of the thicker part joined, exceeds $\frac{1}{2}$ in. To ensure proper fusion to the plate or angle, the weld size should be less than the member thickness by the amounts indicated in Fig. 11-46.

Figure 11-43.   Square groove butt weld.

Figure 11-44.   Fillet weld.

The fillet weld is usually placed along the sides of the connected member as shown in Fig. 11-47. The applied load P tends to shear the fillet welds across the face of the section subjected to the highest shear stress. This corresponds to the section of minimum area and is located in the plane that bisects the root angle. The shearing area is therefore equal to the product of the throat and length dimensions.

The general practice is to make the legs of the fillet weld equal, its transverse cross section being in the form of a right isosceles triangle. Such a fillet weld is specified by its size and length. Its strength is expressed in terms of the allowable load per unit length of weld that is equal to the product of the shear area per unit length a_v and the allowable shear stress f_v. The AISC Manual lists two shear stresses, namely: 13,600 psi and 15,800 psi. Unless a problem specifies otherwise, assume that welding procedure and steel grade require that the 13,600-psi stress be used. For example, what would be the allowable load per unit length

---

*No allowable shear stress is given in the problem; therefore, it is assumed that A141 hot-driven type rivets are used and the allowable shear stress is 15,000 psi.

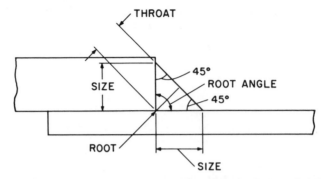

Figure 11-45.   Fillet weld nomenclature. Size dimension is also called the leg of the weld.

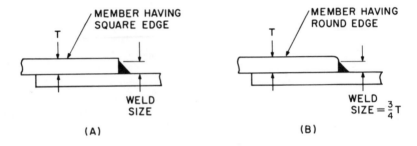

Figure 11-46.   Permissible weld sizes: (A) Square edge: For $T\frac{1}{2}$ maximum effective fillet size = T; for $T\frac{1}{4}$ maximum effective fillet size = $T - \frac{1}{16}$. (B) Round edge: Fillet size at round edges of channels, flanges, or angles should not be greater than three-fourths of the thickness T.

of a $\frac{3}{8}$-in. fillet weld? The designation "$\frac{3}{8}$ in." is the weld size and means that the leg dimension Z is $\frac{3}{8}$ in. Referring to Fig. 11-47, since the weld transverse cross section is a right isosceles triangle, the throat is equal to 0.707(Z) and

$$\text{Allowable load/in. fillet weld} = a_v f_v = 0.707(Z)(1) f_v$$
$$= 0.707(\tfrac{3}{8})(1)(13,600)$$
$$= 3600 \text{ lb}$$

Sometimes there is insufficient space to put down side welds long enough to provide adequate strength. In such circumstances, an end fillet weld can be added, which develops a combined shear and tension or compression stress to resist the applied load. However, for the purposes of design, it is assumed that the end fillet weld tends to shear across the same throat surface as do the side welds. The total required weld length in inches is equal to the applied load divided by the allowable load per inch of fillet weld.

An eccentric load will tend to rotate the connected member with respect to a rigid base plate and cause the welds to develop a nonuniform stress distribution. In order that the welded connection not be eccentrically loaded, the welds

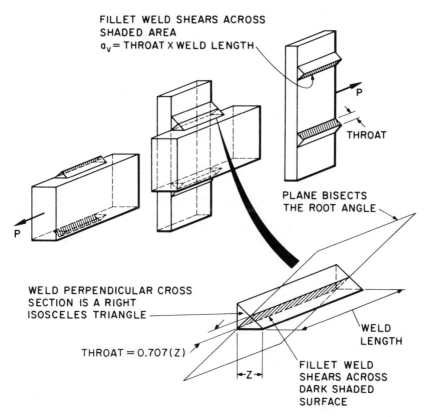

FILLET WELD SHEARS ACROSS
SHADED AREA
a_v = THROAT X WELD LENGTH

P

THROAT

PLANE BISECTS
THE ROOT ANGLE

WELD PERPENDICULAR CROSS
SECTION IS A RIGHT
ISOSCELES TRIANGLE

WELD
LENGTH

THROAT = 0.707(Z)

Z

FILLET WELD
SHEARS ACROSS
DARK SHADED
SURFACE

Figure 11-47. Welded connection before and after fillet weld shear failure showing the surface across which shear failure takes place.

should be located so that their centroid coincides with the line of action of the applied load. Proper placement of the welds will ensure that the load will be distributed uniformly over all the throat shearing surfaces.

Problem 11-10 Design of a welded connection

Design a welded connection for the 4 X 4 X $\frac{5}{16}$-in. angle and gusset plate shown in Fig. 11-48. The connection is to be designed to develop the full tensile strength of the angle based on a 20,000-psi allowable stress in tension.

(a) Determine the size, location, and lengths of the fillet welds required.

(b) Assume that the space requirements permit the angle to overlap the fixed plate a distance of only 18 in. What fillet weld lengths would be required to make a welded connection that will not be loaded eccentrically? As in part (a), the angle is to develop its full tensile strength.

Solution:

(a) The problem states that the angle is to develop its full tensile strength based on a 20,000-psi allowable stress in tension. This means that the welds will require a strength sufficient to support an applied load P equal to the product of

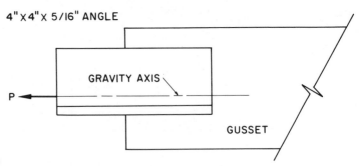

Figure 11-48

the angle cross-sectional area and the allowable 20,000-psi tensile stress. From the AISC Manual, the area of a 4 × 4 × $\frac{5}{16}$-in. angle is 2.40 in.^{2} and the applied load P is equal to (2.40)(20,000) or 48,000 lb.

The angle legs have a rounded edge that limits the size fillet weld that may be used to $\frac{3}{4}$ of the $\frac{5}{16}$-in. angle leg thickness.

Maximum allowable fillet weld size = $(\frac{3}{4})(\frac{5}{16})$ = $\frac{15}{64}$

A $\frac{1}{4}$-in. weld size is too large; therefore use a $\frac{3}{16}$-in. weld, $Z = \frac{3}{16}$ in., which is the minimum size that may be used to make a structural connection.

The total required weld length in inches is equal to the applied load divided by the allowable load per unit inch of fillet weld. The applied load P will tend to shear a fillet weld across its throat surface. The shear strength of a fillet weld is equal to the product of the shear area per unit length a_v and the allowable shear stress f_v. Since no welding procedure and steel grade are specified, it is assumed that the 13,600-psi allowable shear stress (AISC) be used. For a $\frac{3}{16}$-in. fillet weld

$$\text{Allowable load/in. of fillet weld} = a_v f_v = 0.707(Z)(1)f_v$$
$$= 0.707(\tfrac{3}{16})(1)(13,600)$$
$$= 1800 \text{ lb}$$

and

$$\text{Total required weld length} = \frac{\text{applied load}}{\text{allowable load/in. of fillet weld}}$$
$$= 48,000/1800 = 26.7 \text{ in.}$$

Fillet welds of yet undetermined length L_a and L_b are placed as shown in Fig. 11-49 and $1800L_a$ and $1800L_b$ are the reaction forces that resist the applied load P and act at these respective welds. Figure 11-48 shows that the line of action of P is coincident with the gravity axis of the angle. The AISC Manual lists this axis to be at a distance of 1.12 in. away from each angle leg.

The applied load P should not tend to rotate the angle with respect to the fixed plate in the plane of the welds, since this would cause unwanted bending action and a nonuniform stress distribution to develop along the weld throat section. To preclude such eccentric loading, the total 26.7-in. weld length re-

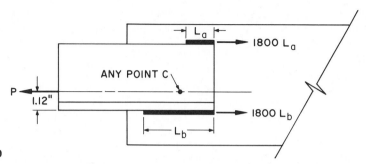

Figure 11-49

quired to resist P must be apportioned to weld lengths L_a and L_b such that the centroid of these two weld lengths lies on the line formed by the perpendicular intersection of the plane of the welds and the plane passing through the line of action of P. The equation to establish the proper proportion between the weld lengths is obtained by taking a moment summation about any point c on the line formed by the perpendicular intersection of the two planes specified in the preceding sentence.

$$\left(\! + \Sigma M_c = 0 \qquad 1800L_a(2.88) - 1800L_b(1.12) = 0\right.$$
$$L_a/1.12 = L_b/2.88 \qquad \text{and} \qquad L_a + L_b = 26.7 \text{ in.}$$

Solving for L_a and L_b,

$$L_a = 7.48 \text{ in.}$$
$$L_b = 19.22 \text{ in.} \qquad \textit{Answer}$$

(b) Side welds of yet undetermined length L_a and L_b are placed in the same positions as in part (a) and a fillet weld, the full 4-in. width of the angle leg, is placed at the end of the angle. See Fig. 11-50. For the purposes of design, it is assumed that the end fillet weld tends to shear across the throat surface in the same manner as do the side welds. Since the $3/16$-in. fillet weld develops a shear strength of 1800 lb/in., the end fillet weld will resist a total of 4(1800) or

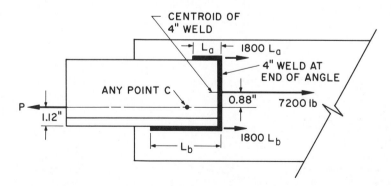

Figure 11-50.   Angle need not overlap gusset by more than 18 in.

7200 lb. It was determined in the solution to (a) that 26.7 in. of $\frac{3}{16}$-in. size fillet weld are required to resist the applied load of 48,000 lb. With a 4-in. weld length placed at the end of the angle, there remains 22.7 in. of weld length to be apportioned to L_a and L_b in a way that will locate the weld centroid on the line formed by the perpendicular intersection of the same two planes considered in the solution to (a). This design procedure will prevent unwanted bending and the consequent nonuniform stress distribution. To establish a relationship between L_a and L_b, a moment summation is taken about any point c on the line defined by the perpendicular intersection of the planes referred to above. For the moment summation, the 7200-lb load resisted by the entire length of the end weld is represented by a resultant vector acting at the end weld centroid.

$$\zeta + \Sigma M_c = 0 \qquad 1800L_a(2.88) + 7200(0.88) - 1800L_b(1.12) = 0$$

and $L_a + L_b = 22.7$ in.

Solving for L_a and L_b,

$$L_a = 5.5 \text{ in.}$$
$$L_b = 17.2 \text{ in.} \qquad \textit{Answer}$$

11-9   TORSION IN CIRCULAR SHAFTS

Torsion in a circular shaft occurs when a shaft is fixed at one end and has a twisting moment T applied to it at the free end as shown in Fig. 11-51. The twisting moment or torque is applied in a plane perpendicular to the longitudinal shaft axis. The twisting moment may be considered as being transmitted from one end of the shaft to the other by imaginary elemental circular shaft sections of thickness ΔL. These elemental sections act in shear upon each other at their contacting surfaces. Consequently, at any distance r from the shaft axis, a shear stress $(f_v)_r$ develops.

The equation relating the applied torque T and the shear stress $(f_v)_r$ is

$$T = (f_v)_r J / r \qquad (11\text{-}26)$$

where $(f_v)_r$ = shear stress, lb/in.^{2}, at any distance r in. from the shaft axis

       J = polar moment of inertia, in.^{4}

       T = twisting moment, lb-in.

The maximum shear stress $(f_v)_R$ is developed at the shaft surface and for a given twisting moment T is related to T by

$$T = (f_v)_R J / R \qquad (11\text{-}27)$$

where $(f_v)_R$ = shear stress, lb/in.^{2}, at shaft surface

       R = shaft radius, in.

Sometimes shaft-driven machinery requires that the shaft not be twisted through more than a specified angle. This angle is known as the angle of twist and is measured for a given shaft length L by the angle θ through which the radius

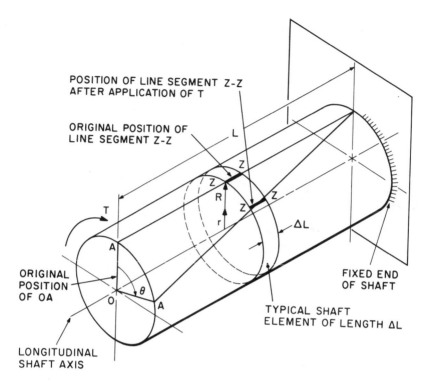

Figure 11-51. Torsion in a circular shaft.

OA in Fig. 11-51 is rotated from its original position by the applied twisting moment T. The angle of twist is related to the applied twisting moment by the equation

$$\theta = TL/E_v J \tag{11-28}$$

where θ = angle of twist, rad

L = shaft length over which twist is measured, in.

E_v = modulus of elasticity in shear

It should be noted that the polar moment of inertia J in Eqs. (11-26) to (11-28) is the moment of inertia of the shaft cross-sectional area about the longitudinal shaft axis. For a solid shaft,

$$J = \pi D^4/32 \tag{11-29}$$

where D = shaft diameter. For a hollow shaft,

$$J = (\pi/32)(D^4 - D_1^4) \tag{11-30}$$

where D = outer diameter

D_1 = inner diameter

In problems involving the transmission of power by a shaft, it is often necessary to be able to relate quantities such as horsepower and shaft rotation speed to the twisting moment. The equation relating these quantities is

$$T = 396,000 \times hp/2\pi N \tag{11-31}$$

where T = twisting moment, lb-in.

hp = horsepower

N = speed of shaft rotation, rpm

Problem 11-11 Shear stress in a solid shaft

A steel shaft of 2-in. diameter is to transmit 60 hp at 250 rpm. The modulus of elasticity in shear is 12,000,000 psi. Find the maximum shearing stress in the shaft and the angle of twist per foot of shaft length.

Solution:

The maximum shear stress $(f_v)_R$ can be expressed in terms of torque using Eq. (11-27)

$$(f_v)_R = TR/J$$

The shaft radius R = 1 in. The polar moment of inertia J for a solid shaft is given by Eq. (11-29).

$$J = \pi D^4/32 = \pi(2)^4/32 = \pi/2$$

The torque T can be found from Eq. (11-31)

$$T = \frac{396,000 \times hp}{2\pi N} = \frac{396,000(60)}{2\pi(250)} = 15,130 \text{ lb-in.}$$

And substituting

$$(f_v)_R = \frac{TR}{J} = \frac{(15,130)(1)}{\pi/2}$$

$$= 9650 \text{ psi} \qquad Answer$$

The angle of twist is calculated using Eq. (11-28). It is required that the angle of twist per foot of shaft length be calculated; therefore L = 12 in.

$$\theta = \frac{TL}{E_v J} = \frac{(15,130)(12)}{(12 \times 10^6)(\pi/2)}$$

$$= 0.00965 \text{ rad/ft} \qquad Answer$$

Problem 11-12 Shear stress in a shaft key

A 2-in. shaft is transmitting 30 hp at 200 rpm. A pulley that delivers the entire amount of power is keyed to the shaft by a ⅜ × ½ × 3-in. flat key. The shaft is in pure torsion. Determine the stresses in the key.

Solution:

The key prevents the pulley from moving with respect to the shaft and transmits the torque force from the shaft to the pulley. In so doing, the key develops very substantial shearing stresses. A typical pulley and flat key configuration is shown

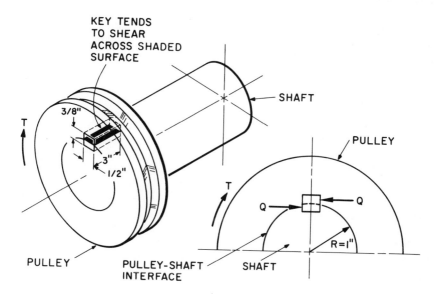

Figure 11-52

in Fig. 11-52. This diagram also shows that the torque force Q tends to shear the key across the surface of the section in the plane defined by the mutually contacting surfaces of the pulley and shaft. An equal and opposite reaction force also shown as Q is applied by the pulley to the other half of the key. The shearing area of the key is $A_v = (\frac{1}{2})(3) = 1.5$ in.^{2} The torque is found using Eq. (11-31):

$$T = \frac{396,000 \times hp}{2\pi N} = \frac{396,000(30)}{2\pi(200)} = 9460 \text{ lb-in.}$$

and the torque force Q is

$$Q = T/R = 9460/1 = 9460 \text{ lb}$$

The shaft is a 2-in. shaft. Shafts are usually specified by their shaft diameter; therefore, the radius R equals 1 in. And the shear stress developed in the key

$$f_v = Q/A_v = 9460/1.5$$
$$= 6310 \text{ lb/in.}^2 \qquad Answer$$

Problem 11-13 Shear stress in a hollow shaft
A hollow steel shaft is designed to transmit 500 hp at 1800 rpm. If the outside diameter of the shaft is 3 in., how large may the inside diameter be so as not to exceed a shearing stress of 10,000 psi?

Solution:
The problem states that the shearing stress is not to exceed 10,000 psi; this maximum value is designated as $(f_v)_R$ and would occur at the outer shaft surface. Solving Eq. (11-27) for J

$$J = RT/(f_v)_R$$

and expressing J in terms of the inner and outer diameters using Eq. (11-30)

$$J = (\pi/32)(D^4 - D_1^4)$$

Equating, $RT/(f_v)_R = (\pi/32)(D^4 - D_1^4)$

Solving for the inner diameter D_1

$$D_1^4 = D^4 - \frac{RT}{(\pi/32)(f_v)_R}$$

where D = 3 in., O.D.

R = $D/2$ = 1.5 in., the shaft radius to the outer surface

$(f_v)_R$ = 10,000 psi, the shear stress at the outer surface

The torque T is calculated using Eq. (11-31):

$$T = \frac{396{,}000 \times hp}{2\pi N} = \frac{396{,}000(500)}{2\pi(1800)} = 17{,}500 \text{ lb-in.}$$

Solving for D_1

$$D_1^4 = 3^4 - \frac{(1.5)(17{,}500)}{(98.2 \times 10^{-3})(10{,}000)}$$

$$D_1 = 2.714 \text{ in.}   \textit{Answer}$$

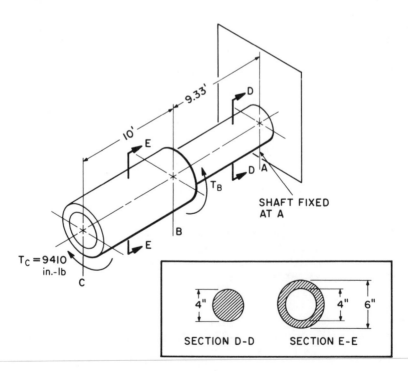

Figure 11-53

Problem 11-14 Composite shaft

A hollow shaft BC is shown connected to a solid shaft AB in Fig. 11-53. The system is properly supported so that no bending exists. Assume E_v = 12,000,000 psi.
(a) Find the torque T_B such that the maximum unit shear stress is the same in both parts.
(b) Find the angle of twist in BC.

Solution:

(a) The problem states that the torque T_B should have a value that makes the maximum unit shear stress in both shafts equal. The maximum shear stress occurs at the farthest distance from the longitudinal shaft axis and is calculated in terms of torque T, radius R, and polar moment of inertia J for each shaft length using Eq. (11-27). The two expressions thus determined are equated.

Shaft length AB: $(f_v)_{R[AB]} = \dfrac{TR}{J} = \dfrac{(T_C - T_B)R_{AB}}{J_{AB}}$

The resultant torque that acts at B to twist the shaft with respect to the fixed end A is the sum of all torques that act on the composite shaft to the right of point B, namely: $T_C - T_B$.

Shaft length BC: $(f_v)_{R[BC]} = TR/J = T_C R_{BC}/J_{BC}$

Calculating the polar moments of inertia J_{AB} and J_{BC} using Eqs. (11-29) and (11-30), respectively,

Shaft length AB: $J_{AB} = \pi D^4/32 = \pi(4)^4/32 = 25.1$ in.^{4}

Shaft length BC: $J_{BC} = (\pi/32)(D^4 - D_1{}^4) = (\pi/32)[(6)^4 - (4)^4] = 102.2$ in.^{4}

Equating $(f_v)_{R[AB]}$ and $(f_v)_{R[BC]}$

$$\frac{(T_C - T_B)R_{AB}}{J_{AB}} = \frac{T_C R_{BC}}{J_{BC}}$$

$$\frac{(9410 - T_B)(2)}{25.1} = \frac{(9410)(3)}{102.2}$$

$$T_B = 5950 \text{ lb-in.} \qquad Answer$$

(b) The angle of twist of shaft length BC is determined using Eq. (11-28):

$$\theta_{BC} = \frac{TL}{E_v J} = \frac{T_C L}{E_v J_{BC}} = \frac{(9410)(10)(12)}{(12 \times 10^6)(102.2)}$$

$$= 0.921 \times 10^{-3} \text{ rad} \qquad Answer$$

11-10   FLANGE COUPLINGS

Power is often transmitted along shaft lengths that are connected by flange couplings, as shown in Fig. 11-54. When a twisting moment is applied at end A, the flange coupling at B will develop a resisting torque T equal to the sum of the products of the shearing force Q acting at each bolt and its moment arm distance to the longitudinal shaft axis that in Fig. 11-54 is the bolt circle radius R_Q. This is expressed by the equation

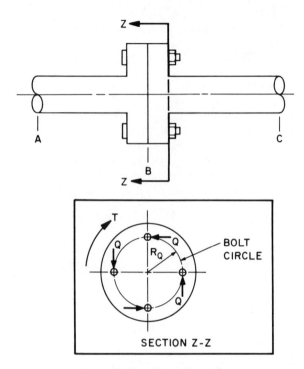

Figure 11-54.   Flanged coupling.

$$T = nR_Q Q \qquad (11\text{-}32)$$

where n is the number of bolts, R_Q is in in., Q is in lb, and T is in lb-in. Each bolt in the same bolt circle is subjected to the shearing force Q, which is assumed to act uniformly over the bolt cross section. Then the shear stress f_v developed in each bolt is

$$f_v = \frac{Q}{\pi d^2/4} \qquad (11\text{-}33)$$

where d is the bolt diameter in in., f_v is in psi, and Q is in lb. By combining Eqs. (11-32) and (11-33), the shear stress f_v may be expressed in terms of the torque T, which is transferred from one shaft flange to the other:

$$f_v = 4T/\pi n d^2 R_Q \qquad (11\text{-}34)$$

For a flange coupling having two concentric bolt circles, as shown in Fig. 11-55, the shearing force U acting on a bolt of the outer circle of radius R_U is related to the shearing force Q acting on a bolt of the inner circle of radius R_Q by the proportionality

$$Q/R_Q = U/R_U \qquad (11\text{-}35)$$

The algebraic and geometric proportions upon which the relation between Q and U is based are shown in Fig. 11-55. The torque transferred from one shaft flange

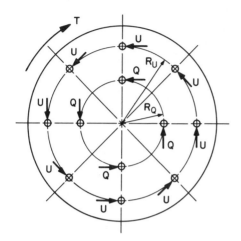

Figure 11-55. Flanged coupling having concentric circles.

to the other in a shaft flange assembly having two concentric bolt circles is given by

$$T = n_Q R_Q Q + n_U R_U U \qquad (11\text{-}36)$$

where n_Q is the number of bolts in the inner bolt circle and n_U is the number of bolts in the outer bolt circle.

Problem 11-15 Design of a flanged coupling

A flanged bolt coupling is used to connect a solid shaft of 3-in. diameter to a hollow shaft of $3\frac{1}{2}$-in. O.D. and 3-in. I.D. How many $\frac{1}{2}$-in.-diameter bolts must be used on an 8-in. diameter bolt circle so that the shearing stress will not exceed 8000 psi anywhere in the assembly?

Solution:

From the statement of the problem a sketch of the composite shaft is drawn in Fig. 11-56. Shear stress develops in three places, namely: in both shaft lengths because of torsion and in the connecting bolts that transfer the torque from one flange to the other by the shearing force Q. This latter force acts at each bolt in the plane of the flange contacting surfaces and in a direction tangent to the bolt circle.

The shear stress is not to exceed 8000 psi anywhere in the assembly; therefore, it first will be necessary to calculate the torque for each shaft length that will develop a stress of 8000 psi at the farthest distance from the longitudinal shaft axis. The lower value of these two torques will be the maximum torque that the shaft assembly may safely transmit. Then calculate the number of $\frac{1}{2}$-in.-diameter bolts required to transfer this latter torque from one shaft flange to the other without developing a shear stress of more than 8000 psi in the bolts.

For each shaft length, calculate the torque that will develop a maximum shear stress of 8000 psi using Eq. (11-27):

Shaft length AB: $T_{AB} = (f_v)_R J_{AB}/R_{AB}$

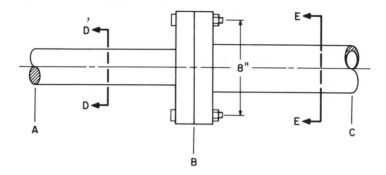

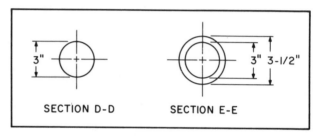

SECTION D-D   SECTION E-E

Figure 11-56

Shaft length AB is solid; therefore use Eq. (11-29) to calculate J_{AB}:

$$J_{AB} = \pi D^4/32 = \pi(3)^4/32 = 7.94 \text{ in.}^4$$

and $T_{AB} = (f_v)_R J_{AB}/R = (8000)(7.94)/1.5 = 42,400$ lb-in.

Shaft length BC: $T_{BC} = (f_v)_R J_{BC}/R_{BC}$

Shaft length BC is hollow; therefore use Eq. (11-30) to calculate J_{BC}:

$$J_{BC} = (\pi/32)(D^4 - D_1^4) = (\pi/32)[(3.5)^4 - (3)^4] = 6.8 \text{ in.}^4$$

and $T_{BC} = (f_v)_B J_{BC}/R_{BC} = (8000)(6.8)/1.75 = 31,100$ lb-in.

Therefore, the maximum torque that the shaft assembly may transmit is 31,100 lb-in. It remains now to calculate the number of ½-in. bolts n needed to transfer this torque load from one shaft flange to the other. Solving Eq. (11-34) for n, and remembering that the shear stress is not to exceed 8000 psi anywhere in the shaft assembly,

$$n = 4T/\pi f_v d^2 R_Q$$

where T = 31,100 lb-in. torque transferred from one flange to the other

f_v = 8000 psi, shear stress developed in the flange bolts

d = ½ in., the bolt diameter

R_Q = 8 in., the bolt circle radius

$$n = \frac{4(31,100)}{\pi(8000)(\tfrac{1}{2})^2(8)} = 2.47 = 3 \text{ bolts} \qquad Answer$$

chapter 12
SHEAR AND BENDING MOMENT

12-1 TYPES OF BEAMS AND LOADING

A beam is classified by the method used to support it and from the positions along the length of the beam which the supports occupy. Figure 12-1 shows a *simple* beam that is supported by a roller support at one end and a pin connection at the other. Figure 12-2 shows an *overhanging* beam that has the same supports as the simple beam except that they occupy different positions along the length of the beam. A *cantilever* beam is shown in Fig. 12-3; it is free at one end and fixed at the other. These three beam configurations are all statically determinate, i.e., the reactions can be determined using the equations of static equilibrium. If all the loads are transverse, i.e., perpendicular to the longitudinal beam axis, then the statically determinate beams have only two unknown reactions and only two equilibrium equations are used for their

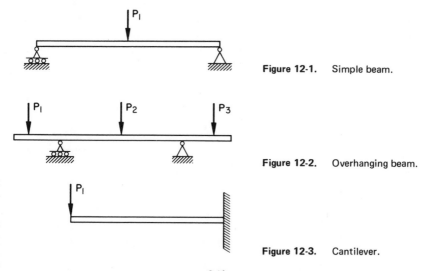

Figure 12-1. Simple beam.

Figure 12-2. Overhanging beam.

Figure 12-3. Cantilever.

solution, namely: $\Sigma F_Y = 0$ and $\Sigma M = 0$; or $\Sigma M = 0$ may be used twice with each moment summation taken at a different point.

A beam that has more unknown reactions than there are equations of static equilibrium is said to be statically indeterminate. The *continuous, propped-cantilever*, and *fixed-ended* beams are statically indeterminate and are shown in Figs. 12-4 through 12-6, respectively. The reactions are determined by supplementing the equations of static equilibrium with equations that concern beam deflection. A study of indeterminate beams and their deflection is taken up in Chap. 17.

There are two principal types of transverse loading that may be applied to a beam, namely: concentrated and distributed. The concentrated load is applied over such a small length of beam that it may be considered to be acting at a point. The distributed load may be *uniform, uniformly varying,* or *nonuniform* and may act over any part of the beam length or over the entire beam length. Figure 12-7 shows a beam subjected to a loading of each type.

12-2   SHEAR AND BENDING MOMENT

Consider the simple beam of Fig. 12-8 to which are applied the concentrated loads P_1 and P_2. Referring to Fig. 12-9, imagine the beam to be cut at any selected transverse section a-a and make a vertical summation of all forces acting on the beam to the left of the section.

$$\Sigma(F_Y)_L = R_1 - P_1 = \text{shear V at the selected section}$$
$$\Sigma(F_Y)_L = V \qquad (12\text{-}1)$$

The resultant V is the shear force or simply *shear* at the section selected. The upward-acting forces are considered positive, and the downward-acting forces negative. If the shear V is positive, then it acts upward as indicated by the dotted vector and tends to move the left-hand beam segment upward with respect to the right-hand beam segment. A negative shear would exist if the summation $\Sigma(F_Y)_L$ yields a negative value. The V would be directed downward tending to move the left-hand beam segment downward with respect to the right-hand beam segment. This sign convention, which makes a tendency of upward movement of the left-hand beam segment relative to the right-hand beam segment correspond to positive shear and downward movement correspond to negative shear, requires that the vertical force summation be made only of the forces acting on the beam segment to the left of the selected transverse section.

In addition to shear, the reactions and loads subject the beam to a bending moment. At any selected section a-a, the bending moment is equal to the summation of all moments either to the left or to the right of the section about an axis passing through the centroid of the section and perpendicular to the plane of

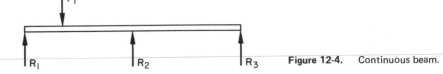

Figure 12-4.   Continuous beam.

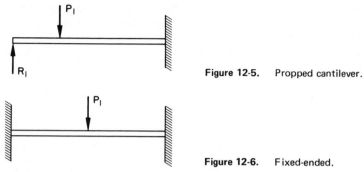

Figure 12-5. Propped cantilever.

Figure 12-6. Fixed-ended.

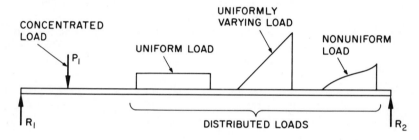

Figure 12-7. Types of loading.

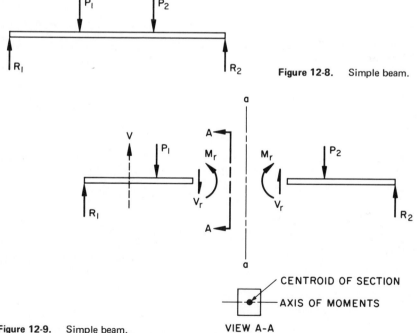

Figure 12-8. Simple beam.

Figure 12-9. Simple beam.

VIEW A-A

the paper, i.e., perpendicular to the plane containing the applied loads and reaction forces. See view A-A of Fig. 12-9. For the forces acting on the left-hand beam segment, clockwise rotation is considered positive and for the forces acting on the right-hand beam segment, counterclockwise rotation is considered positive.

$$(+ \Sigma M_L = +) \Sigma M_R = \text{bending moment M at selected section} \qquad (12\text{-}2)$$

A beam may be thought of as consisting of an infinite number of flexible longitudinal fibers. If the above moment sign convention is followed and a positive value for bending moment is obtained, then the beam will bend concave up as shown in Fig. 12-10. This means that the bending moment produces the effect that the fibers in the upper part of the beam are shortened and in compression and the fibers in the lower part are lengthened and in tension. A negative value of bending moment obtained following the above moment sign convention results in a beam bending as shown in Fig. 12-11. Along the entire length of the beam between the fibers in compression and tension, there lies a surface in which the fibers are neither shortened nor lengthened; this surface is called the *neutral surface*.

To maintain a condition of static equilibrium, the beam of Fig. 12-8 opposes the shear V and bending moment M by developing internal stresses that are evidenced by a resisting shear V_r and a resisting moment M_r. As shown in Fig.

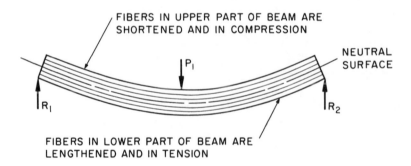

Figure 12-10.   Beam subjected to positive bending moment.

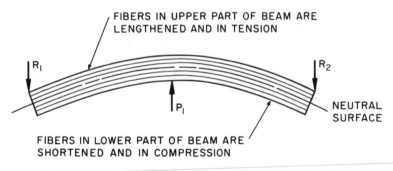

Figure 12-11.   Beam subjected to negative bending moment.

12-9, the resisting shear V_r is equal and opposite to the shear V and acts across the face of the transverse section. The resisting moment M_r is equal to and acts in a rotational direction opposite to the bending moment M. The V_r and M_r of Fig. 12-9 are acting in a direction opposing an assumed positive shear and positive bending moment condition.

12-3 SHEAR AND MOMENT DIAGRAMS

The loads on a beam cause it to be subjected to shear and moment and in Sec. 12-2 it was indicated that a beam responds by developing opposing internal stresses. The study of these stresses will be taken up in Chap. 13. In addition to causing the beam to develop internal stresses, the beam loading deflects the beam from its unloaded position. The study of deflections for both statically determinate and indeterminate beams will be taken up in Chap. 17. It is sufficient at this point to realize that the problems involving the determination of deflection and internal stresses require that the vertical shear and bending moment along the length of the beam be known. A graphical representation of the shear and bending moment is the most convenient and informative means for conveying this information. These graphs are constructed using Eqs. (12-1) and (12-2) in the manner outlined in the following paragraphs and are called shear and moment diagrams.

A shear diagram can best be prepared by dividing the beam into interval lengths, calculating the shear at each interval using Eq. (12-1) and graphically displaying the results. The interval lengths are taken between discontinuous load changing points on the load diagram. The loaded beam by itself is the load diagram. As an example, consider the overhanging beam of Fig. 12-12. The corresponding shear and moment diagrams also appear on Fig. 12-12. The points on the load diagram designated A, B, etc., are all points of load discontinuity. The shear diagram is drawn directly beneath the load diagram and the coordinates are formed by measuring the shear on a vertical axis and the distance x to any point along the length of the beam on the horizontal axis. The left-hand end of the beam coincides with the origin of the coordinates. The shear diagram will be drawn to correspond to the following set of typical load and beam length values.

$P_1 = 5$ kips	$L_{AB} = 5$ ft
$P_2 = 12$ kips	$L_{AC} = 11$ ft
$W_1 = 8$ kips (triangular load)	$L_{AD} = 18$ ft
$W_2 = 1.5$ k/ft	$L_{AE} = 26$ ft
$P_3 = 10$ kips	$L_{AF} = 33.5$ ft
$R_1 = 33.55$ kips	$L_{AG} = 40.0$ ft
$R_2 = 26.25$ kips	$L_{AH} = 50.0$ ft

A comparison of the load and moment diagrams of Fig. 12-12 shows that for those portions of the beam at which the concentrated loads act exclusively and at unloaded intervals between uniform loads such as interval EF, the moment diagram is composed of slanted straight-line segments. At the beam intervals over which a downward uniform load acts, the moment diagram curvature is

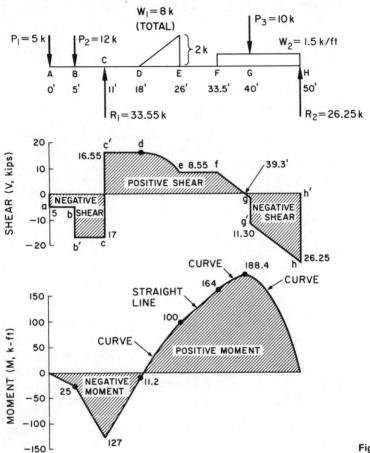

Figure 12-12

concave down. For a uniform upward load, the moment diagram curvature would be concave upward.

The positions on the moment diagram where the slope is zero or where the slope must pass through zero in order to change its sign correspond to locations of zero shear; this means that the maximum moment must exist at one of the zero shear locations. Therefore, if a particular beam problem requires that the maximum moment be known, it is not necessary to first draw the moment diagram. All that is necessary is to determine the points at which the shear diagram crosses the zero shear axis and calculate the moments at these points. The largest absolute moment value so obtained would be used in the particular beam problem. Such largest absolute moment value may of course be either positive or negative. In the case of a cantilever beam, the maximum moment occurs at the fixed end of the beam. Maximum shear also occurs at the fixed end of a cantilever beam. This is illustrated in Problem 12-1.

From Sec. 12-2 recall that the adopted sign convention states that positive bending moment causes the beam to bend concave up and that a negative bending moment causes the beam to bend concave down. To illustrate this bending action an elastic curve is often drawn; this curve is defined by the line formed by the intersection of the plane of the neutral surface and the plane of the loads. It is usually necessary to exaggerate the actual beam deflection and bending in order to see this action clearly. The elastic curve for the beam of the example appears in Fig. 12-12 and is sketched with a curvature corresponding to the moment sign. The points at which the bending moment changes sign and passes through zero correspond to points on the elastic curve where the concavity changes in accordance with a change in moment sign. Such points on the elastic curve are known as points of inflection. For example, at the point of inflection of the elastic curve of Fig. 12-12, the beam curvature changes from concave down to concave up and this corresponds to a moment sign change of from negative to positive.

The moment diagram shows that the bending moment becomes zero within the interval DE. Therefore, to locate the point of inflection, the moment equation for interval DE is set equal to zero and solved for x. A trial and error solution will indicate quickly that x = 19.3 ft, or the value may be determined from the moment diagram.

12-4   RELATION BETWEEN SHEAR AND MOMENT

It is known that a *change* in moment between any two points on a beam is equal to the *net* area under the shear diagram between those two points. This may be expressed as

$$M_2 - M_1 = (\text{area})_{\text{shear}} \tag{12-3}$$

where the subscripts 1 and 2 denote successive points on a beam going from left to right. The location of point 2 is to the right of point 1. For example, use Eq. (12-3) to calculate the moments at zero shear for the beam of Fig. 12-12, i.e., at points C and G.

Moment at Point C:

$$M_C - M_A = A_{AB} + A_{BC}$$

where A_{AB} is the area under the shear diagram for beam interval AB and A_{BC} is the area under shear diagram for beam interval BC.

$$M_C - M_A = (-5)(5) + (6)(-17) = -127.0 \text{ k-ft}$$

Since there is no force and moment arm to the left of point A, the moment at A is zero and the change in moment between points A and C is equal to the moment at point C.

$$M_C - 0 = -127.0 \text{ k-ft}$$
$$M_C = -127.0 \text{ k-ft} \qquad Answer$$

Similarly, the moment at each point on the moment diagram (Fig. 12-12) is obtained by summing the areas of the shear diagram from left to right or from right to left.

The moment at a particular point can often be calculated more expeditiously by considering the areas under the shear diagram that are to the right of the point. For example, an inspection of the shear diagram of Fig. 12-12 shows that only the area under the shear diagram for beam interval GH need be calculated to find the change in moment between points G and H. Since the moment at H is zero, the change in moment between points G and H is equal to the moment at point G.

The slope of the moment diagram at any point x along the length of the beam is given by the ordinate of the shear diagram and is expressed by

$$dM/dx = V \qquad\qquad (12\text{-}4)$$

Positive shear then means that the moment diagram has a positive slope and negative shear indicates a moment diagram having a negative slope. Consider the simply supported beam of Fig. 12-13. From x = 0 to midspan the beam is subjected to an ever decreasing positive shear; this corresponds to a moment diagram having an ever decreasing positive slope. At midspan, where the shear diagram passes through zero, the slope of the moment diagram is zero. Then from midspan to x = L the beam is subjected to negative shear; this corresponds to a moment diagram having an ever increasing negative slope.

12-5   SEMIGRAPHICAL METHOD FOR DRAWING THE SHEAR AND MOMENT DIAGRAMS

The semigraphical method of constructing the shear and moment diagrams requires much less time and effort than does a mathematical method. If a problem requires that the shear and moment diagram be drawn:

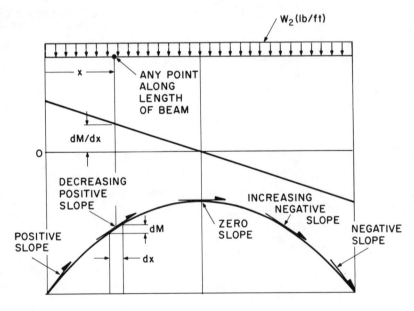

Figure 12-13

1. Find the end reactions, and in the case of a cantilever, the fixed-end reaction and the fixed-end moment.
2. Draw the shear diagram; this usually can be done by inspection.
3. Draw the moment diagram.

In this connection certain observations made toward the end of Sec. 12-3 are well worth repeating. For those portions of the beam at which concentrated loads act exclusively and at unloaded intervals between uniform loads, the moment diagram is composed of slanted straight-line segments. At the beam intervals over which a downward uniform load acts, the moment diagram curvature is concave down. For a uniform upward load, the moment diagram curvature is concave upward.

The shape of the moment diagram at the points where the shear diagram *crosses* the zero shear axis requires special attention. These points on the moment diagram will be maximum points and the slope of the moment curve will change sign when passing from one side of the point to the other. Whether the transition from one side of the point to the other is discontinuous or smooth depends upon the beam loading at that same point. If a maximum moment occurs at the location of a concentrated load or support, then the transition will be discontinuous. Otherwise the transition will be smooth.

Problem 12-1 Semigraphical method of constructing shear and moment diagrams

Use the semigraphical method to draw the shear and moment diagram for the cantilever beam shown in Fig. 12-14. The beam has a weight of 2 k/ft.

Solution:

1. The beam is of the cantilever type and the fixed-end reaction and the fixed-end moment are calculated. The fixed-end reaction and fixed-end moment are assumed to take the directions shown in Fig. 12-15. Label the change of load points as shown in Fig. 12-15.

$\zeta + \Sigma M_C = 0 \qquad M_C - (10 \text{ k})(10) - (15 \text{ k})(6) - (2 \text{ k/ft})(10 \text{ ft})(5 \text{ ft}) = 0$

$\qquad\qquad\qquad M_C = 290 \text{ k-ft}$

$\Sigma F_Y = 0 \qquad R_C - 10 \text{ k} - 15 \text{ k} - (2 \text{ k/ft})(10 \text{ ft}) = 0$

$\qquad\qquad\qquad R_C = 45 \text{ k}$

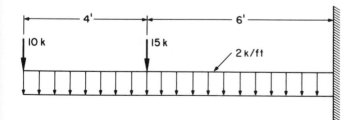

Figure 12-14

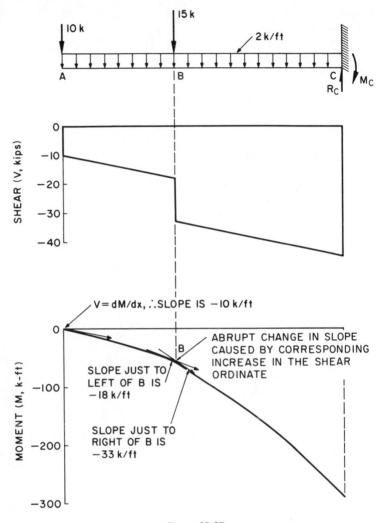

Figure 12-15

The positive values for M_C and R_C merely indicate that the assumed directions are correct. It does not mean that M_C is a positive bending moment. It will be shown later that M_C is indeed a negative bending moment.

2. The shear diagram is easily drawn by inspection. Starting at the left end of the beam, the 10-k concentrated load causes the shear to drop abruptly to -10 k at point A. From point A the uniform load causes the shear to drop at the rate of 2 k/ft and at an infinitesimal distance to the left of point B the *total* shear is -2 k/ft (4 ft) plus -10 k or -18 k. The 15-k concentrated load at point B abruptly drops the shear 15 k to -33 k. Since the uniform load acts over the entire length of the beam, it causes the shear to continue to drop at the rate of 2 k/ft to the fixed end of the beam where at an infinitesimal distance to the left

of point C the *total* shear is -2 k/ft (6 ft) plus -33 k or -45 k. The concentrated fixed-end reaction of 45 k abruptly returns the shear to zero at point C.

The -10-k value at point A is connected to the -18-k value at point B by a slanted straight line having a slope equal in magnitude to the uniform load. Since the load is downward, the slope is a negative 2 k/ft.

Again, between the -33-k value at point B and the -45-k value at point C, the shear diagram is a slanted straight line having a slope of -2 k/ft.

3. Draw the moment diagram. There is no force and moment arm to the left of point A nor is point A fixed ended; therefore, the moment at point A must be zero. The *change* in moment between points A and B is then the total moment at point B. Using Eq. (12-3),

$$M_B - M_A = (area)_{shear}$$
$$M_B - M_A = (-10)(4) + \tfrac{1}{2}(-8)(4) = -56 \text{ k-ft}$$
$$M_A = 0$$
$$\therefore M_B = -56 \text{ k-ft}$$

It is not necessary to use Eq. (12-3) to calculate the bending moment at point C since it was already determined to be 290 k-ft using an equation of static equilibrium. From an inspection of the loading of the cantilever beam, it can be seen that the beam must bend concave down causing the upper-beam fibers to be in tension and the lower-beam fibers to be in compression. The adopted sign convention considers a bending moment causing this effect to be a negative bending moment. Therefore, the bending moment at point C is negative and equal to -290 k-ft.

The moment diagram is now sketched with approximate curvature between the determined moment values. An inspection of the shear diagram shows that at point A the shear has a negative value. This means the moment diagram starts at point A not with a zero slope but with a definite negative slope equal to -10 k/ft. Since the shear ordinate has a larger negative value as point B is approached, the moment diagram has an increasingly negative slope. Such an increasingly negative slope results in a moment curve which is concave down as shown in Fig. 12-15. At point B the sudden increase in the shear ordinate causes the slope of the moment diagram to become abruptly more negative. From point B toward point C the shear ordinate acquires a progressively greater negative value; this causes the slope of the moment diagram to become ever more negative with the result that the moment diagram continues to curve concave down until the -290 k-ft value at point C is reached. Notice that the moment curve stops at -290 k-ft at point C; it does not return to zero. It cannot, since the bending moment at point C is -290 k-ft. Also notice that for a cantilever beam both maximum moment and maximum shear occur at the fixed end.

Problem 12-2 Value and location of maximum bending moment

Determine the maximum bending moment in foot-pounds for the beam loaded as shown in Fig. 12-16. Use the semigraphical method to draw the shear and moment diagrams.

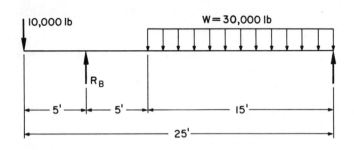

Figure 12-16

Solution:

1. Label the change of load points as shown in Fig. 12-17 and determine the reactions.

$$\{ + \Sigma M_D = 0 \qquad -(10\text{ k})(25) + R_B(20) - (30\text{ k})(7.5) = 0$$

$$R_B = 23.75\text{ k}$$

$$\{ + \Sigma M_B = 0 \qquad -(10\text{ k})(5) + (30\text{ k})(12.5) - R_D(20) = 0$$

$$R_D = 16.25\text{ k}$$

2. Draw the shear diagram. This can be easily done by inspection. Starting at the left end of the beam, the 10-k concentrated load causes the shear to drop abruptly to -10 k at point A. From point A to an infinitesimal distance to the left of point B there is no load; therefore, over this interval the shear remains constant and equal to -10 k. The 23.75-k concentrated reaction at point B abruptly raises the shear to 13.75 k; this causes the shear diagram to cross the zero shear axis. From point B to point C there is no load and the shear remains constant and equal to 13.75 k. From point C rightward the uniform downward load causes the shear to drop at the rate of 2 k/ft. At this rate the shear diagram will cross the zero shear axis at a distance of 6.88 ft to the right of point C; this distance is determined from

$$13.75\text{ k} = (2\text{ k/ft})x$$

$$x = 6.88\text{ ft}$$

This zero shear cross-over point is designated as point E. The uniform load continues to drop the shear at the rate of 2 k/ft so that at an infinitesimal distance to the left of point D the total shear is equal to -16.25 k. The concentrated reaction of 16.25 k abruptly returns the shear to zero at point D.

Maximum moment occurs at the points where the shear diagram *crosses* the zero shear axis, i.e., at points B and E. The moment must be calculated at both points to determine which moment is actually of the greatest absolute value. This will answer part of the problem. The maximum moment values are also useful when sketching the moment diagram.

Moment at Point B: Since there are no loads to the left of point A and point A is not fixed ended, there can be no moment at point A and the moment at point B is equal to change in moment between points A and B. Implementing Eq. (12-3),

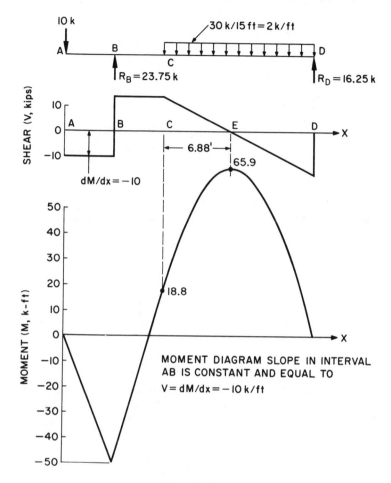

Figure 12-17

$$M_B - M_A = (\text{area})_{\text{shear}}$$
$$M_B - M_A = (-10)(5) = -50 \text{ k-ft} = -50,000 \text{ lb-ft}$$
$$M_A = 0 \qquad \therefore M_B = -50,000 \text{ lb-ft}$$

Moment at Point E: The moment at point E can be more expeditiously calculated by considering the area under the shear diagram that is to the right of point E. An inspection of the shear diagram of Fig. 12-17 shows that only the area under the shear diagram for the beam length ED need be calculated to find the *change* in moment between points E and D. There are no forces to the right of point D that could cause a moment at D; therefore the moment at D is zero and the *change* in moment between points E and D is equal to the moment at point E. Using Eq. (12-3),

$$M_D - M_E = (\text{area})_{\text{shear}}$$

$$M_D - M_E = \tfrac{1}{2}(-16.25)(8.12)$$
$$M_D = 0 \qquad \therefore -M_E = -65.9 \text{ k-ft}$$
$$M_E = 65,900 \text{ lb-ft}$$

In this example point D lies to the right of point E. Notice carefully that the moments at the successive points E and D maintain the same positions as do the successive points in Eq. (12-3).

A comparison of the moments at points B and E shows that the moment at point E has the greatest absolute value. Therefore, the maximum bending moment is

$$M_E = 65,900 \text{ lb-ft} \qquad \textit{Answer}$$

3. Draw the moment diagram. In connection with ascertaining the maximum bending moments, the moment values at points B and E were established. Since the moments at A and D are known to be zero, there remains only the change of load point C at which the moment should be calculated. Using Eq. (12-3),

$$M_C - M_B = (\text{area})_{\text{shear}}$$
$$M_C - M_B = (13.75)(5) = 68.8 \text{ k-ft}$$
$$M_B = -50 \text{ k-ft} \qquad \therefore M_C - (-50) = 68.8$$
$$M_C = 18.8 \text{ k-ft}$$

Equation (12-3) can now be used to sketch in the moment diagram through the determined moment values with the approximate curvature. This equation states that the shear ordinate is equal to the slope of the moment diagram at any particular point. Since the slope is expressed in k/ft and the shear ordinate is constant over the entire interval AB, the slope of the moment diagram is also constant over this same interval and equal to -10 k/ft.

Similarly, over interval BC the shear ordinate is positive and constant, which causes the slope of the moment diagram to be positive and constant.

From point C to point E the positive value of the shear ordinate becomes less and less; this causes the moment diagram to have an ever decreasing positive slope. At point E where the shear ordinate is zero, the slope of the moment diagram is zero. From point E to the end of the beam at point D, the shear ordinate has an ever increasing negative value; this causes the moment diagram to have an ever increasing negative slope.

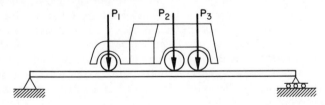

Figure 12-18.   Point loads $P_1, P_2,$ and P_3 always are at fixed positions relative to each other irrespective of the position on the beam that the moving load occupies.

As was stated earlier the points B and E at which the shear diagram crosses the zero shear axis correspond to points of maximum moment. At these points the slope of the moment diagram changes sign when passing from one side of the point to the other. Since the maximum moment at point B occurs at the location of a concentrated load, the transition from one side of the point to the other is discontinuous. The maximum moment at point E occurs within a beam interval over which a uniform load acts and the transition from one side of the point to the other is smooth and continuous.

12-6   MOVING LOADS

A locomotive, truck, or other vehicle crossing a bridge constitutes a moving load on the beams that support the roadbed. Such a moving load comprises a set of point loads at fixed positions relative to each other as shown in Fig. 12-18. The problem is to locate the positions on the beam of the moving load at which the beam is subjected to the *absolute* maximum bending moment and to determine this moment. The position of the moving load at which it will cause the *absolute* maximum shear is also of importance. These two positions usually do not coincide.

It is known that a maximum bending moment will occur when the moving load is located such that one of its point loads and the resultant of its point loads *on the span* occupy positions relative to the beam such that the distance separating the particular point load and the resultant is bisected by a line drawn perpendicular to the longitudinal axis of the beam at the midspan point. When one of the point loads occupies this special position relative to the resultant and the midspan point of the beam, the moving load will cause the beam to develop a maximum bending moment greater than that which is developed by the other point loads when occupying the similar position with respect to the resultant and the midspan point; the maximum moment is the *absolute* maximum moment and is determined by placing each point load in the requisite position relative to the resultant and midspan point and in turn calculating the maximum bending moment. The largest value so calculated is the absolute maximum bending moment. The resultant includes only those point loads of the moving load that are on the beam in each instance.

The maximum shear occurs at and is equal to the reaction having the greatest value. The reaction having the greatest value is that reaction to which the resultant is closest; this corresponds to a moving load position wherein the outside point load closest to the resultant is acting at a reaction.

Also, the shear values should be calculated for positions of the moving load at which first one outermost load is off the span and second at which the other outermost load is off the span. The load adjacent to the load off the span acts at the support. In each case the resultant will have to be recalculated and will include only those forces that remain on the beam. If it should happen that the moving load contains many point loads, this procedure should be continued, i.e., determine the shear value (1) for the moving load position where one outermost load and its adjacent load are off of the span, and (2) for the moving load position where the other outermost load and its adjacent load are off the span. A comparison of the calculated shearing values will determine which is the *absolute* maximum shear.

Problem 12-3 Maximum shear and bending moment developed by a moving load

As shown in Fig. 12-19, a moving load with wheels at fixed distances apart rolls across the 24-ft beam. Calculate the maximum moment developed in ft-lb. Also calculate the maximum shear in pounds.

Solution:

In turn, place each point load in the position at which a maximum moment will be developed. For the point load under consideration, this position is such that the midspan point is half way between the point load and the resultant. The resultant here referred to is the resultant of all loads on the beam at the time the load under consideration is at the position of maximum moment.

Determine the resultant R of P_1, P_2, and P_3 and its position. Use the line of action of P_1 as a reference as shown in Fig. 12-20.

Position of Resultant R:

$$(7 \text{ k} + 1 \text{ k} + 4 \text{ k})x_c = (7 \text{ k})(0) + (1 \text{ k})(8) + (4 \text{ k})(16)$$

$$x_c = 6 \text{ ft}$$

Value of Resultant R:

$$R = 7 \text{ k} + 1 \text{ k} + 4 \text{ k}$$

$$= 12 \text{ k}$$

Place P_1 in the position where the moving load will cause a maximum moment to be developed as shown in Fig. 12-21. With P_1 in this position, P_3 is shifted to a location not on the span. Since the resultant must

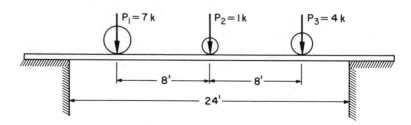

Figure 12-19

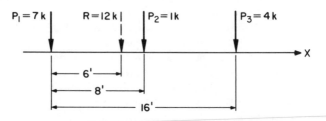

Figure 12-20

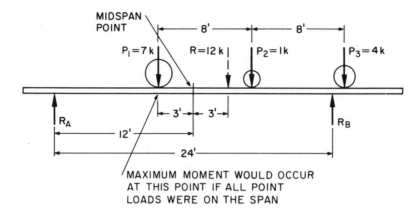

Figure 12-21

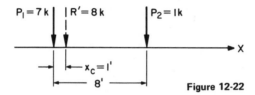

Figure 12-22

include only those loads that are on the span, it becomes necessary to calculate the resultant of P_1 and P_2 and its position. Use the line of action of P_1 as a reference as shown in Fig. 12-22.

Position of Resultant R':

$$(7 \text{ k} + 1 \text{ k})x_c = (7 \text{ k})(0) + (1 \text{ k})(8)$$
$$x_c = 1 \text{ ft}$$

Value of Resultant R':

$$R' = P_1 + P_2 = 7 \text{ k} + 1 \text{ k}$$
$$= 8 \text{ k}$$

The new resultant R' is only 1 ft distant from P_1 and the position of P_1 at which a maximum moment is developed is shown in Fig. 12-23. Now calculate the reaction at end A and use it to determine the moment at the point under P_1.

$$\curvearrowleft + \Sigma M_B = 0 \qquad (R_A)(24) - (8 \text{ k})(11.5) = 0$$
$$R_A = 3.84 \text{ k}$$
$$M = \curvearrowleft + \Sigma M_L \qquad M_{P1} = \curvearrowleft + \Sigma M_L = (R_A)(11.5) = (3.84 \text{ k})(11.5)$$
$$= 44.1 \text{ k-ft}$$

Place P_2 in the position where the moving load will cause a maximum moment to be developed at that same position. For this the load P_2 must be positioned with respect to the midspan point and the resultant R of all three loads; this position is shown in Fig. 12-24. It is also shown in Fig. 12-24 that it is

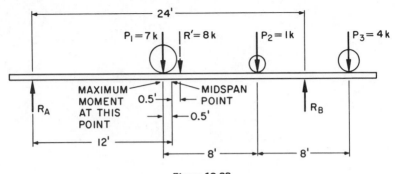

Figure 12-23

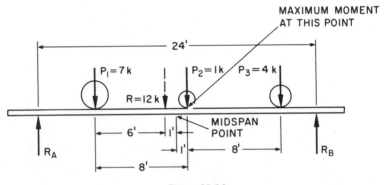

Figure 12-24

not necessary to make another calculation for the resultant since all three loads remain on the span. Now calculate the reaction at end A and use it in determining the moment at the point under P_2.

$$\curvearrowleft + \Sigma M_B = 0 \qquad (R_A)(24) - (12 \text{ k})(13) = 0$$

$$R_A = 6.5 \text{ k}$$

$$M = \curvearrowleft + \Sigma M_L \qquad M_{P2} = (R_A)(13) - (7 \text{ k})(8) = (6.5 \text{ k})(13) - (7 \text{ k})(8)$$

$$= 28.4 \text{ k-ft}$$

Place P_3 in the position where the moving load will cause a maximum moment to be developed at that same position. For this the load P_3 must be positioned with respect to the midspan point and the resultant R of all three loads as shown in Fig. 12-25. Here too it is not necessary to make another calculation for the resultant because all three loads remain on the span. Now calculate the reaction at end A and use it in determining the moment at the point under P_3.

$$\curvearrowleft + \Sigma M_B = 0 \qquad (R_A)(24) - (12 \text{ k})(17) = 0$$

$$R_A = 8.5 \text{ k}$$

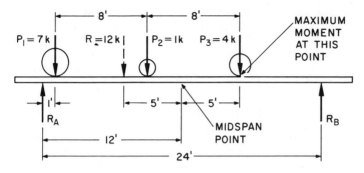

Figure 12-25

$$M = \langle + \Sigma M_L \qquad M_{P3} = (R_A)(17) - (7\text{ k})(16) - (1\text{ k})(8)$$
$$= (8.5\text{ k})(17) - (7\text{ k})(16) - (1\text{ k})(8)$$
$$= 24.5\text{ k-ft}$$

Observe in the calculation for the moment under P_3 that although the resultant is to the left of P_3, it is not used in lieu of the individual point loads P_1 and P_2 to the left of P_3. This is so because the resultant includes point load P_3, which acts at the point under P_3 and the equation $M = \langle + \Sigma M_L$ includes only those moments that are developed by loads acting to the left of point load P_3.

A comparison of all the maximum bending moments M_{P1}, M_{P2}, and M_{P3} shows that

$$M_{P1} = 44.1\text{ k-ft} = 44,100\text{ lb-ft} \qquad \textit{Answer}$$

is the absolute maximum bending moment that the moving load can cause in its movement across the span. The position that the moving load must occupy on the span to cause this absolute maximum bending moment is shown in Fig. 12-23.

It remains to determine the absolute maximum shear that will occur at and be equal to the end reaction having the greatest value. The end reaction closest

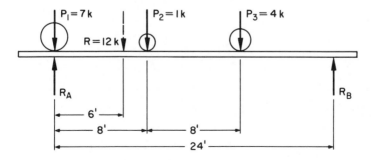

Figure 12-26

to the resultant will have a maximum value; this corresponds to a position of the moving load where the resultant R is only 6 ft away from end reaction R_A, as shown in Fig. 12-26. Notice that the outermost load nearest the resultant acts at the end support. Calculating R_A:

$$\curvearrowleft + \Sigma M_B = 0 \qquad (R_A)(24) - (12\ k)(18) = 0$$
$$R_A = 9\ k$$
$$V_{max} = R_A = 9\ k = 9000\ lb$$

Now it must be ascertained whether this shear of 9000 lb is the absolute maximum value. Consider the situation where point load P_1 has moved off of the span and P_2 is located at end reaction A. The resultant of P_2 and P_3 is 5 k and R_A is only 3.67 k. R_B could not be greater than R_A because the 5-k resultant is closer to end A.

Consider next the situation where point load P_3 has moved off of the span and P_2 is located at end reaction B. The resultant of P_1 and P_2 is 8 k and R_B is only 5.67 k. In this instance R_A could not be greater than R_B because the 8-k resultant is closer to end B.

A comparison of the calculated shear values shows that the absolute maximum shear is indeed 9000 lb and occurs at support A.

Absolute maximum shear $= (V_A)_{abs\ max} = 9000\ lb$ *Answer*

chapter 13
BEAM DESIGN

13-1   FLEXURAL STRESS AND SECTION MODULUS

Consider the simply supported beam of Fig. 13-1. When it is transversely loaded as shown, the upper fibers, under compression, are shortened and the lower fibers, under tension, are lengthened. The fiber segment a-a$'$ is not longitudinally deformed; it lies in the lateral plane known as the neutral surface.

For the concave-up curvature shown, starting upward from the neutral surface, the longitudinal fiber segments become continuously shorter; this decrease in fiber segment length being directly proportional to the distance from the neutral surface. Similarly, in the downward direction from the neutral surface, fiber segment length increases in direct proportion to the distance from the neutral surface.

Since the segment lengths vary linearly with distance from the neutral surface, the following proportion may be set up:

$$(\Delta L_{yy'})/y = (\Delta L_{cc'})/c$$

Divide both numerators by the initial length L of the fiber segments before the transverse load is applied. Thus,

$$\frac{(\Delta L_{yy'})/L}{y} = \frac{(\Delta L_{cc'})/L}{c}$$

$(\Delta L_{yy'})/L$ is the longitudinal strain ϵ_y in the beam at a distance y from the neutral surface and $(\Delta L_{cc'})/L$ is the longitudinal strain ϵ_c at a distance c from the neutral surface. Thus, $\epsilon_y/y = \epsilon_c/c$.

Assuming that the proportional limit referred to in Sec. 11-3 is not exceeded, the stress-strain equation is valid, i.e.,

$$f = \epsilon E \tag{11-6}$$

where it will be recalled that E is the modulus of elasticity which for steel is 30×10^6 psi and f is the stress in lb/in.^{2} Since the stress that is of concern

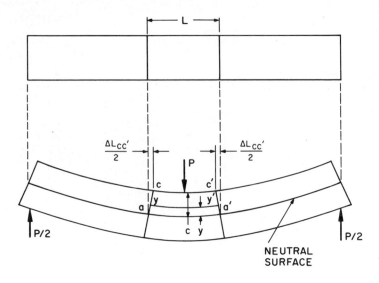

Figure 13-1

here is bending stress, the designation f_b will be used. It is assumed that the moduli of elasticity in tension and compression are equal. Expressing strain in terms of stress and substituting

$$\frac{(f_b)_y/E}{y} = \frac{(f_b)_c/E}{c}$$

$$(f_b)_y/y = (f_b)_c/c \qquad (13\text{-}1)$$

The stress f_b is the flexural or bending stress developed by the beam in response to the bending action caused by applied external load. Equation (13-1) is very important and enables one knowing the bending stress at an outer fiber to determine the stress at any other fiber; this equation makes it clear that the bending stress varies in direct proportion to the distance from the neutral surface. The stress $(f_b)_y$ acts normal to an element of area across the width of the beam at a distance y from the neutral surface and similarly $(f_b)_c$ acts normal to the element of area at the outer fiber; this is shown in Fig. 13-2 together with a stress distribution diagram that illustrates Eq. 13-1 geometrically. It can be seen from this diagram that it is possible, knowing a stress above the neutral surface, to calculate a stress at any point below the neutral surface.

The section taken at A-A in Fig. 13-2 is a transverse cross section, and as such it is perpendicular to the longitudinal plane of symmetry. The line formed by the intersection of the transverse section and the neutral surface is known as the neutral axis.

Sometimes an examination problem will state: "Assume the beam is laterally supported." This means that the beam is supported from the sides so as to constrain deflection in the plane of the loads, i.e., in the longitudinal plane of symmetry. Ideally, a beam loaded exclusively with transverse loads

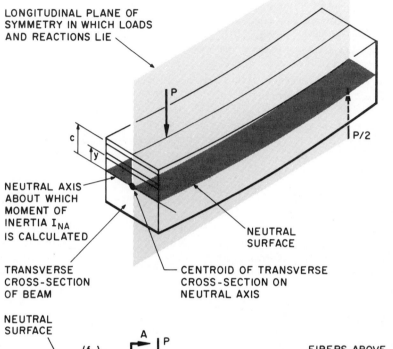

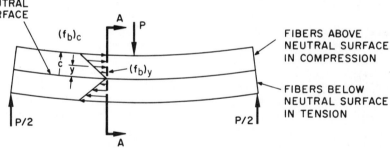

Figure 13-2

lying in the longitudinal plane of symmetry will only deflect in that same plane. Also, it is known[*] that for a beam so loaded, the neutral axis passes through the centroid of the transverse cross section.

It can be shown[†] that the bending stress f_b is related to the externally applied moment M by the equation

$$(f_b)_y = My/I_{NA} \tag{13-2}$$

---

[*] *Strength of Materials*, F. L. Singer, pp. 126 and 127.
[†] Ibid., pp. 124-128.

This equation is known as the flexure formula and is used to determine the bending stress at any distance y above or below the neutral surface. As shown above, this formula is based upon the assumption that the beam material does not exceed its proportional limit and obeys the stress-strain relation, $f = \epsilon E$. Other assumptions are that a transverse section plane before bending remains plane after bending and that the beam material is homogeneous. The latter assumption is significant in the study of reinforced concrete and timber beams.

The bending moment M is the bending moment at the particular transverse cross section along the length of the beam at which the bending stress is to be calculated. The moment of inertia I_{NA} is calculated about the neutral axis. For a given transverse loading, the maximum flexure stress $(f_b)_{max}$ at a given transverse cross section occurs at the fibers outermost from the neutral surface; this distance is designated as c and $(f_b)_{max}$ is found from

$$(f_b)_{max} = Mc/I_{NA} \tag{13-3}$$

For a beam having a constant transverse cross section along its entire length, the ratio I/c is a constant and is called the *section modulus*. The section modulus is designated by the letter S and is an important property of structural members. It is expressed in in.^{3}

$$f_b = M/S \tag{13-4}$$

Occasionally a beam will not be symmetrical about the neutral axis. In this instance the magnitude of the stress in the outermost fibers above the neutral surface will be different in magnitude from the outermost fibers below the neutral surface. The fibers farthest from the neutral surface will of course be stressed the most. A structural member having a section unsymmetrical about the neutral axis will have two different sections of modulus.

Figure 13-3 shows a typical symmetrical and unsymmetrical section. The symmetrical section is that of a wide flange member, whereas the unsymmetrical section is a channel member.

Often a structural member is built up from simpler sections and such a member is commonly called a built-up section. Figure 13-4 illustrates a symmetrical and unsymmetrical built-up section. For each section in Figs. 13-3 and 13-4 it is presupposed that the loading is exclusively transverse; therefore the neutral axis passes through the centroid of the section.

Problem 13-1 Bending stress at points in a given beam section

A beam 12 in. wide and 18 in. deep is subjected to a shear of 21,800 lb and a bending moment of 29,160 ft-lb at a particular section.

(a) Find the extreme fiber stress due to bending at this section.

(b) What is the bending stress 6 in. from the neutral axis?

Solution:

(a) The extreme fiber stress due to bending occurs in the fibers outermost from the neutral surface and can be determined by using Eq. (13-3), which is the form of the flexure formula for calculating the bending stress in the outermost fiber.

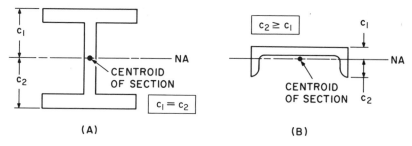

Figure 13-3. (A) Symmetrical section: $c_1 = c_2$; therefore the outermost fibers would be of the same magnitude as in the outermost lower fibers. (B) Unsymmetrical section: $c_2 \geqslant c_1$; therefore the bending stress in the outermost fibers would be less than in the outermost lower fibers.

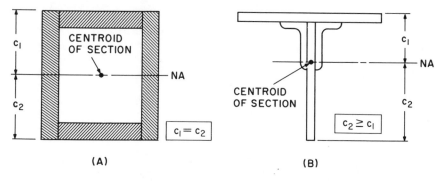

Figure 13-4. (A) Symmetrical built-up section: $c_1 = c_2$; therefore the bending stress in the outermost upper fibers would be of the same magnitude as in the outermost lower fibers. (B) Unsymmetrical built-up section: $c_2 \geqslant c_1$; therefore the bending stress in the outermost upper fibers would be less than in the outermost lower fibers.

$$(f_b)_{max} = Mc/I_{NA} \tag{13-3}$$

The bending moment at the section where the extreme fiber stress is required is given as 29,160 ft-lb. Therefore, it remains to determine c, the distance between the neutral surface and the outermost fiber, and the moment of inertia I_{NA}.

The centroid of the transverse cross section lies in the neutral surface. Thus, locating the centroid locates the neutral surface. The centroid is here easily determined by inspection. (See Fig. 13-5.) If the beam section were unsymmetrical as in Fig. 13-3(B) or 13-4(B), then the centroid would have to be located with respect to the outermost fibers using the method outlined in Sec. 2-6.

The line formed by the intersection of the transverse cross section and the neutral surface is the neutral axis. The distance from the neutral axis to both outermost fibers is the same, namely, 9 in., i.e., c = 9 in. Therefore, the stress in both outermost fibers will be of the same magnitude but of opposite types, i.e., above the neutral surface compressive, and below the neutral sur-

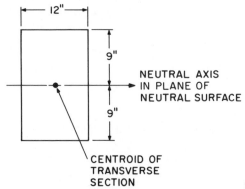

CENTROID OF
TRANSVERSE
SECTION

Figure 13-5

face tensile. This condition presupposes that the given bending moment is positive, which results in a concave-up curvature.

The moment of inertia I_{NA} is the moment of inertia of the transverse cross section *with respect to the neutral axis* and is calculated using the formula $I_{NA} = \frac{1}{12} bh^3 = \frac{1}{12} (12)(18)^3 = 5830$ in.[4] This and other formulas for different geometric sections are found in the AISC Manual.

Calculating the extreme fiber bending stress,

$$(f_b)_{max} = \frac{(12 \text{ in./ft}) (29{,}160 \text{ ft-lb}) (9 \text{ in.})}{5830 \text{ in.}^4}$$

$$= 539 \text{ psi} \qquad Answer$$

(b) The bending stress at 6 in. from the neutral axis may be determined by using Eq. (13-2), which is the flexure formula for calculating bending stress at any distance y from the neutral axis.

$$(f_b)_y = My/I_{NA} \tag{13-2}$$

$$(f_b)_{y=6 \text{ in.}} = \frac{(12) (29{,}160) (6)}{5830}$$

$$= 360 \text{ psi} \qquad Answer$$

Or Eq. (13-1) could be used to find the bending stress at y = 6 in., since the stress at some other distance from the neutral axis is known. The stress at 9 in. from the neutral axis was calculated in (a) to be 539 psi. Therefore,

$$(f_b)_y/y = (f_b)_c/c \tag{13-1}$$

$$(f_b)_{y=6 \text{ in.}} = y(f_b)_c/c = (6)539/9$$

$$= 360 \text{ psi} \qquad Answer$$

Problem 13-2 Maximum bending stress in a beam member

A lintel is formed as an inverted T by welding a 12-in. $\times$ $\frac{1}{2}$-in. horizontal plate to a 10-in. $\times$ $\frac{1}{2}$-in. vertical plate. This member spans an 8-ft opening and supports a wall weighing 1000 lb/linear ft. Find the maximum stresses in the lintel. (Assume adequate lateral bracing and simple support.)

Solution:

A lintel is a structural member that is used to span an opening in a wall and is usually simply supported at its ends. The lintel could be supporting the wall over a window.

The problem states that the maximum stresses are to be found. The word "stresses" is in the plural indicating that more than only bending stress is wanted. The other stress sought here is shear stress and it is calculated in Problem 13-4. Maximum shear stress and maximum bending stress do not necessarily occur at the same section of the beam. Usually they do not. Maximum shear stress occurs at that section along the length of the beam where shear is a maximum and maximum bending stress at that section where the bneding moment is a maximum.

At any particular section, the maximum bending stress occurs in the fiber outermost from the neutral axis. The bending stress in the outermost fiber at the section corresponding to the maximum bending moment will be found. The flexure formula for calculating the bending stress in the fibers outermost from the neutral surface is given by Eq. (13-3). Referring to Fig. 13-6, draw the shear diagram and determine the value and location of the maximum bending moment.

The maximum bending moment occurs where the shear diagram *crosses over* the zero shear axis; this cross-over point is at midspan. The change in moment between points A and B can be calculated using Eq. (12-3). Since there are no forces to the left of point A, the moment at that point is zero. The change in moment between points A and B is therefore equal to the moment at point B.

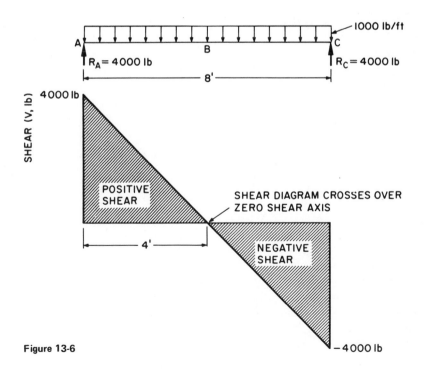

Figure 13-6

$$M_B - M_A = (area)_{shear} = \tfrac{1}{2}(4000)(4) = 8000 \text{ ft-lb}$$
$$M_A = 0$$
$$\therefore M_B = 8000 \text{ ft-lb}$$

In this example, the shear diagram crossed over the zero shear axis at only one point, namely, at midspan. Should the shear diagram have crossed over at more than one point, as in the instance of the beam in Fig. 12-12, then the bending moment at both cross-over points would have to be calculated and compared to determine which value is the absolute maximum.

Next, locate the centroid of the transverse cross section. This will determine the position of the neutral axis and establish the distance c to the outermost fiber. Also, the moment of inertia about the neutral axis can then be calculated. The transverse cross section of the lintel is shown in Fig. 13-7. The vertical coordinate of the centroid cannot be located by inspection because the section is unsymmetrical; therefore, its position must be determined by calculation.

$$(a_1 + a_2)(\bar{y}) = a_1 y_1 + a_2 y_2$$
$$(5 + 6)\,\bar{y} = (5)(5.5) + (6)(\tfrac{1}{4})$$
$$\bar{y} = 2.64 \text{ in.}$$

Again refer to Fig. 13-7 and calculate the moment of inertia about the neutral axis using the method of Sec. 2-6.

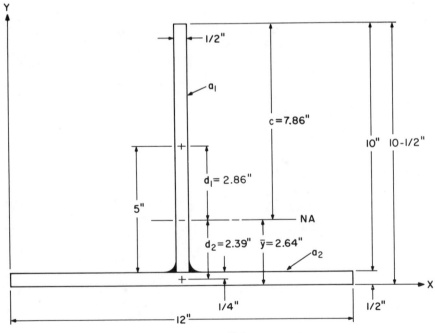

Figure 13-7

$$I_{NA} = \sum_{n=1}^{n=p} (I_{OXn}) + \sum a_n y_{cn}^2$$

$$= \frac{1}{12} bh^3 + \frac{1}{12} b_2 h_2^3 + a_1 d_1^2 + a_2 d_2^2$$

$$= \frac{1}{12}(\frac{1}{2})(10)^3 + \frac{1}{12}(12)(\frac{1}{2})^3 + (5)(2.86)^2 + (6)(2.39)^2$$

$$= 116.9 \text{ in.}^4$$

An inspection of Fig. 13-7 shows that upper outermost fibers are the farthest distant from the neutral axis, i.e., $c = 7.86$ in. Calculating the maximum bending stress in these fibers at the midspan section,

$$(f_b)_{max} = \frac{Mc}{I} = \frac{12(8000)(7.86)}{116.9}$$

$$= 6460 \text{ psi} \quad Answer$$

13-2 BEAM SHEAR STRESS

A beam loaded as shown in Fig. 13-8 is subjected to both horizontal and vertical shear stresses. Imagine the beam to comprise several layers of longitudinal fibers as shown. These fibers would ordinarily slide past one another but a horizontal shear stress $(f_v)_H$ is developed that prevents this action.

Figure 13-9 shows the shearing stresses acting across the orthogonal faces of a typical element. It is known that the shearing stress acting across one face of an element is attended by a shearing stress of equal value acting across an orthogonal surface of the same element. Therefore, at any point within the beam the horizontal shear stress $(f_v)_H$ is equal to the vertical shear stress $(f_v)_V$: $(f_v)_H = (f_v)_V$.

The stress $(f_v)_V$ is the shear stress that acts across the vertical face of the typical element. The product of the stress $(f_v)_V$ and the elemental area $(\Delta A)_V$ is the elemental resisting shear $(\Delta V)_r$. A summation of elemental resisting shears across the entire face of the transverse section is the resisting shear V_r. The beam develops the shear V_r to resist the tendency of the shear V to shear the beam across the transverse section. It will be recalled that shear V

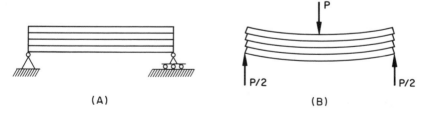

(A)   (B)

Figure 13-8.   (A) Simple beam imagined to comprise several layers of longitudinal fibers. (B) Longitudinal fiber layers would slide past each other as shown, if no horizontal shear stress developed.

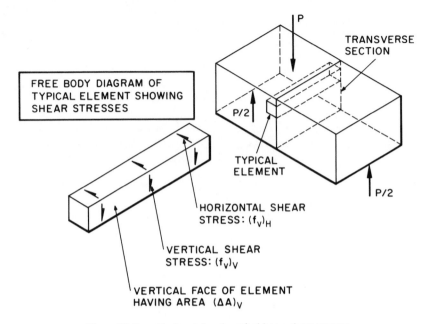

Figure 13-9.   Horizontal and vertical beam shear stresses.

is the vertical summation of all forces acting on the beam to the left of any particular transverse section.

It is known* that the horizontal and vertical shearing stresses at any point within a beam can be determined from

$$f_v = (f_v)_H = (f_v)_V = VQ_{NA}/I_{NA}b \tag{13-5}$$

where V = shear at transverse section containing the point

   Q_{NA} = moment about neutral axis of area between point within beam at which shear stress is required and either outermost fiber

   I_{NA} = moment of inertia of area of entire transverse section about neutral axis

   b = width of beam *at* point at which shear stress is required

The transverse section of a rectangular beam is shown in Fig. 13-10. If the shear stress f_v at a point at a distance y above the neutral axis were required, then Q_{NA} may be calculated using the area A above the point $Q_{NA} = A\bar{y}$, where $\bar{y}$ is the distance between the centroid of A and the neutral axis. Or, the area A' below the point may be used, $Q_{NA} = A'\bar{y}'$, where $\bar{y}'$ is the distance between the centroid of A' and the neutral axis. The area used to calculate Q_{NA} is that area A or A', whichever requires the least amount of computation to determine.

---

*F. L. Singer, *Strength of Materials*, pp. 151-56.

   F. E. Miller and H. A. Doeringsfeld, *Mechanics of Materials*, pp. 148-51.

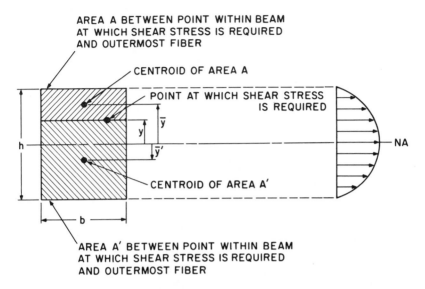

AREA A BETWEEN POINT WITHIN BEAM
AT WHICH SHEAR STRESS IS REQUIRED
AND OUTERMOST FIBER

CENTROID OF AREA A

POINT AT WHICH SHEAR STRESS
IS REQUIRED

NA

CENTROID OF AREA A′

AREA A′ BETWEEN POINT WITHIN BEAM
AT WHICH SHEAR STRESS IS REQUIRED
AND OUTERMOST FIBER

Figure 13-10. Transverse section of a rectangular beam.

The graph to the right of the rectangular section in Fig. 13-10 shows how the shear stress varies through the section. The shear stress is a maximum at the neutral axis and the formula for its computation may be determined using Eq. 13-5,

$$f_v = \frac{VQ_{NA}}{I_{NA}b} = \frac{V(A)(\bar{y})}{I_{NA}b} = \frac{V(\frac{1}{2}bh)(h/4)}{\frac{1}{12}bh^3(b)}$$

For a rectangular section,

$$(f_v)_{max} = \frac{3}{2}(V/bh) \tag{13-6}$$

The maximum shear stress for a rectangular section is 1.5 times the average shear stress V/bh.

The maximum shear stress in a beam will occur within the section at which maximum shear V acts. The value of the maximum shear V and the location of the section along the length of the beam at which it acts is most easily determined from an inspection of the shear diagram. In most geometric sections the maximum shear stress $(f_v)_{max}$ occurs at the neutral axis; this applies also to unsymmetrical sections such as a T section.

Sections in which the maximum shear stress does not occur at the neutral axis are not commonly used. Typical of these sections are the trapezoidal and isosceles sections shown in Fig. 13-11.

Figure 13-12 shows the transverse section of an I beam and its shear stress distribution; this curve shows that the shear stress distribution is very nearly uniform over the web of the beam and further, that the web resists most of the shear. For an I beam the average stress is not very much less than the maximum shear stress at the neutral axis. Since the flanges do little to

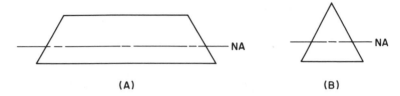

Figure 13-11.   Sections in which shear stress does not occur at neutral axis: (A) trapezoidal section and (B) isosceles section.

resist shear and the shear stress distribution over the web is almost uniform, the average shear stress at any point in the web of an I beam may be found from

$$f_v = V/ht \tag{13-7}$$

where h and t are the dimensions indicated in Fig. 13-12. It is customary to take h as the overall height of the beam and not as the distance between flanges. Equation (13-7) gives the average stress in the web and is of course applicable also to wide flange beams.

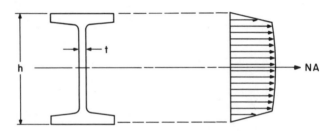

Figure 13-12.   Transverse section of I-beam and shear stress distribution.

Problem 13-3 Shear stress at points in a given beam section
For the beam section of Problem 13-1, (a) find the maximum shearing stress, and (b) find the stresses caused by shearing 6 in. from the neutral axis.

Solution:
(a) The maximum shear stress occurs at the neutral axis. For a rectangular section this may be determined using Eq. (13-6).

$$(f_v)_{max} = \frac{3}{2}\left(\frac{V}{bh}\right) = \frac{3}{2}\left(\frac{21,800}{(12)(18)}\right)$$

$$= 151.3 \text{ psi} \quad \textit{Answer}$$

(b) The stress at any position y away from the neutral axis is determined using Eq. (13-5).

$$f_v = VQ_{NA}/I_{NA}b$$

Refer to Fig. 13-13 and calculate Q_{NA}.

$$Q_{NA} = (3)(12)(7.5) = 270 \text{ in.}^3$$

The moment of inertia I_{NA} of the section about the neutral axis was determined in Problem 13-1 to be 5830 in.[4] The width b of the section at the point where the shear stress is to be calculated is 12 in. Substituting into Eq. (13-5),

$$f_v = \frac{VQ_{NA}}{I_{NA}b} = \frac{(21,800)(270)}{(5830)(12)}$$

$(f_v)_{y=6 \text{ in.}} = 84.2 \text{ psi}$ *Answer*

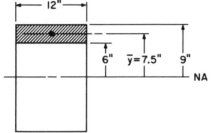

Figure 13-13

Problem 13-4 Maximum shear stress in a beam member

Determine the maximum shear stress in the lintel member of Problem 13-2.

Solution:

The maximum shear stress occurs within the section at which maximum shear V acts. An inspection of the shear diagram in Fig. 13-6 shows that this section is located an infinitesimal distance to the right of the reaction at Point A and the shear value is 4000 lb.

Within the section, the maximum shear stress occurs at the neutral axis. The position of this axis was determined in Problem 13-2 and is shown again in Fig. 13-14. The shear stress at the neutral axis is determined using Eq. (13-5).

$$f_v = VQ_{NA}/I_{NA}b$$

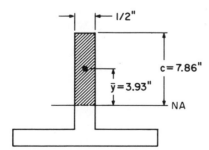

Figure 13-14

Referring to Fig. 13-14, the moment of area Q_{NA} can be determined using either the area of the section above the neutral axis or the area below it. The area above the neutral axis is simply a rectangle whose centroid is easily located by inspection whereas the area below the neutral axis is a composite of two rectangles the centroid of which must be determined by computation. Therefore, Q_{NA} is calculated using the area above the neutral axis.

$$Q_{NA} = A\bar{y} = (7.86)(\tfrac{1}{2})(3.93)$$
$$= 15.43 \text{ in.}^3$$

The moment of inertia I_{NA} was found in Problem 13-2 to be 116.9 in.[4] The dimension b is the width of the section at which the shear stress is to be calculated. In this problem b = $\tfrac{1}{2}$ in.

Substituting into Eq. (13-5),

$$f_v = \frac{VQ_{NA}}{I_{NA}b} = \frac{(4000)(15.43)}{(116.9)(\tfrac{1}{2})}$$
$$= 1057 \text{ psi} \qquad Answer$$

13-3   ECONOMIC SECTIONS

An examination of Eq. (13-3) shows that the bending stress $(f_b)_{max}$ is inversely proportional to the section modulus I_{NA}/c, which is designated as S.

$$(f_b)_{max} = \frac{M}{I_{NA}/c} = \frac{M}{S} \tag{13-3}$$

From this it is concluded that in order to keep the bending stress low, it is necessary for the beam section to have a large moment of inertia and consequently a large section modulus. This is achieved by distributing the bulk of the beam material at the farthest practical distance from the neutral axis. This is very logical because from the flexural stress distribution diagram of Fig. 13-2 it is evident that the fibers outermost from the neutral axis sustain the greatest flexural stress. Therefore, the greatest amount of beam material should be concentrated at these fibers. The wide-flange (symbolized as WF) and American Standard (also known as I beam) beams have structural sections that are shaped to utilize this principle.

The wide-flange beam is specified by the following successive designations: (1) the nominal overall depth of the section in inches between outermost flange fibers, (2) the symbol WF, and (3) the weight in pounds per foot of length. Thus a beam specified as an 8 WF 48 has an overall depth of 8.5 in. and weighs 48 lb/ft.

Often it is necessary to select a beam to meet given specifications, as, for example, load and length of span. A beam satisfactory in bending will have a section modulus of sufficient magnitude to ensure that the allowable bending stress is not exceeded. This may be expressed by rearranging Eq. (13-3) and substituting for M the maximum moment value M_{max}

$$S \geqslant M_{max}/f_b \tag{13-8}$$

where f_b is the allowable bending stress. Equation (13-8) shows that a beam having a section modulus equal to or greater than the ratio M_{max}/f_b will be adequate in bending.

Tensile and compressive allowable stress in the extreme fibers of laterally supported, compact members having an axis of symmetry in the plane of loading is given in the AISC Manual as

$$f_b = 0.66f_y \tag{13-9}$$

A7 and A36 steels are the most commonly used structural steels. Practically all rolled WF and I shapes made of these steels are compact sections as are most members made of the very high strength A242, A440, and A441 steels. A member qualifies as a compact section when it meets certain flange width-thickness ratio and web depth-thickness ratio requirements as defined in the Specification of the AISC Manual.

The allowable tensile and compressive bending stresses for laterally supported noncompact members is given by

$$f_b = 0.60f_y \tag{13-10}$$

A few rolled WF-shaped members that do not qualify as compact sections are so designated by a footnote reference in the Design Properties of applicable sections in the AISC Manual.

A laterally supported beam is supported from the side at its compression flange; this can be done with bracing members at intervals along the length of the beam. The lateral support acts to prevent a sideward or lateral deflection of the beam because of buckling in its compression flanges. Figure 13-15 shows a member

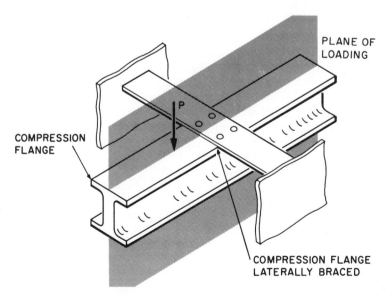

Figure 13-15.   Laterally supported beam.

having a compression flange laterally braced and having an axis of symmetry in the plane of loading.

Steel beams usually do not fail in shear unless they are relatively short or very heavy loads are placed near the ends of the span. A selected WF- or I-beam selection may be checked for shear by using Eq. (13-7), $f_v = V/ht$. The value of shear having the greatest magnitude is taken from the shear diagram and substituted into this equation so that

$$f_v = V_{max}/ht \qquad (13\text{-}11)$$

The value of average shear stress f_v is calculated and compared with the allowable shear stress f_v given in the Manual as

$$f_v = 0.40f_y \qquad (13\text{-}12)$$

where again f_y is the specified yield stress of the particular steel used. The average shear stress f_v may be used as a basis of comparison for WF- and I-beam members because as was discussed in Sec. 13-2, in these members the average shear stress approximates closely the value of maximum shear stress at the neutral axis.

The beam affording the greatest economy is the beam that weighs the least. The following problem will illustrate the procedure to be followed in selecting the most economic laterally supported section for a given load requirement.

Problem 13-5 Selection of the economic beam section

A steel beam 20 ft long rests on two bearings, one at the right end and one 5 ft from the left end. The beam is uniformly loaded with 1 k/lineal ft. Determine the necessary section modulus and design the economical American Standard beam section. Assume the beam to be laterally supported.

Solution:

The necessary section modulus is determined from Eq. (13-8), $S \geqslant M_{max}/f_b$. This equation requires that the maximum moment be calculated. From the statement of the problem prepare a sketch, calculate the reactions, draw the shear diagram and determine the maximum moment. The shear diagram is shown in Fig. 13-16. Since the shear diagram crosses the zero shear axis at two points, B and D, there are two values of maximum moment both of which have to be calculated to determine which is of the greater magnitude. For this purpose, use Eq. (12-3).

Moment at Point B:

$$M_B - M_A = (area)_{shear} = \tfrac{1}{2}\,(5)(-5) = -12.5 \text{ k-ft}$$

There are no loads to the left of point A and M_A must therefore equal zero. Thus $M_B = -12.5$ k-ft.

Moment at Point D:

$$M_D - M_B = (area)_{shear} = \tfrac{1}{2}(8.33)(8.33) = 34.7 \text{ k-ft}$$
$$M_D - (-12.5) = 34.7$$
$$M_D = 22.2 \text{ k-ft}$$

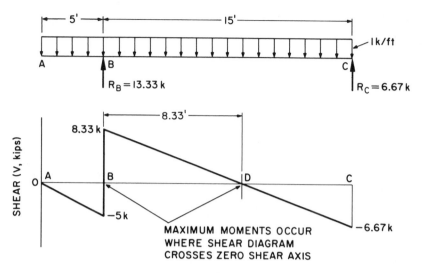

Figure 13-16

The maximum bending moment having the greatest magnitude occurs at point D, $M_D = M_{max} = 22.2$ k-ft. The beam is laterally supported and the allowable stress f_b is found using Eq. (13-9). Use a steel having, say, a 33,000-psi specified yield point. Then $f_b = 0.66f_y = 0.66$ (33,000) = 22,000 psi. Using Eq. (13-8) to find the necessary section modulus

$$S \geqslant \frac{M_{max}}{f_b} = \frac{22.2 \text{ k-ft}}{22,000 \text{ lb/in.}^2} = \frac{(22.2)(1000)(12)}{22,000}$$

$$\geqslant 12.12 \text{ in.}^3 \qquad Answer$$

Recall that the section modulus S is with respect to the horizontal neutral axis. Refer now to the AISC Manual for the design properties of American Standard Beams. Look down column S of the group of columns headed Axis X-X until a section modulus greater than 12.12 is found. A beam having a section modulus of 14.2 has a weight of 18.4 lb/ft. This shows that an I beam capable of supporting the given load should weigh, say, 20 lb/ft.

The estimated weight of the beam should be considered when computing the section modulus S. Use the estimated value of 20 lb/ft and calculate the bending moment that it causes at the location where the absolute maximum value of bending moment due to the load occurs, namely, at point D. Considering only the estimated weight of the beam, the bending moment at point D is 442 lb-ft.

Calculate the required section modulus based upon the moment effect of both the given beam loading and estimated beam weight.

$$S \geqslant \frac{(22,200)(12) + 442(12)}{22,000} = 12.36 \text{ in.}^3$$

The 8I18.4 American Standard section is the lightest and therefore the most economical member having a section modulus equal to or greater than the calculated value of 12.36 in.[3]

The selected member has a weight of 18.4 lb/ft that is not greater than the estimated value of 20 lb/ft. If the only beams available having the requisite section modulus were those with a weight per foot in excess of the estimated value, then a greater weight would have to be assumed and a new section modulus calculated. This calculation would be based upon the moment caused by the given beam loading and the new estimated beam weight. With the new section modulus, another beam selection could be made.

Check the 8I18.4 beam for shear. From the shear diagram, the largest value of shear is 8.33 kips acting at point B. The design properties of appropriate I beams in the AISC Manual show the beam to have an overall depth h of 8 in. and a web thickness t of 0.270 in. Substituting these values into Eq. (13-11)

$$f_v = \frac{V_{max}}{ht} = \frac{(8.33)(1000)}{(8)(0.270)} = 3860 \text{ psi}$$

The allowable shear stress f_v is obtained from Eq. (13-12)

$$f_v = 0.40f_y = 0.40(33,000) = 13,200 \text{ psi}$$

The average shear stress f_v is much less than the allowable shear stress F_v and therefore the selected number is satisfactory in shear.

13-4   BUILT-UP SECTIONS

In Sec. 13-2 it was observed that a load-carrying beam develops a shearing stress along the interface of the longitudinal beam fibers. If it were not for this shear stress, the fibers would slide past each other, as shown in Fig. 13-8. Recall that at any point within a transverse section, the working shear stress f_v is given by Eq. (13-5),

$$f_v = VQ_{NA}/I_{NA}b$$

Also recall that b is the width of the member at the point where the shear stress is desired.

At a given horizontal surface of a beam comprising only one structural member, the beam material must withstand a horizontal shear P_v in pounds. Consider the rectangular beam of Fig. 13-17. The horizontal shear P_v acting at the shaded parts of the given horizontal surface is equal to the product of the shear stress f_v and the area of the shaded part (p)(b), i.e., $P_v = f_v(p)(b)$.

Examine next the built-up section of Fig. 13-18 wherein two WF members are rivet joined to form a compound beam. The horizontal shear P_v acting over the shaded area must now be resisted by the rivets within this area and will be designated as $(P_v)_{riv}$. Since the horizontal shearing action can also cause a bearing failure in the flange of a member, the value of $(P_v)_{riv}$ should be the lowest of either the allowable rivet shear load or the allowable bearing load, $(P_v)_{riv} = f_v(p)(b)$. The longitudinal length p is now the required rivet spacing. Solving for p,

$$p = (P_v)_{riv}/f_v b \qquad (13\text{-}13)$$

Equation (13-5) shows that the shear stress f_v is directly proportional to the vertical shear V, which for any point along the length of the beam may be taken directly from the shear diagram. The value of shear V often varies from point to point along the beam length causing corresponding variations in shear stress f_v. The largest value of shear V in a longitudinal rivet spacing interval is used to calculate the shear stress f_v for that interval. It should be carefully noted that shear stress f_v is calculated for the position in the transverse section of the compound beam that lies in the plane defined by the interface of the joining surfaces.

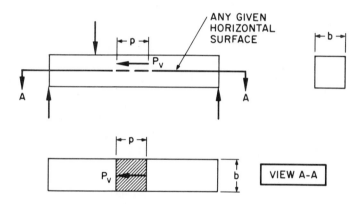

Figure 13-17.   Rectangular beam.

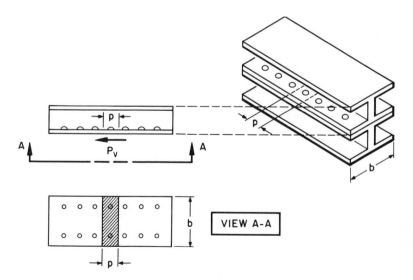

Figure 13-18.   Built-up section.

Since the shear stress f_v varies with shear along the beam length, the required rivet spacing will vary also. Of course, for any length of beam over which the vertical shear V is constant, the shear stress f_v and consequently the rivet spacing are constant. Problem 13-6 will use the above material to determine the spacing required between rivets at a location along the length of a built-up beam. In Problem 13-7 these ideas will be extended to a built-up beam whose structural elements are joined by welding.

Problem 13-6 Design of a riveted built-up section

Two 30-in. WF 116 steel beams are connected by riveting flange to flange to form a compound beam 60 in. deep. The beam is to carry concentrated loads at the center and at each of the quarter points, a total of 3 loads of 68 kips each. How many ¾-in. rivets will be required between the end of the beam and the first load point, 10 ft in from the end, to resist the horizontal shear developed under this load condition? The yield stress f_y is 33,000 psi.

Solution:

The problem states that the first quarter point is 10 ft from the end of the beam. Therefore, the beam is 40 ft long and is sketched with its shear diagram in Fig. 13-19. From the end of the beam lay off a part of the horizontal surface at the interface plane as shown by the shaded area in Fig. 13-20. The horizontal shear, which would act over the entire shaded area if the beam were one single homogeneous member, must in the compound beam be resisted by the joining rivets. The yet undetermined longitudinal length p will be the required rivet spacing for the first pair of rivets; these two rivets are positioned

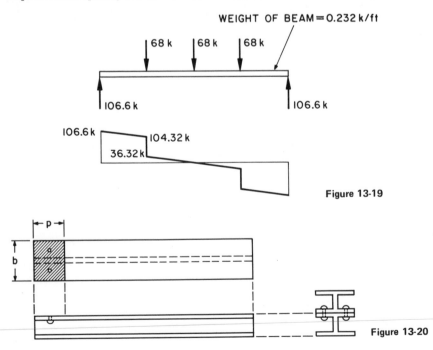

WEIGHT OF BEAM = 0.232 k/ft

68 k   68 k   68 k

106.6 k   106.6 k

106.6 k   104.32 k

36.32 k

Figure 13-19

|← p →|

b

Figure 13-20

with respect to p as shown in Fig. 13-20. Determine the allowable rivet load for shear and bearing failure.

Shear Failure: The allowable shear stress f_v is not specified. This is obtainable from the AISC Manual. The type of rivet is not specified in the problem; therefore assume that the examiners intended that the A 141 hot-driven type be used and the allowable shear stress would be the indicated 15,000 psi. Use Eq. (11-24) and substitute for the working shear stress f_v, the allowable shear stress f_v.

$$f_v = \frac{P}{\pi d_r^2/4}$$

Solving for P:

$$P = f_v [\pi d_r^2/4] = 15,000 [\pi(0.75)^2/4] = 6630 \text{ lb}$$

The allowable shear load for a single rivet is 6630 lb

Bearing failure: The allowable bearing stress f_p is found from Eq. (11-23),

$$f_p = 1.35 f_y = (1.35)(33,000) = 44,600 \text{ psi}$$

where f_y is the yield stress of the steel against which the shank of the rivet bears, i.e., the flange of the beam. The beam has a yield stress f_y of 33,000 psi. Use Eq. (11-22) and substitute for the working bearing stress f_p, the allowable bearing stress.

$$f_p = P/d_r t$$

Solving for P:

$$P = f_p d_r t = (44,600)(0.75)(0.850) = 28,400 \text{ lb}$$

where t is the thickness of the flange of the 30 WF 116 beam. The allowable bearing load for a single rivet is 28,400 lb. The value of t can be found in the AISC Manual.

Failure is most likely to occur in shear and the maximum load that a single rivet may withstand is 6630 lb. Therefore, for a pair of rivets the maximum allowable load $(P_v)_{riv}$ is 13,260 lb.

Before Eq. (13-13) can be used to solve for the rivet spacing p, it is necessary to calculate f_v. It should be remembered that the value of f_v required in Eq. (13-13) is that value which occurs at the position within the rivet spacing p at which the vertical shear V is a maximum. For the rivet spacing p shown in Fig. 13-20, the maximum vertical shear is 106.6 kips and occurs at its left end, which is also the left end of the beam. Shear stress f_v is calculated for the vertical position in the transverse section of the compound beam that lies in the plane defined by the interface of the joining surfaces.

A transverse cross section of the compound beam is shown in Fig. 13-21. Calculating the moment of inertia using Eq. (2-7).

$$I_{NA} = \sum_{n=1}^{n=p} I_{OXn} + \sum_{n=1}^{n=p} a_n y_{cn}^2$$

$$= I_{OX1} + I_{OX2} + a_1 y_{c1}^2 + a_2 y_{c2}^2$$

$$= 4919 + 4919 + (34.1)(15)^2 + (34.1)(15)^2 = 25,200 \text{ in.}^4$$

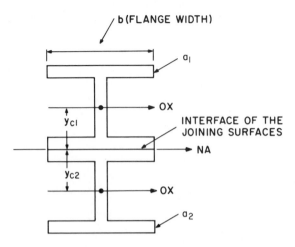

Figure 13-21.   Transverse cross section of beam.

The value of I_{OX} is found in the AISC Manual in the group of columns headed Axis X-X. The value of area a_1 and a_2 is also listed.

The moment of area Q_{NA} is $Q_{NA} = A\bar{y} = a_1 y_{c1} = (34.1)(15) = 511$ in.^{3} Using Eq. (13-5) to solve for f_v,

$$f_v = \frac{VQ_{NA}}{I_{NA}b} = \frac{(106,600)(511)}{(25,200)(10.5)} = 206 \text{ psi}$$

where b is the width of the beam at the point where the shear stress is desired. In this problem that point is at the interface of the two contacting surfaces and b is the flange width. The value of b here is found in the beam tables in the AISC Manual. Flange width in the beam tables means the horizontal width from flange tip to flange tip. (See Fig. 13-21.)

Substituting into Eq. (13-13) and solving for p,

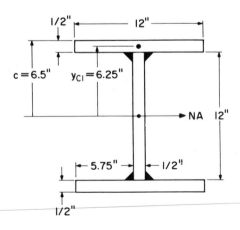

Figure 13-22

$$p = \frac{(P_v)_{riv}}{f_v b} = \frac{(13,260)}{(206)(10.5)}$$

$$= 6.13 \text{ in.} \qquad \text{say, } p = 6 \text{ in.}$$

Therefore, the rivet spacing for the first pair of rivets at the left end of the beam is 6 in. Since the vertical shear drops off only very slightly from the left end toward the first load point (less than 3 kips in 10 ft), the rivet pairs may be spaced on 6-in. centers in this first quarter-beam length. Therefore, in 10 ft of the beam it is necessary to have 20 pairs of rivets at 6-in. spacing per pair. Thus 40 rivets are required. *Answer*

Problem 13-7 Design of a welded built-up section
A wide-flange beam is made up by welding three 12-in. $\times$ $\frac{1}{2}$-in. plates. What is the maximum centerline spacing of $\frac{1}{4}$-in. $\times$ 2-in. long fillet welds joining flange plates to web plate if this beam is to support a maximum allowable concentrated load at the center of its 10-ft simple span? The allowable bending stress f_b is 19,800 psi.

Solution:
A single beam that supports a concentrated load P at midspan has its maximum bending moment also at midspan, i.e., $M = PL/4$, where L is the length of the beam. The maximum allowable value of P is that value which will cause bending stress f_b to reach its allowable value. The maximum allowable value of P will be calculated using the flexure formula, as shown in Eq. (13-3).

The section of the built-up member is shown in Fig. 13-22 and from symmetry, the neutral axis is located at middepth. Calculating the moment of inertia I_{NA} using Eq. (2-7).

$$I_{NA} = \sum_{n=1}^{n=p} I_{OXn} + \sum a_n y_{cn}^2$$

$$= 2I_{OX1} + I_{OX2} + 2a_1 y_{c1}^2 + a_2 y_{c2}^2$$

$$= 2\tfrac{1}{12}b_1 h_1^3 + \tfrac{1}{12}b_2 h_2^3 + 2(b_1)(h_1)y_{c1}^2 + (b_2)(h_2)y_{c2}^2$$

$$= 2\tfrac{1}{12}(12)(\tfrac{1}{2})^3 + \tfrac{1}{12}(\tfrac{1}{2})(12)^3 + 2(12)(\tfrac{1}{2})(6.25)^2 + (\tfrac{1}{2})(12)(0)$$

$$= 541 \text{ in.}^4$$

Substituting into the flexure formula Eq. (13-3), and solving for P,

$$f_b = Mc/I_{NA}$$

$$= \frac{(PL/4)c}{I_{NA}}$$

$$P = \frac{4I_{NA}f_b}{Lc} = \frac{4(541)(19,800)}{(10)(12)(6.5)} = 55,000 \text{ lb}$$

The built-up beam and its shear diagram are shown in Fig. 13-23. The weight of the beam is neglected. Although the shear changes sign at midspan, it is nonetheless constant in magnitude over the entire length of the beam.

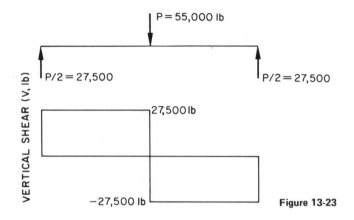

Figure 13-23

Therefore, the centerline spacing of welds will be the same along the entire length of the beam. The centerline spacing p is found using Eq. (13-13), which is modified by substituting $(P_v)_{weld}$ for $(P_v)_{riv}$.

$$p = (P_v)_{weld}/f_vb$$

The quantity $(P_v)_{weld}$ is the horizontal shear force that a pair of ¼-in. × 2-in. welds, one on either side of the web plate, can resist. Referring to Chap. 11, Sec. 11-8, and using an allowable weld shear stress f_v of 13,600 psi:

Allowable load per inch of fillet weld = $0.707Zf_v$

$$= 0.707(¼)(13,600)$$

$$= 2400 \text{ lb}$$

A pair of 2-in. welds would resist a load of 4(2400) or 9600 lb, i.e., $(P_v)_{weld}$ = 9600 lb.

The shear stress f_v is calculated for the position in the transverse section of the built-up beam that lies in the plane of the surface at which web plate and flange plate are joined. It is at this interface where the welds must resist the tendency of the structural elements to slide past each other.

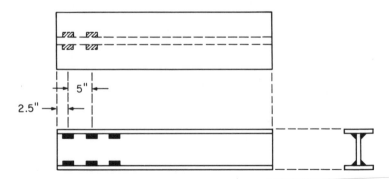

Figure 13-24

Calculating the moment of area Q_{NA},

$$Q_{NA} = A\bar{y} = (\tfrac{1}{2})(12)(6.25) = 37.5 \text{ in.}^3$$

Take the vertical shear V from the shear diagram and solve for f_v, using Eq. (13-5),

$$f_v = \frac{VQ_{NA}}{I_{NA}b} = \frac{(27,500)(37.5)}{(541)\,b} = \frac{1906}{b}$$

Digression: The value of b is $\tfrac{1}{2}$ in., the width of the member at the position within transverse cross section at which the shear stress is calculated. Where two surfaces of unequal width are joined and it is desired to know the shear stress f at their interface, the narrower width is used.

Solving for the weld spacing p,

$$p = \frac{(P_v)_{weld}}{f_v b} \quad \frac{9600}{(1906/b)b} = 5.04 \text{ in.}$$

The 2-in. weld pairs should be placed on, say, 5-in. centers, as shown in Fig. 13-24.   *Answer*

chapter 14
BEAM DEFLECTIONS

A beam responds to the application of a load by bending and moving in the direction of the load. The vertical distance at any point along the length of the beam between its loaded position and its initially straight unloaded position is known as the deflection at that point.

Often the design of a beam is governed by its deflection rather than by its strength. For example, a floor beam that supports a plaster ceiling must not deflect an amount more than 1/360th of its length if the plaster is not to crack. Also, where floor beams are required to support precision instruments, excessive deflection could interfere with their proper operation. Beam deflection is related to the applied bending moment and herein lies a second very important reason for determining deflection. This relationship provides an equation that supplements the equations of static equilibrium and makes possible the evaluation of statically indeterminate beams. Deflection as applied to such evaluations is treated in Chap. 15.

The reference to which deflections are measured in a beam from the straight-line unloaded position is the elastic curve. It will be recalled that this curve lies in the neutral surface and is defined by the intersection of the latter surface and the longitudinal plane of symmetry. In the material that follows, the elastic curve is always shown greatly exaggerated for instructional purposes.

There exist a number of methods for determining beam deflections. To name a few, there are the double integration method, the superposition method, the conjugate beam method, and the area-moment method. Most all texts on strength of materials discuss these and other methods. This book considers only the area-moment method, which is widely used in practice and is relatively simple to apply.

14-1 THE TWO THEOREMS OF THE AREA-MOMENT METHOD

The area-moment method is a semigraphical means for determining slope and deflection at any point along the length of a beam. The method involves the use of the area beneath the moment diagram and the moment of this area. It is assumed that the beam is homogeneous and has a constant cross section, i.e., E and I are constant.

The area-moment method is expressed by two theorems, the first of which follows:

Theorem I *The change in slope θ measured in radians between the slopes at any two points A and B on the elastic curve of a loaded beam is equal to the net area beneath the moment diagram included between the ordinates at these two points multiplied by 1/EI.*

Consider the loaded beam of Fig. 14-1. The slope at each point is measured from the horizontal x axis to the tangent using the sign convention that a slope down to the right is negative and a slope up to the right is positive. The *change* in slope θ_{AB} between the two points A and B is obtained by subtracting the slope at the left-hand point A from the slope at the right-hand point B. The calculated value of θ_{AB} will have a sign corresponding to the sign of the net area under the moment diagram between the two points. Referring still to Fig. 14-1, Theorem I can be expressed algebraically as

$$\theta_{AB} = \theta_B - \theta_A = (1/EI)(A)_{AB} \qquad (14\text{-}1)$$

where $(A)_{AB}$ is the area shown shaded in Fig. 14-1(B).

A calculated value of θ_{AB} having a positive sign indicates that a counterclockwise angle must be traversed when going from the tangent at the left-hand point A to the tangent at the right-hand point B, the vertex of the said angle being formed by the intersection of the two tangents. A negative value for θ_{AB} means that a clockwise angle must be traversed.

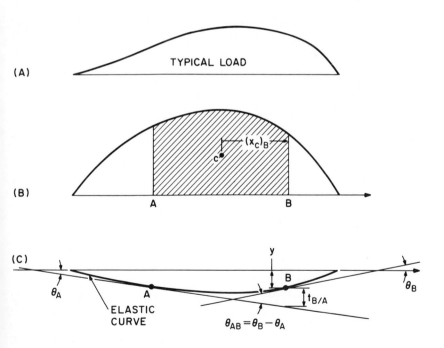

Figure 14-1

The second theorem of the moment area method follows:

Theorem II   *The vertical distance t between any point B on the elastic curve and the tangent drawn to any other point A on the elastic curve is equal to the moment of the net area beneath the moment diagram included between the ordinates at these two points multiplied by 1/EI about the ordinate of the moment diagram corresponding to the point at which the vertical distance t is to be determined*

The vertical distance t is often referred to as the tangential deviation and is not to be confused with the beam deflection y. (See Fig. 14-1.) With respect to specific points such as A and B in Fig. 14-1, a subscript designation B/A is appended to the tangential deviation, i.e., $t_{B/A}$. The first letter indicates the point on the elastic curve from which the tangential deviation is to be measured and the second letter denotes the point on the elastic curve to which the tangent is drawn.

Referring to Fig. 14-1, Theorem II can be expressed algebraically as

$$t_{B/A} = (1/EI)(A)_{AB}(x_c)_B \tag{14-2}$$

where $(x_c)_B$ is the distance from the area centroid perpendicular to the moment diagram ordinate corresponding to the point at which the tangential deviation is to be determined. The outside subscript designates the point on the beam through which this moment ordinate passes.

The sign of the computed tangential deviation indicates in which vertical direction from the elastic curve it is measured. A positive value means that the elastic curve lies above the tangent and a negative value means that the elastic curve lies below the tangent. (See Fig. 14-2.) In those cases where the shape of the elastic curve is not evident from the given loading, this rule will be of assistance in establishing its general shape.

The ease of implementation of the area-moment method depends largely upon the shape of the moment diagram. By preparing a separate moment diagram for each load and reaction, it becomes necessary to deal only with simple geometric forms such as rectangles, triangles, and complements of half parabolas. These

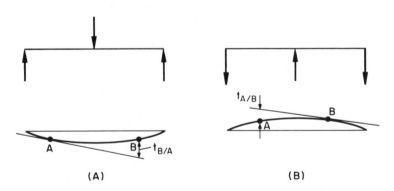

(A)   (B)

Figure 14-2.   Tangential deviation: (A) positive and (B) negative.

shapes have areas that are simple to calculate and centroids that are readily located. This procedure is commonly known as moment diagrams by parts and is discussed in the next section. In Sec. 14-3 the separate moment diagrams are used in the application of the area-moment method to specific problems wherein slope and deflection are determined.

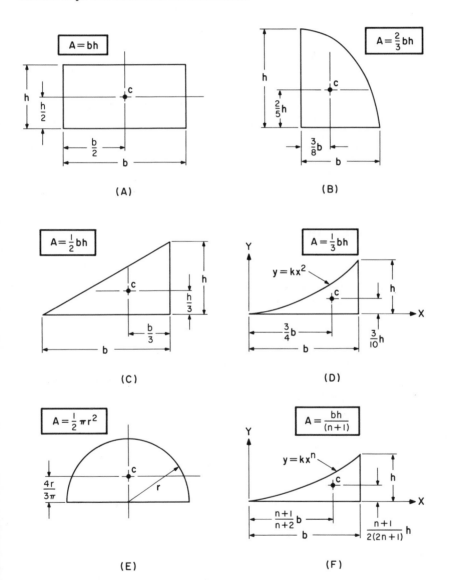

Figure 14-3. Properties of certain areas: (A) rectangle, (B) half parabola, (C) right triangle, (D) complement of a second-degree half parabola, (E) semi-circle, and (F) complement of an nth-degree half parabola.

14-2   DEFLECTIONS AND SLOPES BY THE AREA-MOMENT METHOD

In these applications of the area-moment theorems, it will be necessary to know the geometric properties of certain areas. Figure 14-3 lists the geometric sections most frequently encountered.

The area-moment method for determining the slope and deflection for several beam configurations will be illustrated with problems in the following Secs. 14-3, 14-4, and 14-5.

14-3   SLOPE AND DEFLECTION—CANTILEVER BEAMS

The slope and deflection of cantilever beams are the easiest to calculate because of the convenient reference afforded by the tangent to the elastic curve at the fixed end of the beam. As shown in Fig. 14-4, the tangent line at the fixed end B is horizontal and consequently has a zero slope. The change in slope between the tangent to any other point A and this horizontal tangent is therefore equal to the actual slope at point A. Also, the tangential deviation $t_{A/B}$ is equal to the deflection at any point A. It will be shown in Secs. 14-4 and 14-5 that other beam configurations such as unsymmetrically loaded simple beams require that similar triangle geometry be used with tangential deviations to arrive at the beam deflection.

Problem 14-1 Maximum slope and deflection for a cantilever beam

Determine the maximum slope and deflection of the cantilever beam shown in Fig. 14-5. $E = 2 \times 10^6$ psi, $I = 80$ in.^{4}

Solution:

For a cantilever beam, it is usually most convenient to select the reference section for the preparation of the moment diagram at the fixed end. This eliminates the necessity of calculating the end moment and reaction and preparing the corresponding moment diagrams.

Only one load acts on the beam and its moment diagram is shown in Fig. 14-6.

An inspection of the beam support and loading indicates that the elastic curve will have the general form shown in Fig. 14-6 and that maximum slope and deflection will occur at the free end point A.

Determination of Slope: From Theorem I only the change in slope between two points is obtainable. To ascertain the value of slope at a given point, this change in slope must be referred to a known value of slope. The slope at the fixed end of the cantilever is zero and constitutes a convenient reference. Therefore, in this instance, the change in slope between the slopes at point A and the fixed end point B is the actual slope at the free end. Between these two points apply Theorem I as exemplified by Eq. 14-1,

$$\theta_{AB} = \frac{1}{EI}(A)_{AB} = \frac{1}{(2 \times 10^6)(80)} \left[\tfrac{1}{2}(108)(-54,000) \right]$$

$$= -0.01822 \text{ rad}$$

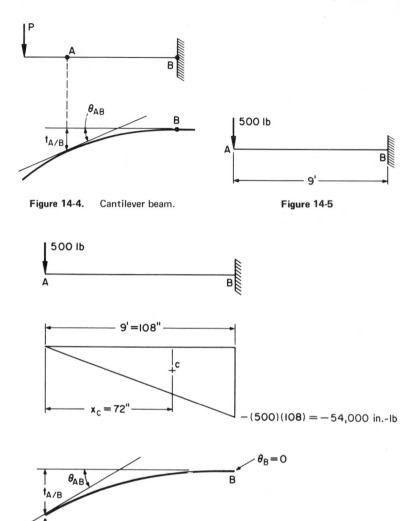

Figure 14-4. Cantilever beam.

Figure 14-5

Figure 14-6

The calculated value of θ_{AB} is negative indicating that a clockwise angle must be traversed to go from the tangent at the left-hand point A to the tangent at the right-hand point B. This is shown in Fig. 14-6 and affirms that the general shape of the elastic curve assumed earlier is indeed correct.

The slope θ_A is here equal to the change in slope θ_{AB}, i.e., $\theta_A = \theta_{AB}$ = 0.01822 rad. The negative sign is omitted because its significance pertains to the position of the slope at A relative to the slope at B.

Determination of Deflection: From Theorem II only the vertical distance between a point on the elastic curve and the tangent drawn to some other point is obtainable. This vertical distance (tangential deviation) is usually not equal to the beam deflection. However, as shown in Fig. 14-6, in the instance of the cantilever beam, the tangent drawn to the fixed end point B will deviate from the free endpoint A of the elastic curve by an amount equal to the deflection. Between these two points apply Theorem II as exemplified by Eq. (14-2),

$$t_{A/B} = \frac{1}{EI}(A)_{AB}(x_c)_B = \frac{1}{(2 \times 10^6)(80)}[\tfrac{1}{2}(108)(-54,000)](72)$$

$$= -1.311 \text{ in.}$$

The area-moment is taken about the ordinate of the moment diagram at which the tangential deviation is to be determined. (See Fig. 14-6.)

The negative sign of the computed tangential deviation indicates that the elastic curve lies below the tangent line. This too affirms that the general shape of the elastic curve assumed initially by visual inspection is correct.

The deflection and tangential deviation are synonymous for this beam configuration

$$y_A = 1.311 \text{ in.} \qquad Answer$$

The omission of the negative sign indicates that a downward deflection is considered to be positive.

Problem 14-2 Deflection at any point along a cantilever beam

For the cantilever beam shown in Fig. 14-7, find the slope and deflection at any point B under the uniform distributed load w lb/ft.

Solution:

The procedure of drawing the moment diagrams by parts is followed in implementing the area-moment theorems. An appropriate reference section must be chosen. Although it is usually more convenient to select the fixed end of the cantilever beam, this beam carries a distributed load and, to minimize computations, a section corresponding to one end of the distributed load is selected. For convenience, select the end of the distributed load corresponding to the free end of the beam.

Had one end of the distributed load coincided with the fixed end, then of course, the fixed end would have been selected as the reference section. A reference at a section other than the fixed end requires that the end moment and reaction be calculated and their moment effect included when drawing the moment diagrams by parts. The end reaction and moment are computed using the equations of statics with the results shown in Fig. 14-8(A).

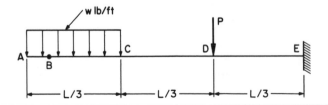

Figure 14-7

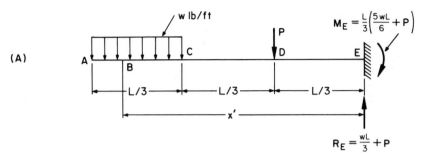

(A)

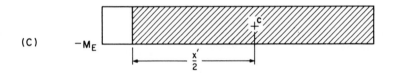

(B)

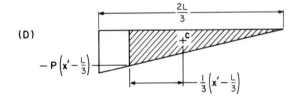

(C)

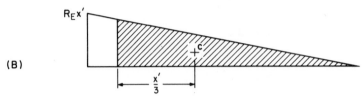

(D)

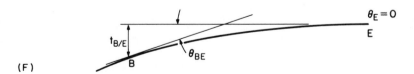

(E)

(F)

Figure 14-8

Figure 14-8 also shows the separate moment diagrams drawn for each load and reaction as if each alone were acting on the beam. An inspection of the beam support and loading indicates that the elastic curve should assume the general shape shown in Fig. 14-8(F).

Determination of Slope at Point B: The slope at the fixed end point E is zero and constitutes a convenient reference to which the change in slope obtained from Theorem I may be referred. Because the slope at point E is zero, the change in slope between B and E is the actual slope at point B.

Refer to Fig 14-8 and apply Theorem I, Eq. (14-1), making certain to include the area under the moment diagram between points B and E for the end moment, end reaction, and each load.

$$\theta_{BE} = \frac{1}{EI}(A)_{BE} = \frac{1}{EI}\left\{ \frac{1}{2}(x')(R_Ex') + (x')(-M_E) - \frac{1}{2}(x' - L/3)P(x' - L/3) \right.$$
$$\left. - \frac{1}{3}(x' - 2L/3)\frac{1}{2}w(x' - 2L/3)^2 \right\}$$

where $\theta_E = 0$ and the area formula of the half-parabolic complement is given in Fig. 14-3.

The slope θ_B is here equal to the change in slope θ_{BE}:

$$\theta_B = \theta_{BE} = \frac{1}{EI}\left\{ \frac{1}{2}(R_E)(x')^2 - M_Ex' - \frac{1}{2}P(x' - L/3)^2 \right.$$
$$\left. - \frac{1}{6}w(x' - 2L/3)^3 \right\} \qquad Answer$$

Determination of Deflection at Point B: Because the beam is cantilevered, a tangent drawn to point E at the fixed end is horizontal and will deviate from point B on the elastic curve by an amount equal to the deflection, i.e., $y_B = t_{B/E}$. Apply Theorem II, Eq. (14-2), by including the area-moment effect between points B and E for the end moment, end reaction, and each load. The area-moments are taken about the ordinate at which the tangential deviation is to be determined. (See Fig. 14-8.)

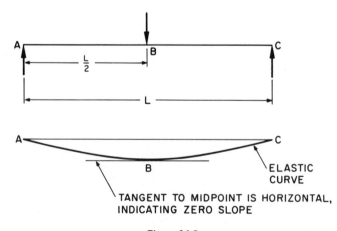

Figure 14-9

$$t_{B/E} = \frac{1}{EI}(A)_{BE}(x_c)_B = \frac{1}{EI}\left\{ [\tfrac{1}{2}(R_E)(x')^2](x'/3) - [(M_E)(x')](x'/2) \right.$$
$$\left. - [\tfrac{1}{2}(P)(x' - L/3)^2]\frac{(x' - L/3)}{3} - [\tfrac{1}{6}(w)(x' - 2L/3)^3]\frac{(x' - 2L/3)}{4} \right\}$$

The location of the centroid for the parabolic complement and the other areas are listed in Fig. 14-3.

The deflection and tangential deviation are synonymous for this beam configuration.

$$y_B = t_{B/E} = \frac{1}{EI}\left\{ \tfrac{1}{6}(R_E)(x')^3 - \tfrac{1}{2}(M_E)(x')^2 - \tfrac{1}{6}(P)(x' - L/3)^3 \right.$$
$$\left. - \tfrac{1}{24} w(x' - 2L/3)^4 \right\} \qquad Answer$$

14-4   SLOPE AND DEFLECTION–SIMPLE AND OVERHANGING BEAMS

In Sec. 14-3 it was a relatively simple matter to obtain slope and deflection because of the convenient reference afforded by the tangent to the elastic curve at the fixed end; this tangent always had a slope of zero that was evident by inspection.

For a simple supported beam symmetrically loaded, the slope at the midpoint is zero. (See Fig. 14-9.) For this beam, the deflection at the midpoint is a maximum as is also evident by inspection.

However, there is no point on the unsymmetrically loaded, simply supported beam or the overhanging beam at which the slope may be determined by visual inspection to have a known value. Slope is determined using a calculated value of tangential deviation. For example, consider the beam configuration shown in Fig.

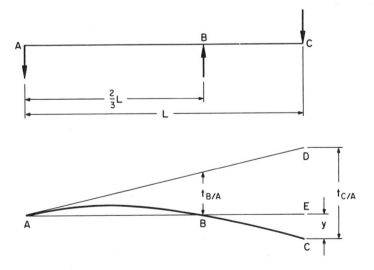

Figure 14-10

14-10. The tangential deviation $t_{B/A}$ is calculated by applying the second area-moment theorem

$$t_{B/A} = (1/EI)(A)_{AB} (x_c)_B$$

and the slope at point A is given by

$$\theta_A \approx \tan \theta_A = \frac{t_{B/A}}{2L/3}$$

Deflection is calculated by using calculated values of tangential deviation and similar triangle geometry. In Fig. 14-10 it is required that deflection y at the free end be determined. $t_{B/A}$ having already been calculated, the length DE is found from similar triangles.

$$\frac{t_{B/A}}{2L/3} = \frac{DE}{L} \qquad \text{and} \qquad DE = \tfrac{3}{2}\, t_{B/A}$$

Tangential deviation $t_{C/A}$ is calculated by applying the second area-moment theorem

$$t_{C/A} = (1/EI)(A)_{AC} (x_c)_C$$

and the deflection y is given by the difference of $t_{C/A}$ and DE, $y = t_{C/A} - DE$.

Problem 14-3 Deflection of a simple beam
Determine the deflection at the quarterpoint of the simple beam loaded as shown in Fig. 14-11. $E = 30 \times 10^6$ psi, $I = 500$ in.^{4}

Solution:
The end reactions are computed using the equations of statics with the results shown in Fig. 14-12(A).

In implementing the area-moment theorems, the procedure of drawing moment diagrams by parts is used because this enables the moment effect of each load and reaction to be evaluated in terms of a simple geometric form. A reference section to which the separate moment diagrams are drawn is selected at one end of the distributed load to minimize computations. For convenience, select the end of the distributed load corresponding to the end of the beam.

The separate moment diagrams, drawn for each load and reaction as if each alone were acting on the beam, are shown in Fig. 14-12(A) through 14-12(D). Notice that all moment quantities are expressed in in.-lb.

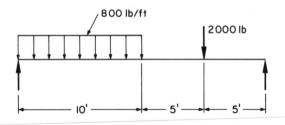

Figure 14-11

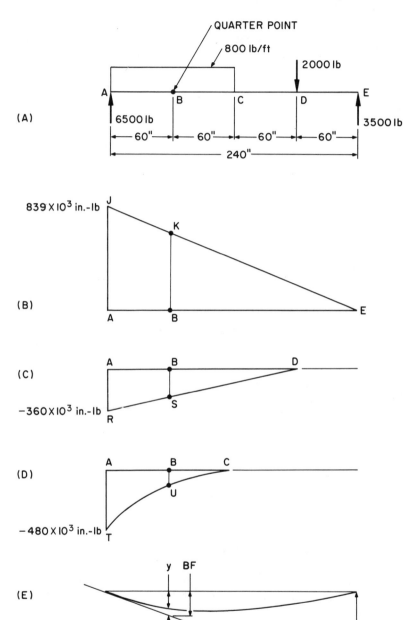

Figure 14-12

A visual inspection of the loading diagram in Fig. 14-12(A) indicates that the elastic curve should assume the shape shown in Fig. 14-12(E). This assumption will be checked using the sign of the computed tangential deviation.

Deflection is determined by using calculated values of tangential deviation and similar triangle geometry. Referring to Fig. 14-12, the deflection y at the quarterpoint is equal to the dimension BF less $t_{B/A}$, i.e., $y = BF - t_{B/A}$. Dimension BF is calculated using tangential deviation $t_{E/A}$ with similar triangle geometry.

$$t_{E/A} = (1/EI)(A)_{AE} (x_c)_E$$

Compute $1/EI$:

$$E = 30 \times 10^6 \text{ psi}$$
$$I = 500 \text{ in.}^4$$
$$1/EI = 1/(30 \times 10^6)(500) = 66.7 \times 10^{-12}$$
$$t_{E/A} = 66.7 \times 10^{-12} \left\{ \tfrac{1}{2}(839 \times 10^3)(240) [\tfrac{2}{3}(240)] \right.$$
$$- \tfrac{1}{2}(360 \times 10^3)(180) [\tfrac{2}{3}(180) + 60] - \tfrac{1}{3}(480$$
$$\left. \times 10^3)(120) [\tfrac{3}{4}(120) + 120] \right\}$$
$$= 0.418 \text{ in.}$$

The positive sign of the computed tangential deviation indicates that the tangent line should lie below the elastic curve. This affirms that the general shape of the elastic curve assumed initially from a visual inspection of the load diagram is indeed correct.

From similar triangles and referring to Fig. 14-11(E),

$$BF/60 = t_{E/A}/240$$
$$BF = \tfrac{1}{4}t_{E/A} = \tfrac{1}{4}(0.418)$$
$$= 0.1045 \text{ in.}$$

Tangential deviation $t_{B/A}$ is next determined:

$$t_{B/A} = (1/EI)(A)_{AB} (x_c)_B$$

In order to solve for $t_{B/A}$, it will be necessary to compute the component moments of area between points A and B about an ordinate through B. In each instance, Fig. 14-12(B), (C), and (D), the moment diagram does not have a regular shape, i.e., the moment diagrams do not correspond to the common shapes listed in Fig. 14-3. However, regular shapes are dealt with by making an area-moment summation and expressing the area moment of the irregular shapes in terms of the area moments of the regular shapes.

It was indicated in Sec. 2-6 that the area moment of a composite area is equal to the algebraic sum of the area moments of its component areas, e.g., the triangular area JAE of Fig. 14-12(B) is a composite comprising the component areas JABK and KBE. Implementing this principle with respect to the ordinate through B and referring to Fig. 14-13 where Fig. 14-12(B) is redrawn,

$$-\text{Moment of area JAE} = -\text{moment of area KBE} - \text{moment of area JABK}$$

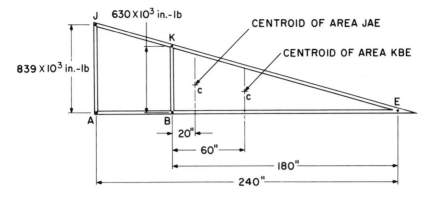

Figure 14-13

The quantities "moment of area JAE" and "moment of area KBE" have negative signs because their centroids lie on a side of the ordinate through B opposite to that on which the centroid of area JABK lies.

Moment of area JABK = − moment of area KBE + moment of area JAE

Moment of area JABK = $\frac{1}{2}(630 \times 10^3)(180)(60) - \frac{1}{2}(839 \times 10^3)(240)(20)$

The other moment diagrams in Fig. 14-12(C) and (D) are redrawn in Figs. 14-14 and 14-15, respectively, and are similarly treated. Solving for $t_{B/A}$,

$$t_{B/A} = \frac{1}{EI}(A)_{AB}(x_c)_B = 66.7 \times 10^{-12} \left\{ [\frac{1}{2}(630 \times 10^3)(180)(60) \right.$$
$$- \frac{1}{2}(839 \times 10^3)(240)(20)] + [\frac{1}{2}(-240 \times 10^3)(120)(40)$$
$$+ \frac{1}{2}(-360 \times 10^3)(180)(0)] + [\frac{1}{3}(-120 \times 10^3)(60)(15)$$
$$+ \left. \frac{1}{3}(-480 \times 10^3)(120)(30)] \right\}$$

$t_{B/A} = 0.0128$ in.

Again, the positive sign of the tangential deviation indicates that the tangent line should lie below the elastic curve as shown in Fig. 14-12(E).

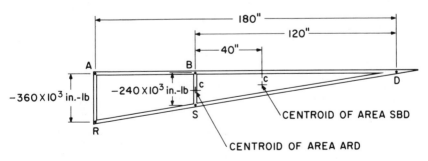

Figure 14-14

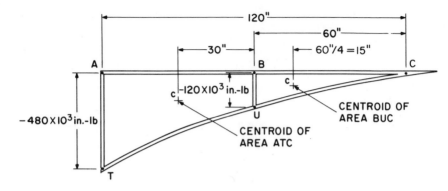

Figure 14-15

Computing the deflection y,

$$y = BF - t_{B/A} = 0.1045 - 0.0128$$
$$= 0.0917 \text{ in.} \qquad Answer$$

Problem 14-4 Deflection of an overhanging beam

Determine the deflection at the free end of the overhanging beam loaded as shown in Fig. 14-16. $E = 30 \times 10^6$ psi, $I = 500$ in.^{4}

Solution:

The end reactions are computed using the equations of statics with the results shown in Fig. 14-17(A).

The procedure of drawing moment diagrams by parts is used in implementing the area-moment theorem. A reference section to which the separate moment diagrams are drawn is selected at the left end of the distributed load. The separate moment diagrams are shown in Fig. 14-17(B) through 14-17(D). To accommodate the units of E and I, all dimensions are in inches and all moments are in in.-lb.

Assume that the elastic curve takes the form shown by the dashed line in Fig. 14-17(E). The algebraic sign of tangential deviation will indicate if this assumption is correct or, if not correct, what general form the curve should take.

Deflection is determined by using calculated values of tangential deviation and similar triangle geometry. A set of similar triangles can be established by

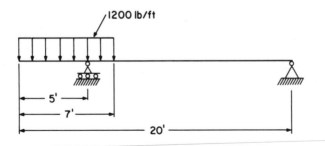

Figure 14-16

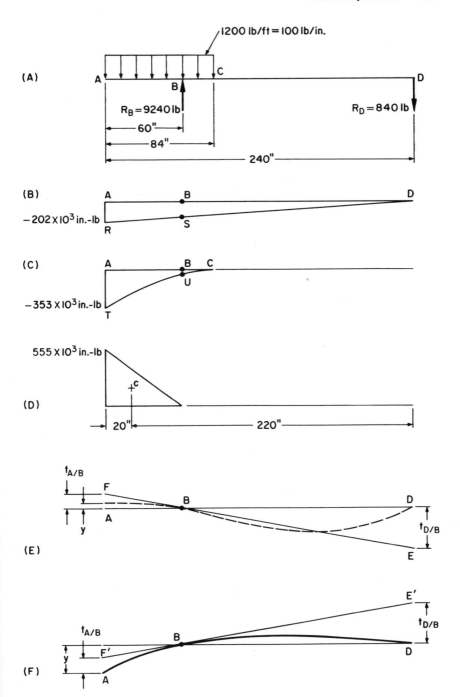

Figure 14-17

drawing a tangent to the elastic curve at either point B or D. Draw a tangent to point B as shown in Fig. 14-17(E). The deflection y can be found by knowing dimension AF and tangential deviation $t_{A/B}$. Figure 14-17(E) indicates that y is the numerical difference between AF and $t_{A/B}$, i.e., $y = AF - t_{A/B}$. This expression is based on the geometry shown in Fig. 14-17(E). If it turns out that the general shape of the elastic curve is otherwise, a new expression based on the new geometry will be written.

Dimension AF is determined using $t_{D/B}$ and similar triangle geometry.

$$t_{D/B} = (1/EI)(A)_{BD} (x_c)_D$$
$$= \frac{1}{(30 \times 10^6)(500)} \left\{ \frac{1}{2}(-151.2 \times 10^3)(180)(120) + \frac{1}{3}(-29.8 \times 10^3)(24)(174) \right\}$$
$$= -0.112 \text{ in.}$$

The negative sign of $t_{D/B}$ indicates that the elastic curve should lie below the tangent line at point D. The elastic curve is redrawn in Fig. 14-17(F) to reflect this condition. The segment of the curve extending from point B to point A is assumed to occupy a position below the tangent line at point A. The sign of the calculated value of $t_{A/B}$ will determine if this assumption is correct.

From similar triangles the magnitude of the dimension AF$'$ is

$$AF'/60 = t_{D/B}/180$$
$$AF' = (60/180)(t_{D/B}) = \frac{1}{3}(-0.112) = -0.0374 \text{ in.}$$

The areas under the moment diagrams in Fig. 14-17(B) and (C), which are used in the determination of $t_{A/B}$, do not have shapes corresponding to the common shapes listed in Fig. 14-3. Therefore, these areas are to be handled in accordance with the procedure described in Problem 14-3.

Figure 14-17(B) and (C) are redrawn in Figs. 14-18 and 14-19, respectively. In these figures the composite diagram and its components are drawn to facilitate

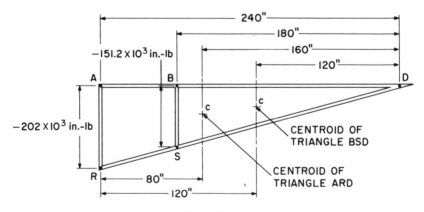

Figure 14-18

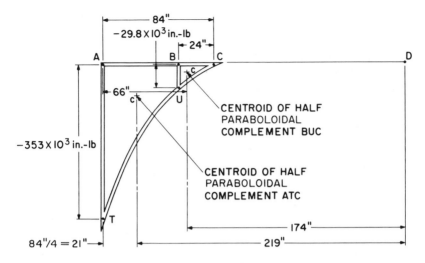

Figure 14-19

implementation of the concept that the area moment of the composite area is equal to the algebraic sum of the area moments of its component areas; this makes it possible to express the area-moment of the irregular shape in terms of the area moments of the regular shapes. For example in Fig. 14-18, the area moment of irregular shape ARSB can be expressed in terms of the area moments of regular shapes ARD and BSD. Since the tangential deviation $t_{A/B}$ is located at point A, the area moments will be taken with respect to an ordinate through A.

Solving for $t_{A/B}$,

$$t_{A/B} = (1/EI)(A)_{AB} (x_c)_A$$

$$= \frac{1}{(30 \times 10^6)(500)} \{[\tfrac{1}{2}(-202 \times 10^3)(240)(80) - \tfrac{1}{2}(-151.2$$
$$\times 10^3)(180)(120)] + [\tfrac{1}{3}(-353 \times 10^3)(84)(21) - \tfrac{1}{3}(-29.8$$
$$\times 10^3)(24)(66)] + [\tfrac{1}{2}(555 \times 10^3)(60)(20)]\} = -0.0114 \text{ in.}$$

The negative sign of $t_{A/B}$ indicates that the tangent line should lie above the elastic curve at the point A where $t_{A/B}$ is measured. This shows that the assumption made in Fig. 14-17(F) as to the general position of the segment AB of the elastic curve is correct. The geometry of Fig. 14-17(F) shows that the deflection y is the sum of the quantities AF' and $t_{A/B}$.

$$y = AF' + t_{A/B}$$
$$= -0.0374 + (-0.0114)$$
$$= 0.0488 \text{ in.} \qquad Answer$$

The omission of the negative sign indicates that a downward deflection is considered to be positive.

14-5   MAXIMUM DEFLECTION OF THE SIMPLE BEAM

For a simple beam not symmetrically loaded it is not evident from inspection at which point along its length the maximum deflection y_{max} occurs. However, the beam interval within which maximum deflection occurs is usually apparent and an equation in terms of the dimension x shown in Fig. 14-20 can be established by using the first area-moment theorem between points A and B. This will yield an expression for θ_{AB} in terms of x.

A value for θ_A can be easily found by using the tangential deviation $t_{C/A}$ obtained from the second area-moment theorem.

$$\theta_A \approx \tan \theta_A = t_{C/A}/L$$

The tangent to the elastic curve at the point of maximum deflection is horizontal. Consequently, the change in slope θ_{AB} is equal to the slope θ_A. The expressions for θ_A and θ_{AB} are equated and solved for x. Having established its location, the maximum deflection is calculated in the same manner as taught in Sec. 14-4.

Problem 14-5 Location and value of the maximum deflection for a simple beam

A simple beam 12 ft long carries a concentrated load of 9 kips at the third point. Locate the point, and calculate the amount, of maximum deflection in inches. E = 1.6 × 10⁶ psi, I = 400 in.⁴

Solution:

From the statement of the problem, the beam schematic is drawn in Fig. 14-21(A). A visual inspection of the loaded beam indicates that the point of maximum deflection must be somewhere to the right of the 9-kip load. This point will be at some distance x' from the right end of the beam and is designated B in Fig. 14-21(D).

The moment diagrams for end reaction R_C and for the 9-kip load are drawn in Fig. 14-21(B) and (C), respectively. An expression for θ_{BC} in terms of x' is obtained by applying the first area-moment theorem between points B and C.

$$\theta_{BC} = \frac{1}{EI}(A)_{BC} = \frac{1}{EI}\left[\frac{1}{2}(3000)(x')(x')\right] = \frac{1.5 \times 10^3 \ (x')^2}{EI}$$

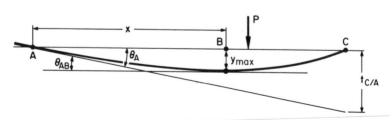

Figure 14-20

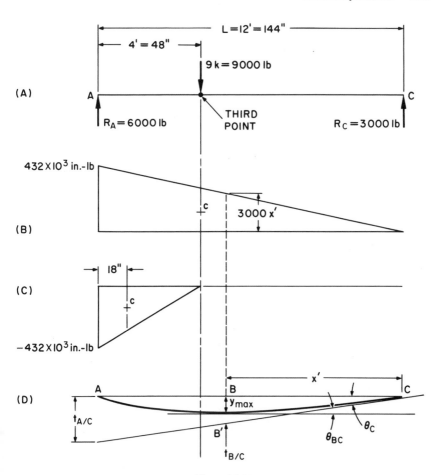

Figure 14-21

The tangent to the elastic curve at the point of maximum deflection is horizontal and the change in slope θ_{BC} is equal to the slope θ_C, which is obtained using the tangential deviation $t_{A/C}$.

$$t_{A/C} = \frac{1}{EI}(A)_{AC}(x_c)_A = \frac{1}{EI}\{[\tfrac{1}{2}(432 \times 10^3)(144)(48)]$$
$$+ [\tfrac{1}{2}(-432 \times 10^3)(48)(18)]\}$$
$$= \frac{1.308 \times 10^9}{EI}$$

and

$$\theta_C \approx \tan \theta_C = \frac{t_{A/C}}{L} = \frac{\dfrac{1.308 \times 10^9}{EI}}{144}$$

Equating θ_{BC} and θ_C,

$$\frac{1.5 \times 10^3 (x')^2}{EI} = \frac{\dfrac{1.308 \times 10^9}{EI}}{144}$$

$$x' = 77.7 \text{ in.}$$

Now that the location of the maximum deflection has been obtained, it is a simple matter to determine its value. The deflection y_{max} is found by using calculated values of tangential deviation and similar triangle geometry. Referring to Fig. 14-21 (D), y_{max} is given by $y_{max} = BB' - t_{B/C}$. From similar triangles

$$BB'/t_{A/C} = x'/L$$

$$BB' = t_{A/C}\left(\frac{x'}{L}\right) = \frac{1.308 \times 10^9}{EI}\left(\frac{77.7}{144}\right) = \frac{(1.308 \times 10^9)(77.7)}{(1.6 \times 10^6)(400)(144)}$$

$$= 1.101 \text{ in.}$$

Tangential deviation $t_{B/C}$ is next determined:

$$t_{B/C} = \frac{1}{EI}(A)_{BC}(x_c)_C = \frac{1}{(1.6 \times 10^6)(400)}\left[\frac{1}{2}(3000)(77.7)(77.7)(51.8)\right]$$

$$= 0.734 \text{ in.}$$

Computing the deflection y_{max},

$$y_{max} = BB' - t_{B/C} = 1.101 - 0.734$$
$$= 0.367 \text{ in.} \qquad Answer$$

14-6   BEAM NOT OF UNIFORM SECTION

It is occasionally necessary to reinforce a beam over a part of its length to reduce excessive deflection. When this is done, the beam will have a moment of inertia I that is discontinuous at one or more points along its length.

It will be recalled that the area-moment theorems incorporate E and I. Until now, it was assumed that the beam was homogeneous (E constant) and had a constant cross section (I constant). This permitted treating $1/EI$ merely as a constant coefficient of the area under the moment diagram.

Change of slope and tangential deviation are really functions of the area under the M/EI diagram and the moment of the area under this diagram, respectively. When the moment of inertia I is discontinuous, appropriate cognizance must be taken in the preparation of the moment diagram or more precisely, the M/EI diagram. The discontinuity in I causes a corresponding discontinuity in the M/EI diagram, as will be shown in the following problem.

Problem 14-6 Deflection of a composite beam having portions of respective different moments of inertia

A steel-reinforced beam cantilevers as shown in Fig. 14-22 with moments of inertia for each portion of the beam as indicated. How far will point A deflect in inches under a load of two tons? (Neglect beam weight.)

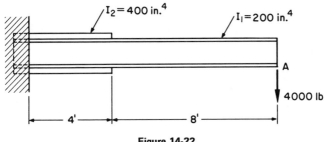

Figure 14-22

Solution:

The beam is shown again in Fig. 14-23(A). Since the beam is cantilevered at point C, a tangent line drawn to this point is horizontal. See Fig. 14-23(D). The tangential deviation $t_{A/C}$ is therefore equal to the deflection y at point A. The quantity $t_{A/C}$ is obtained by applying the second area-moment theorem between points C and A.

Instead of drawing a moment diagram and treating $1/EI$ as a constant coefficient, an M/EI diagram is prepared that reflects the discontinuity in I. The M/EI diagram is shown in Fig. 14-23(C) and a diagram of the moment of inertia I is depicted in Fig. 14-23(B) to emphasize the discontinuity at point B.

For instructional purposes, all dimensions on the M/EI diagram are given in letters. At an infinitesimal distance to the right of point B, the ordinate BE is

$$BE = \frac{1}{EI_1} P\left(\frac{2L}{3}\right) = \frac{2PL}{3EI_1}$$

At an infinitesimal distance to the left of point B, the ordinate BD is

$$BD = \frac{1}{EI_2} P\left(\frac{2L}{3}\right) = \frac{2PL}{3EI_2}$$

At point C, the ordinate CF is

$$CF = \frac{1}{EI_2}(P)(L) = \frac{PL}{EI_2}$$

The determination of $t_{A/C}$ requires that the moment of irregular area CFDEA about the ordinate through A be calculated. Regular shapes are dealt with by implementing the concept that the area-moment of a composite area is equal to the algebraic sum of the area-moments of its component areas.

Moment of area CFDEA = moment of area CFA + moment of area DEA

Area DEA is a somewhat irregular shape, and its moment in terms of regular shapes can be found from

Moment of area DEA = moment of area BEA − moment of area BDA

Apply the second area-moment theorem. Remember that the diagram in Fig. 14-23(C) is an M/EI diagram and therefore includes $1/EI$.

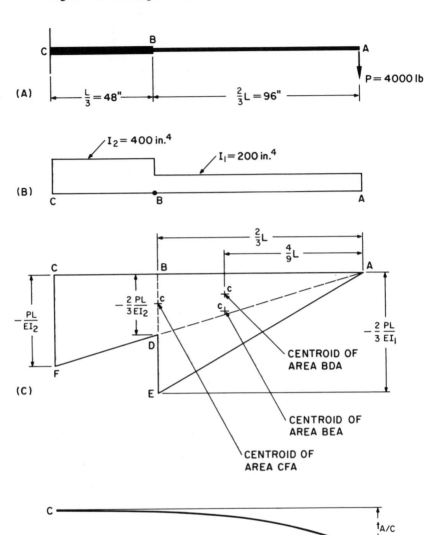

Figure 14-23

$$t_{A/C} = \frac{1}{EI}(A)_{AC}(x_c)_A = \frac{1}{2}\left(-\frac{PL}{EI_2}\right)(L)\left(\frac{2L}{3}\right) + \frac{1}{2}\left(-\frac{2PL}{3EI_1}\right)\left(\frac{2L}{3}\right)\left(\frac{4L}{9}\right)$$

$$- \frac{1}{2}\left(-\frac{2PL}{3EI_2}\right)\left(\frac{2L}{3}\right)\left(\frac{4L}{9}\right)$$

$$= -\frac{PL}{(81)EI_1I_2}[(19)I_1 + (8)I_2]$$

Substituting numerical values

$$t_{A/C} = -\frac{(4000)(144)}{(81)(30 \times 10^6)(200)(400)}\ [(19)(200) + (8)(400)]$$
$$= -0.208 \times 10^{-4}\ \text{in.}$$

The minus sign indicates that the assumed position of the elastic curve with respect to the tangent line in Fig. 14-23(D) is correct. The deflection at point A and $t_{A/C}$ are synonymous.

$$y_A = 0.208 \times 10^{-4}\ \text{in.} \qquad Answer$$

The omission of the negative sign indicates that downward deflection is considered to be positive.

chapter 15

STATICALLY INDETERMINATE BEAMS

A beam is statically indeterminate when it has more unknown loads and reactions than there are equations of static equilibrium. In a planar-force system, only three unknown forces and reactions may be determined because there exist only three equations of static equilibrium, namely: $\Sigma F_H = 0$, $\Sigma F_V = 0$, and $\Sigma M = 0$. However, in this chapter, only beams that have their loads acting perpendicular to the longitudinal beam axis are considered; this means that only two equilibrium equations will be available. The equation $\Sigma F_H = 0$ will be of no use since no force or component of a force acts in the horizontal direction, i.e., in the line of action of the longitudinal beam axis. Therefore, a beam so loaded and acted upon by more than two unknowns is statically indeterminate. The degree of being indeterminate is dependent upon the number of unknowns exceeding the number of equilibrium equations. For example, a beam whose unknowns exceed by two the number of equilibrium equations available is indeterminate to the second degree.

Problem 15-1 Determination of the reactions in a propped cantilever

A 12-in., 31.8-lb standard steel I-beam, 15 ft long, is built in horizontally at the right end. The other end rests on a support. Originally the supports were at the same level. The beam carries a load of 20,000 lb uniformly distributed. If the left support sinks 1 in., what is the reaction in pounds at this point? What are the reactions at the other end?

Solution:

From the statement of the problem, the loading diagram is drawn in Fig. 15-1 (A). Often the weight of the beam is small compared with the load and is neglected. However, here the load is uniformly distributed and the weight of the beam can be conveniently included.

$$w = \frac{20,000}{(15)(12)} + \frac{31.8}{12} = 113.9 \text{ lb/in.}$$

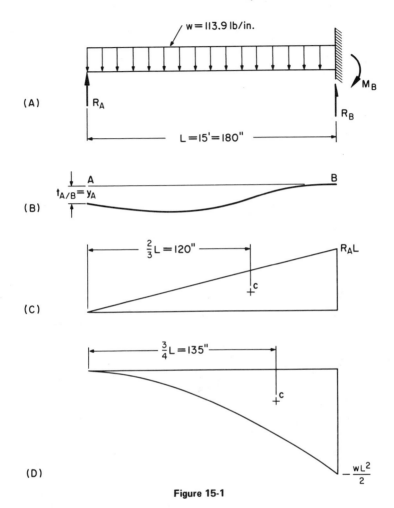

Figure 15-1

There are three unknown reactions, R_A, R_B, and M_B, and only two independent equations of static equilibrium. A third equation is required and it can be obtained from an evaluation of geometric conditions.

As shown in Fig. 15-1 (B), a tangent line drawn to point B of the elastic curve is horizontal and deviates from this curve at point A an amount equal to the deflection y_A. Because the tangent line is horizontal, the deflection y_A is synonymous with tangential deviation $t_{A/B}$ and a third equation is formulated using the second area-moment theorem.

$$\frac{1}{EI}(A)_{AB}(x_c)_A = t_{A/B} = y_A = -1$$

Notice that the 1-in. deflection was given a minus sign. This was done because the sign convention associated with the theorem requires that the tangential deviation be negative when the tangent line is positioned above the elastic curve at the point where the deviation is measured.

The quantities $(A)_{AB}$ and $(x_c)_A$ are obtained from the moment diagrams by parts. These diagrams are drawn in Fig. 15-1 (C) and (D) where the reference section for their preparation is taken at the fixed end of the beam. Selection of this reference section makes it unnecessary to draw moment diagrams for M_B and R_B.

Proceeding with the area-moment equation,

$$\frac{1}{EI}\left\{\left[\frac{1}{2}(R_A L)(L)\left(\frac{2L}{3}\right)\right] + \left[\frac{1}{3}\left(-\frac{wL^2}{2}\right)(L)\left(\frac{3L}{4}\right)\right]\right\} = t_{A/B} = y_A = -1$$

Solving for R_A and substituting numerical values,

$$E = 30 \times 10^6 \text{ psi} \quad \text{and} \quad I = 215.8 \text{ in.}^4$$

(from the AISC Manual of Steel Construction I-beam tables. The value of I is with respect to axis X-X because as the beam deflects, it bends about this axis.)

$$R_A = \frac{3y_A EI}{L^3} + \frac{3wL}{8} = \frac{3(-1)(30 \times 10^6)(216)}{(180)^3} + \frac{3(113.9)(180)}{8}$$
$$= 4360 \text{ lb} \qquad Answer$$

Having found R_A, there remain only two unknowns, M_B and R_B, which are easily determined from two equations of static equilibrium.

$$\Sigma F_V = 0 \qquad\qquad R_A + R_B - wL = 0$$

$$\langle + \Sigma M_B = 0 \qquad R_A(L) - wL\left(\frac{L}{2}\right) + M_B = 0$$

Substituting numerical values and solving for M_B and R_B yields

$$R_B = 16,140 \text{ lb}$$
$$M_B = 1.062 \times 10^6 \text{ in.-lb} \qquad Answer$$

Problem 15-2 Location and value of the maximum deflection for a propped cantilever

For the propped cantilever shown in Fig. 15-2, compute the distance from the left end to the point of maximum deflection and calculate its value. $E = 1.6 \times 10^6$ psi, $I = 400$ in.^{4}

Solution:

The beam is drawn again in Fig. 15-3 (A). Maximum deflection will occur at the point between the ends of the beam at which the slope is zero. The end conditions here are not the same and it is not evident from a visual inspection at which side of the concentrated load this point lies. Assume maximum deflection occurs at point K a distance x from the left end of the beam. The elastic curve defining this situation is shown in Fig. 15-3(B). Point K will have a slope of zero and, since the slope at the fixed end is also zero, the change in slope θ_{KC} is zero. An expression in terms of x is obtained by applying the first area-moment theorem between points K and C.

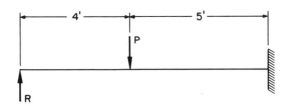

Figure 15-2

$$\frac{1}{EI} (A)_{KC} = \theta_{KC} = 0$$

The quantity $(A)_{KC}$ is obtained from the moment diagrams by parts; these diagrams are given in Fig. 15-3 (C) and (D).

$(A)_{KC}$ = area GFDC + area GHEC = (area ADC − area AFG) + (area BEC − area BHG) = 0

$$\frac{1}{2}[(R_A)(L)](L) - \frac{1}{2}[(R_A)(x)](x) + \frac{1}{2}\left(-\frac{5PL}{9}\right)\left(\frac{5L}{9}\right)$$

$$-\frac{1}{2}\left[-P(x - \frac{4L}{9})\right]\left(x - \frac{4L}{9}\right) = 0$$

Solving for x,

$$x = \frac{L}{2}\left\{ \frac{8P}{9(P - R_A)} \pm \sqrt{\frac{64P^2}{81(P - R_A)^2} - \frac{4(9R_A - P)}{9(P - R_A)}} \right\}$$

From the last expression it is evident that R_A must be known before the solution can be continued. For this beam configuration there can be only two equations of static equilibrium. Since there are three unknowns, R_C, M_C, and R_A, a third equation is required based upon an evaluation of a geometric condition imposed by the reactions.

A tangent line drawn to point C is horizontal; because R_A prevents any deflection at point A, the tangential deviation $t_{A/C}$ is zero. This condition can be expressed by the second area-moment theorem.

$$\frac{1}{EI} (A)_{AC}(x_c)_A = t_{A/C} = 0$$

$$\frac{1}{2}(R_A L)(L)\left(\frac{2L}{3}\right) + \frac{1}{2}\left(-\frac{5PL}{9}\right)\left(\frac{5L}{9}\right)\left(\frac{22L}{27}\right) = 0$$

$$R_A = \frac{275(P)}{729} = \frac{275(9000)}{729} = 3400 \text{ lb}$$

Now return to the first area-moment theorem equation. Substitute values for R_A, L, and P, and solve for x. The solution for x yields two roots, namely, 46.5 in. and 108 in. The second root is not a point of maximum deflection.

The first root is of concern and shows that the point of maximum deflection occurs just 1.5 in. to the left of the 9000-lb load.

$$x = 46.5 \text{ in.} \qquad Answer$$

Since the tangent to point C is horizontal, the deflection y_{max} at point K is equal to the tangential deviation $t_{K/C}$. Apply the second area-moment theorem

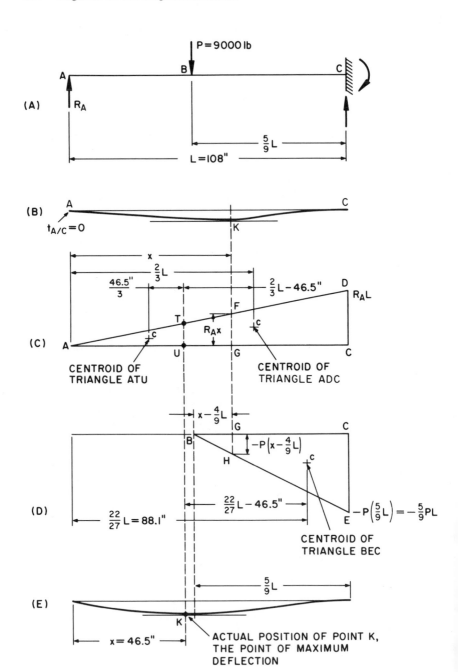

Figure 15-3

between points C and K noting carefully the actual position of point K, as shown in Fig. 15-3 (E).

$$(1/EI)(A)_{KC}(x_c)_K = t_{K/C} = y_{max}$$

$$y_{max}EI = \frac{1}{2}[(R_AL)(L)\left(\frac{2L}{3} - x\right) - \frac{1}{2}(R_Ax)(x)\left(\frac{x}{3}\right)$$

$$+ \frac{1}{2}\left(-\frac{5PL}{9}\right)\left(\frac{5L}{9}\right)\left(\frac{22L}{27} - x\right)$$

Substituting numerical values and solving yields the value

$$y_{max} = 0.348 \text{ in.} \qquad Answer$$

The omission of the negative sign indicates that a downward deflection is considered to be positive.

15-1   BEAM HAVING BOTH ENDS FIXED

A loaded beam fixed at both ends is supported by four reactions R_A, M_A, R_B, and M_B as shown in Fig. 15-4 (A). Because no force or force component acts in the horizontal direction, the static equilibrium equation $\Sigma F_H = 0$ is of no help and only two equations of static equilibrium can be used.

The beam is statically indeterminate to the second degree; thus two additional independent equations, each incorporating an unknown reaction, are required. These equations are obtained by applying the first and second area-moment theorems to geometric conditions imposed by the reactions. Two such conditions are shown in Fig. 15-4 (B). The tangent lines drawn to points A and B at the fixed ends are horizontal. Therefore, the change in slope θ_{AB} between points A and B is zero; this condition is expressed by the first area-moment theorem.

$$(1/EI)(A)_{AB} = \theta_{AB} = 0$$

A second condition is established by the fact that the tangential deviation $t_{B/A}$ is zero; this condition is expressed by the second area-moment theorem

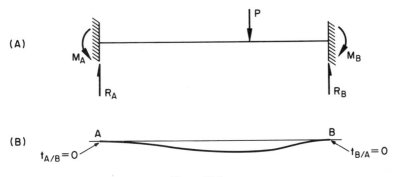

Figure 15-4

$(1/EI)(A)_{AB}(x_c)_B = t_{B/A} = 0$

Since the tangential deviation $t_{A/B}$ is also zero, the second area-moment equation could be written with respect to a moment axis through point A.

$(1/EI)(A)_{AB}(x_c)_A = t_{A/B} = 0$

In the following problem, the reactions for a beam fixed at both ends are determined.

Problem 15-3 Determination of the reactions for a beam fixed at both ends

Determine the end reactions for the beam shown in Fig. 15-5.

Solution:

The beam is fixed at both ends and is held in equilibrium by four reactive elements, R_A, M_A, R_B, and M_B, as shown in Fig. 15-6 (A).

Only two equations of static equilibrium can be applied to this beam configuration; thus two additional independent equations must be established. These supplementary equations are based on the geometry imposed by the reactions.

Refer to Fig. 15-6 (B). Since the slope at points A and B is zero, the change in slope θ_{AB} is zero. Applying the first area-moment theorem to this condition

$(1/EI)(A)_{AB} = 0$

The quantity $(A)_{AB}$ is obtained from the moment diagram by parts shown in Fig. 15-6 (C) through (E).

$$\frac{1}{EI}\left\{ \frac{1}{2}(R_B L)(L) + (-M_B)(L) + \frac{1}{2}[(-P)(a)]a \right\} = 0 \tag{15-1}$$

A second equation based on the condition of zero tangential deviation at point A is obtained using the second area-moment theorem.

$$\frac{1}{EI}(A)_{AB}(x_c)_A = t_{A/B} = 0$$

$$\frac{1}{EI}\left\{ \frac{1}{2}[(R_B)(L)](L)\left(\frac{L}{3}\right) + (-M_B)(L)\left(\frac{L}{2}\right) + \frac{1}{2}[(-P)(a)](a)\left(\frac{a}{3}\right) \right\} = 0 \tag{15-2}$$

Note: The tangential deviation at point B is also zero and the second area-moment theorem could have been taken with respect to a moment axis through

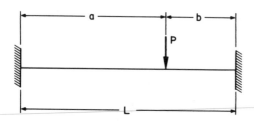

Figure 15-5

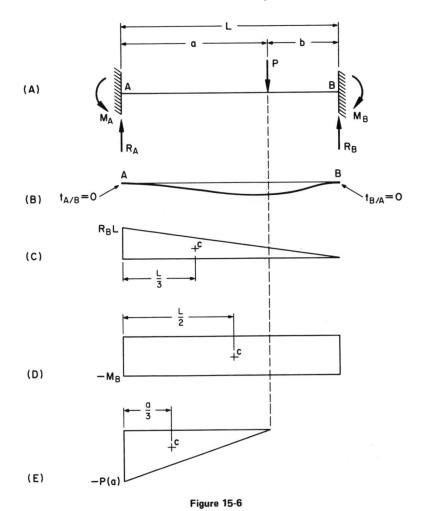

Figure 15-6

this point. The ease of computing moments is usually the basis upon which the selection of a moment axis is made.

Equations (15-1) and (15-2) obtained from the area-moment theorems may be solved simultaneously for R_B and M_B. This yields

$$R_B = \frac{P(a)^2}{(L)^3}(a + 3b) \qquad M_B = \frac{P(a)^2 b}{(L)^2} \qquad \textit{Answer}$$

These values used together with the equations of static equilibrium permit the remaining two reactions to be determined. For example, $\Sigma F_H = 0$ and $R_A + R_B - P = 0$. Substituting for R_B and P and solving for R_A yields

$$R_A = \frac{P(b)^2}{(L)^3}(3a + b) \qquad \textit{Answer}$$

$\big\{$ + ΣM_B = 0 $R_A(L) - P(b) - M_A + M_B = 0$

Substituting for R_A, P and M_B and solving for M_A yields

$$M_A = \frac{Pa(b)^2}{(L)^2} \qquad Answer$$

All the reactions turn out to have positive signs; this indicates that the directions for the reactions assumed in Fig. 15-6 (A) are all correct.

Note: Since both ends are fixed, it is often not difficult to ascertain by visual inspection in which beam interval the point of maximum deflection lies. The techniques developed in Chap. 14 can then be used to calculate its exact position and value. Should the proper beam interval not be evident from visual inspection, the techniques of Chap. 14 as extended in Problem 15-2 can be used.

15-2 CONTINUOUS BEAMS

A continuous beam is a beam that rests on more than two supports, as, for example, the beam shown in Fig. 15-7 (A). It is statically indeterminate since there are more reactions than there are equations of static equilibrium.

The internal bending moments can be calculated using the three-moment equation.

$$\left(\frac{L_1}{E_1 I_1}\right)M_1 + 2\left(\frac{L_1}{E_1 I_1} + \frac{L_2}{E_2 I_2}\right)M_2 + \left(\frac{L_2}{E_2 I_2}\right)M_3 = -\frac{6A_1(x_{c1})_1}{E_1 I_1 L_1} \qquad (15\text{-}3)$$
$$-\frac{6A_2(x_{c2})_3}{E_2 I_2 L_2}$$

For a continuous beam in which the beam material is homogeneous throughout (E constant) and the cross section at each span the same (I constant), Eq. (15-3) may be written as

$$(L_1)M_1 + 2(L_1 + L_2)M_2 + (L_2)M_3 = -\frac{6A_1(x_{c1})_1}{L_1} - \frac{6A_2(x_{c2})_3}{L_2} \qquad (15\text{-}4)$$

Equations (15-3) and (15-4) are based upon the concepts of the area-moment theorems and relate the bending moment at any three successive supports to the loads carried by the intervening spans. For a beam having n unknown moments, a set of n equations is written and solved simultaneously.

The three-moment Eqs. (15-3) and (15-4) may be used to find the bending moment at each support point of a continuous beam for which each support is at the same elevation. These equations incorporate the sign convention adopted in Chap. 12 that a computed value of M having a positive sign has the direction shown in Fig. 15-7 (B). A computed negative value of M would have the opposite direction.

The bending moments M_1, M_2, and M_3 are not part of the factors on the right-hand side of Eqs. (15-3) and (15-4). These factors are obtained by treating each span as a simple beam as shown in Fig. 15-7 (C). The moment diagrams for these simple beams are shown in Fig. 15-7 (D). The quantity $A_1(x_{c1})_1$ for example, represents the area-moment of the area under the moment diagram

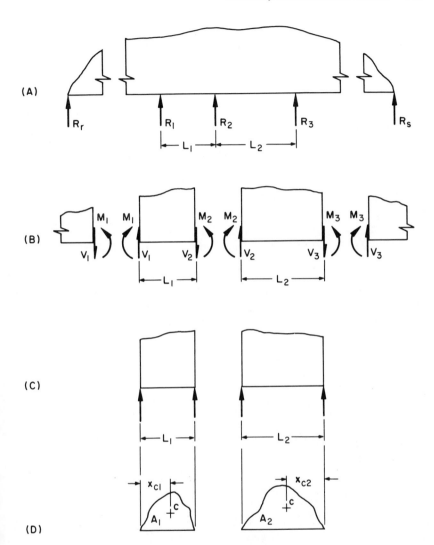

Figure 15-7. Continuous beam.

about an axis through point 1 at the left-hand end of the span having a length L_1. It is usually most convenient to draw the moment diagram by parts.

Problem 15-4 will consider a two-span beam wherein the spans are of different cross-sectional area and Problem 15-5 covers a beam having more than two spans.

Problem 15-4 Reactions for a continuous beam having portions of different moments of inertia

Find the reactions for the beam shown in Fig. 15-8 if the moment of inertia of the cross section of the left span is 10 in.[4] and of the right span is 5 in.[4] The beam is continuous over the three supports.

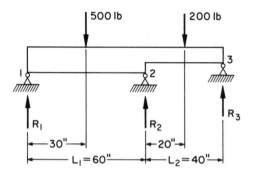

Figure 15-8

Solution:

The beam is continuous and, before the reactions can be calculated, the bending moment within the beam at each reaction must be known. The free-body diagram for each span showing the assumed positive directions of bending moment is given in Fig. 15-9 (A). Since the value of E is not given, assume that the beam material is homogeneous throughout. However, the moments of inertia of the spans are different and the form of the three-moment equation given by Eq. (15-3) is applicable.

$$\left(\frac{L_1}{E_1 I_1}\right)M_1 + 2\left(\frac{L_1}{E_1 I_1} + \frac{L_2}{E_2 I_2}\right)M_2 + \left(\frac{L_2}{E_2 I_2}\right)M_3 = -\left(\frac{6A_1(x_{c1})_1}{E_1 I_1 L_1}\right)$$
$$-\left(\frac{6A_2(x_{c2})_3}{E_2 I_2 L_2}\right)$$

Since $E_1 = E_2 = E$ and $I_1 = 2I_2$,

$$\left(\frac{L_1}{2}\right)M_1 + 2\left(\frac{L_1}{2} + L_2\right)M_2 + (L_2)M_3 = -\left(\frac{6A_1(x_{c1})_1}{2L_1}\right) - \left(\frac{6A_2(x_{c2})_3}{L_2}\right)$$

To determine the quantities on the right-hand side of the three-moment equation, each span is treated as a simple beam in Fig. 15-9 (B) with the corresponding moment diagram given in Fig. 15-9 (C).

$$\left(\frac{6}{2L_1}\right)A_1(x_{c1})_1 = \frac{6}{2(60)}\left[\frac{1}{2}(15,000)(60)(20) + \frac{1}{2}(-15,000)(30)(10)\right]$$
$$= 338 \times 10^3$$
$$\left(\frac{6}{L_2}\right)A_2(x_{c2})_3 = \frac{6}{40}\left[\frac{1}{2}(4000)(40)(13.33) + \frac{1}{2}(-4000)(20)(6.67)\right]$$
$$= 120 \times 10^3$$

The moment M_1 is zero because there is no force acting to the left of reaction R_1 that could cause a moment at point 1. Also, M_3 is zero because no force acts to the right of R_3.

$$M_1 = 0 \qquad \text{and} \qquad M_3 = 0$$

Substitute into the three-moment equation,

$$2\left(\frac{60}{2} + 40\right)M_2 = -(338 \times 10^3) - (120 \times 10^3)$$

$$M_2 = -3.28 \times 10^3 \text{ in.-lb}$$

The negative sign of the computed value of M_2 indicates that it acts in a direction opposite to that depicted in Fig. 15-9 (A).

The reactions are calculated by applying Eq. (12-2) as follows:

Reaction R_1:

$$\circlearrowleft + \Sigma M_L = \text{bending moment } M_2 \text{ at point 2}$$

$$R_1(60) - 500(30) = -3.28 \times 10^3$$

$$R_1 = 195.3 \text{ lb} \qquad Answer$$

Reaction R_2:

$$\circlearrowleft + \Sigma M_L = \text{bending moment } M_3 \text{ at point 3}$$

$$(195.3)(100) - 500(70) + R_2(40) - 200(20) = 0$$

$$R_2 = 487 \text{ lb} \qquad Answer$$

Reaction R_3:

$$+\circlearrowright \Sigma M_R = \text{bending moment } M_2 \text{ at point 2}$$

$$R_3(40) - 200(20) = -3.28 \times 10^3$$

$$R_3 = 18 \text{ lb} \qquad Answer$$

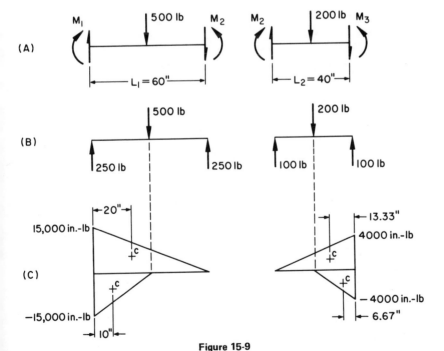

Figure 15-9

Check the results:

$$\Sigma F_V = 0 \qquad R_1 + R_2 + R_3 - 500 - 200 = 0$$
$$195 + 487 + 18 - 500 - 200 = 0$$
$$0 = 0$$

Problem 15-5 Continuous beam having three spans

Calculate the reactions for the beam shown in Fig. 15-10.

Solution:

The beam is continuous and, before the reactions can be calculated, it is necessary to know the moments in the beam at the reactions. A free-body diagram for each span showing the assumed positive directions of bending moment is given in Fig. 15-11 (A). Since the values of E and I are not provided, assume that the beam material is homogeneous throughout and that the beam is everywhere of constant cross section. Therefore the form of the three-moment equation given by Eq. (15-4) is applicable and is applied to the first and second spans and again to the second and third spans.

$$(L_1)M_1 + 2(L_1 + L_2)M_2 + (L_2)M_3 = -\left(\frac{6A_1(x_{c1})_1}{L_1}\right) - \left(\frac{6A_2(x_{c2})_3}{L_2}\right)$$

$$(L_2)M_2 + 2(L_2 + L_3)M_3 + (L_3)M_4 = -\left(\frac{6A_2(x_{c2})_2}{L_2}\right) - \left(\frac{6A_3(x_{c3})_4}{L_3}\right)$$

In Fig. 15-11 (B) each span is treated as a simple beam with the corresponding moment diagrams given in Fig. 15-11 (C). The quantities on the right-hand side of the three-moment equation are determined using these moment diagrams that for convenience are prepared by parts.

$$\left(\frac{6}{L_1}\right)A_1(x_{c1})_1 = \frac{6}{10}\left[\frac{1}{2}(1250)(10)(3.33) + \frac{1}{3}(-1250)(5)(1.25)\right] = 10,930$$

$$\left(\frac{6}{L_2}\right)A_2(x_{c2})_3 = \frac{6}{8}\left[\frac{1}{2}(1600)(8)(2.67) + \frac{1}{2}(-1600)(4)(1.33)\right] = 9570$$

$$\left(\frac{6}{L_2}\right)A_2(x_{c2})_2 = \frac{6}{8}\left[\frac{1}{2}(1600)(8)(5.33) + \frac{1}{2}(-1600)(4)(6.67)\right] = 9570$$

$$\left(\frac{6}{L_3}\right)A_3(x_{c3})_4 = \frac{6}{10}\left[\frac{1}{2}(2500)(10)(3.33) + \frac{1}{3}(-2500)(10)(2.50)\right] = 12,500$$

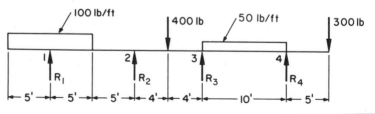

Figure 15-10

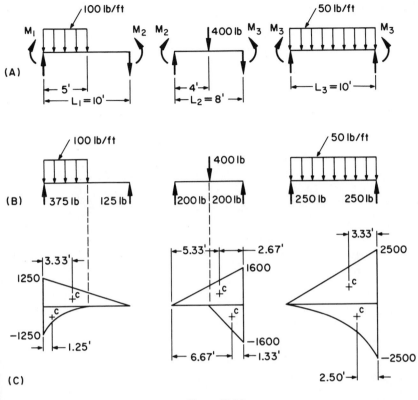

Figure 15-11

The moments M_1 and M_4 are directly calculable by applying Eq. (12-2) as follows.

$\big(\, + \Sigma M_L$ = bending moment M_1 at point $1 - (500)(2.5) = M_1$

$+\,\big)\, \Sigma M_R$ = bending moment M_4 at point $4 - (300)(5) = M_4$

$M_1 = -1250$ ft-lb $\qquad M_4 = -1500$ ft-lb

The values of M_1 and M_4 were computed following the same sign convention incorporated into the three-moment equation. Therefore the proper algebraic signs must be retained when substitution is made into the three-moment equations.

$(10)(-1250) + 2(10 + 8)M_2 + (8)M_3 = -(10{,}930) - (9570)$

$(8)M_2 + 2(8 + 10)M_3 + (10)(-1500) = -(9570) - (12{,}500)$

which reduces to

$(36)M_2 + (8)M_3 = -8000 \qquad\qquad\qquad (15\text{-}5)$

$(8)M_2 + (36)M_3 = -7070 \qquad\qquad\qquad (15\text{-}6)$

Multiply Eq. (15-6) by 4.5 and subtract Eq. (15-6) from Eq. (15-5):

$$(36)M_2 + (8)M_3 = -8000$$
$$(36)M_2 + (162)M_3 = -31,800$$
$$\overline{-(154)M_3 = 23,800}$$
$$M_3 = -154.7 \text{ ft-lb}$$

Solving for M_2,

$$(36)M_2 + 8(-154.7) = -8000$$
$$M_2 = -188.1 \text{ ft-lb}$$

The negative signs of the computed values of M_1, M_2, M_3, and M_4 indicate that these moments act in a direction opposite to that depicted in Fig. 15-11 (A).

The reactions are calculated by applying Eq. (12-2) as follows:

Reaction R_1:

$$\big(+ \Sigma M_L = \text{bending moment } M_2 \text{ at point 2}$$
$$-(1000)(10) + R_1(10) = -188.1$$
$$R_1 = 981 \text{ lb} \qquad \textit{Answer}$$

Reaction R_2:

$$\big(+ \Sigma M_L = \text{bending moment } M_3 \text{ at point 3}$$
$$-(1000)(18) + (981)(18) + R_2(8) - (400)(4) = -154.7$$
$$R_2 = 222 \text{ lb} \qquad \textit{Answer}$$

For determining R_3 and R_4, it is more convenient to make the moment summation from the right. Again apply Eq. (12-2):

Reaction R_4:

$$+\big) \Sigma M_R = \text{bending moment } M_3 \text{ at point 3}$$
$$-(300)(15) + R_4(10) - (500)(5) = -154.7$$
$$R_4 = 685 \text{ lb} \qquad \textit{Answer}$$

Reaction R_3:

$$+\big) \Sigma M_R = \text{bending moment } M_2 \text{ at point 2}$$
$$-(300)(23) + (685)(18) - (500)(13) + R_3(8) - (400)(4) = -188.1$$
$$R_3 = 312 \text{ lb}$$
$$\textit{Answer}$$

Check the results:

$$\Sigma F_V = 0 \qquad R_1 + R_2 + R_3 + R_4 - 1000 - 400 - 500 - 300 = 0$$
$$981 + 222 + 312 + 685 - 1000 - 400 - 500 - 300 = 0$$

chapter 16

COLUMN DESIGN

16-1 COMPRESSION MEMBERS

Compression members are classified in accordance with their mode of failure. A steel compression member that fails by yielding, upon the application of an excessive axial load, is known as a *compression block*. Yield failure is characterized by a lateral bulging, as shown in Fig. 16-1. The stress developed is a direct compressive stress f_a given by Eq. (11-1): $f_a = P/A$, and complete failure occurs if f_a is increased to the point where the ultimate stress is exceeded. The compression block usually has a length of not more than ten times its least lateral dimension.

Compression members in which bending action contributes significantly to failure are known as columns. Bending action results because the applied load cannot be positioned so that its line of action will pass through the centroid of every cross section. In Fig. 16-2 the dashed line passes through the centroid of each cross section of the column and the line of action of the axial load is shown by the heavy solid line. It is impossible to make these

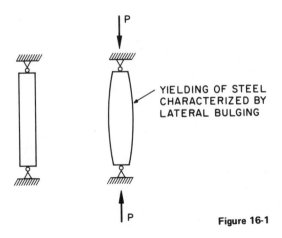

P

YIELDING OF STEEL
CHARACTERIZED BY
LATERAL BULGING

P

Figure 16-1

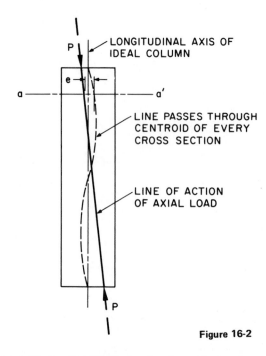

Figure 16-2

lines coincident with the longitudinal axis of an ideal column because of the incapability of so exactly positioning the axial load and because of the inherent imperfections that are incorporated during the column fabrication process such as nonhomogeneity of the material and the inability to make the column perfectly straight. For a typical section aa' the bending moment about its centroid is Pe where e is the eccentricity. A summation of the moments about the centroid of each cross section will result in a net bending moment.

The net bending moment causes flexural stress to develop. The longer a column of a given lateral dimension is made, the greater will be its flexibility and propensity for bending. Bending action occurs in compression blocks but its effect is negligible.

A *long column* is a column in which essentially only flexural stress develops, the effect of any direct compressive stress being insignificant. Failure occurs through the action of excessive bending and is known as buckling.

Between the compression block and the long column is the *intermediate column*. In this member direct compressive stress and flexural stress combine to produce failure by yielding and buckling.

A measure of a column's propensity for bending is indicated by the slenderness ratio L/r, where L is the *unsupported* column length and r is the radius of gyration with respect to the axis about which the column tends to bend. The slenderness ratio forms part of the column design formulas and into these formulas its *maximum value* should be substituted. A column hinged at both ends in a way that imposes no restraint on bending in any direction, and to which no lateral support is applied to any point along its entire

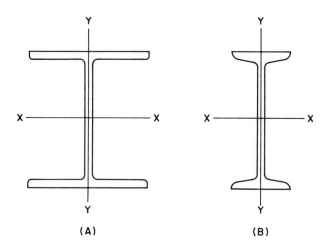

Figure 16-3. (A) WF column section and (B) American Standard I column section.

length, will tend to bend about the axis of the transverse cross-sectional area with respect to which the radius of gyration is a minimum. Therefore, for this column, the minimum value of r should be used in establishing the slenderness ratio L/r.

Transverse cross sections typical of WF and I columns are shown in Fig. 16-3. The axis X-X is known as the *major axis* or *strong axis* and with respect to it the radius of gyration is a maximum. The axis Y-Y is called the *minor axis* or *weak axis*, and with respect to it the radius of gyration is a minimum. In dealing with built-up column sections, the designations OX and OY will be used to indicate the centroidal axes.

Unless it is otherwise specified, the hinged connections at the ends of a column permit it to rotate in any direction, i.e., they impose no restraint on bending. If a column problem does not specify the nature of the end connections, the problem should be solved by assuming hinged-end connections. Other types of end connections, e.g., fixed, free, etc., sometimes require that the value of L used to calculate the slenderness ratio L/r be modified. This is taken up in Sec. 16-3.

If a column is laterally supported at only one principal axis, the maximum slenderness ratio may not necessarily correspond to the minimum radius of gyration. Consider the 30-ft 14WF87 hinged column shown in Fig. 16-4. Lateral support is applied to the Y-Y axis of the column at its midpoint by means of a bracing connection. This connection acts as a hinge and prevents lateral movement of the midpoint. Also and most important, the bracing connection reduces the unsupported length of the column to 15 ft for bending about the Y-Y axis. Therefore, with respect to the Y-Y axis, the slenderness ratio is

$$\left(\frac{L}{r}\right)_{Y\text{-}Y} = \frac{L}{r_{Y\text{-}Y}} = \frac{(15)(12)}{3.70} = 48.7$$

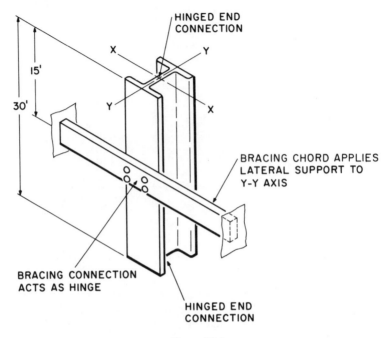

Figure 16-4

The entire 30-ft length of the column is still free to bend about the X-X axis because the lateral support applied to the Y-Y axis does not prevent the movement of the midpoint in the plane perpendicular to the plane of the bracing connection. Therefore, with respect to the X-X axis, the slenderness ratio is

$$\left(\frac{L}{r}\right)_{X\text{-}X} = \frac{L}{r_{X\text{-}X}} = \frac{(30)(12)}{6.15} = 58.6 \text{ max}$$

Because lateral support is applied only to the Y-Y axis, the maximum value of slenderness ratio is with respect to the X-X axis.

If a problem does not specify to which axis the lateral bracing is applied, assume that the bracing is applied to both principal axes. Consider the above 14WF87 column to have lateral support applied to both principal axes at the midpoint. Then the unsupported column length would be 15 ft for bending about both the X-X and Y-Y axes. The maximum value of the slenderness ratio is now with respect to the Y-Y axis. Compare:

$$\left(\frac{L}{r}\right)_{X\text{-}X} = \frac{L}{r_{X\text{-}X}} = \frac{(15)(12)}{6.15} = 29.3$$

$$\left(\frac{L}{r}\right)_{Y\text{-}Y} = \frac{L}{r_{Y\text{-}Y}} = \frac{(15))12)}{3.70} = 48.7 \text{ max}$$

A hinged column laterally unsupported along its entire length will tend to buckle about the axis of the transverse cross section with respect to which the radius of gyration is a minimum. In order to make the column equally resistant to bending about both principal axes, it is necessary to make the radii of gyration with respect to these axes equal.

The moment of inertia I of the transverse cross section of area A about its axis is related to the radius of gyration with respect to that same axis by the relation $I = Ar^2$. Therefore, the column will be made equally resistant to bending about both principal axes if the moments of inertia with respect to these axes are made equal.

Problem 16-1 Design of a column section for equal resistance to bending about both major axes

A column is to consist of two 12-in., 25-lb channels laced together as shown in Fig. 16-5. Find the distance b between channels, back to back, so that moments of inertia about the X-axis and the Y-axis are equal. (Neglect the effect of lacing.)

Solution:

The question might have been worded: "Find the distance b between channels, back to back, so that the column is equally resistant to bending about both principal axes," since this is the condition obtained when the moments of inertia about these axes are made equal.

The distance b is found by setting up the expressions for moment of inertia with respect to the principal axes and equating them. Use Eq. (2-7) to obtain an expression for the moment of inertia about the OX-axis. Refer to the AISC Manual for the geometric properties of the 12-in., 25-lb channels

$$I_X = \sum_{n=1}^{n=p} I_{OXn} + \sum_{n=1}^{n=p} a_n y_{cn}^2$$

$$I_{OX} = \sum_{n=1}^{n=2} I_{OXn} + \sum_{n=1}^{n=2} a_n y_{cn}^2 = 143.5 + 143.5 + (7.32)(0) + (7.32)(0)$$

$$= 287 \text{ in.}^4$$

Use Eq. (2-8) to obtain an expression for the moment of inertia about the OY-axis.

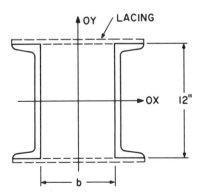

Figure 16-5

$$I_Y = \sum_{n=1}^{n=p} I_{OYn} + \sum_{n=1}^{n=p} a_n x_{cn}^2$$

$$I_{OY} = \sum_{n=1}^{n=2} I_{OYn} + \sum_{n=1}^{n=2} a_n x_{cn}^2 = 4.5 + 4.5 + (7.32)\left(\frac{b}{2} + 0.68\right)^2 + (7.32)$$

$$\times \left(\frac{b}{2} + 0.68\right)^2$$

$$= 9 + 2(7.32)(b/2 + 0.68)^2$$

Notice carefully that the moment arm for the transfer moment of inertia includes the 0.68-in. distance from the back of the channel to its centroid.

Equating I_{OX} and I_{OY} and solving for b,

$$287 = 9 + 2(7.32)\left(\frac{b}{2} + 0.68\right)^2$$

$$b = 7.36, -10.08$$

The negative value of b is meaningless; therefore,

$$b = 7.36 \text{ in.} \qquad Answer$$

Problem 16-2 Least radius of gyration for a column section

A steel column section is made up of a 12-in. X $\frac{3}{8}$ in. web plate and 4 angles 6 in. X 4 in. X $\frac{3}{8}$ in. with the short leg attached to the plate. What is the least radius of gyration of the column?

Solution:

From the statement of the problem, the built-up section is drawn as shown in Fig. 16-6.

The transverse cross-sectional area of the column is symmetrical and the centroidal axes OX and OY can be located by inspection.

The least radius of gyration occurs with respect to one of the principal centroidal axes. The problem is solved by computing the radius of gyration with respect to both principal axes and comparing.

Use Eq. (2-7) to find the moment of inertia of the composite area with respect to its OX-axis. The geometric properties of the angles are listed in the AISC Manual.

$$I_X = \sum_{n=1}^{n=p} I_{OXn} + \sum_{n=1}^{n=p} a_n y_{cn}^2$$

$$I_{OX} = \sum_{n=1}^{n=5} I_{OXn} + \sum_{n=1}^{n=5} a_n y_{cn}^2 = 4(4.9) + \left(\frac{1}{12}\right)\left(\frac{3}{8}\right)(12)^3$$

$$+ 4(3.61)(6 - 0.94)^2 + \left(\frac{3}{8}\right)(12)(0)^2$$

$$= 444 \text{ in.}^4$$

Calculate the radius of gyration with respect to the OX-axis.

$$r_{OX} = \sqrt{I_{OX}/A} = \sqrt{444/18.94} = 4.849 \text{ in.}$$

Use Eq. (2-8) to find the moment of inertia of the composite area with respect to its OY-axis.

$$I_Y = \sum_{n=1}^{n=p} I_{OYn} + \sum_{n=1}^{n=p} a_n x_{cn}^2$$

$$I_{OY} = \sum_{n=1}^{n=5} I_{OYn} + \sum_{n=1}^{n=5} a_n x_{cn}^2 = 4(13.5) + \frac{1}{12}(12)\left(\frac{3}{8}\right)^3$$

$$+ 4(3.61)\left[1.94 + \frac{1}{2}\left(\frac{3}{8}\right)\right]^2 + \left(\frac{3}{8}\right)(12)(0)^2$$

$$= 119.5 \text{ in.}^4$$

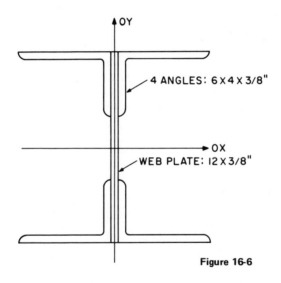

OY

4 ANGLES: 6 X 4 X 3/8"

OX
WEB PLATE: 12 X 3/8"

Figure 16-6

Calculate the radius of gyration with respect to the OY-axis.

$$r_{OY} = \sqrt{I_{OY}/A} = \sqrt{119.5/18.94} = 2.513 \text{ in.}$$

Therefore, the least radius of gyration of the column is with respect to the OY-axis.

$$r_{OY} = 2.51 \text{ in.} \qquad \textit{Answer}$$

If the column is hinged at both ends and no lateral support is applied to its entire length, it will tend to bend about the OY-axis.

16-2   THE COLUMN CURVE AND EULER'S EQUATION

If a great many steel compression members all having a different slenderness ratio L/r are loaded to ultimate failure with axial load P, a column curve approximating that shown in Fig. 16-7 can be plotted. The curve is a plot of the critical load P/A for any given slenderness ratio L/r and is drawn for A7 structural steel, which has a proportional limit of 30,000 psi, a specified yield point stress of 33,000 psi, and an ultimate stress of 40,000 psi. For compression blocks the critical load is synonymous with the actual stress in the column because this stress is for all practical purposes entirely direct compressive.

However, for columns, the critical load P/A is not to be confused with actual stress in the column; it is really the load expressed in pounds per square inch which if exceeded will cause failure. It is not the actual stress because failure is brought about by a combination of compressive and flexural stresses in the case of intermediate columns and by primarily flexural stress in the case of long slender columns.

The lower values of L/r from zero to about 60 correspond to compression blocks and ultimate failure occurs when the compressive stress reaches its ultimate value. Intermediate columns lie in the slenderness ratio range in the vicinity of between 60 and 150. The column curve slopes downward after passing L/r = 60, showing that the critical load that a member can withstand becomes less and less with increasing slenderness ratio. The downward slope is axiomatic of the ever increasing effect of bending action on the ability of a column to support an axial load.

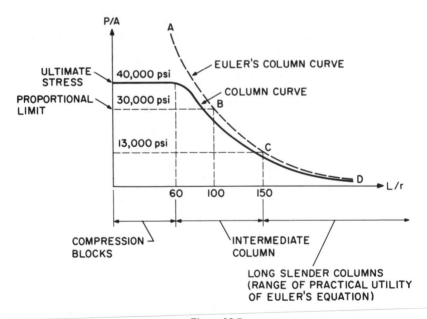

Figure 16-7

Many equations have been developed to express analytically the relation between P/A and L/r for intermediate columns. To name just a few, there are the parabolic, Gordon-Rankine, secant, and straight-line equations, which are all discussed in any texts on strength of materials. These equations are empirical because of the inherent imperfections incorporated during column fabrication and the eccentricity resulting from the practical inability to position the axial load so that its line of action coincides with the longitudinal column axis. The AISC has adopted a form of the parabolic equation that is discussed in Sec. 16-4.

Imagine the long slender steel column of Fig. 16-8 to be loaded with an axial force that is gradually increased. If no eccentricities and fabrication imperfections existed, no bending would occur and since steel is a ductile material, the column would fail by yielding in the same manner as shown for the compression block of Fig. 16-1. But this is not the case and as the axial load is increased, the lateral deflection δ becomes ever greater until a critical load is reached. The critical load is an ultimate load and if the axial load is increased beyond this value, the column will fail through the action of excessive bending and buckling. The critical value of axial load is known as the Euler critical load and is given by Euler's equation $P = EI\pi^2/L^2$, where L is the unbraced column length and I is the moment of inertia of the transverse cross-sectional area A with respect to the axis about which the column tends to bend.

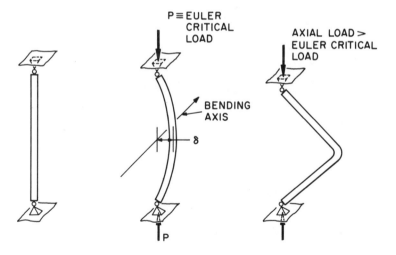

Figure 16-8

It is desirable to write Euler's equation in terms of slenderness ratio L/r. Using Eq. (2-10) to express I in terms of A and the radius of gyration r, and substituting

$$\frac{P}{A} = \frac{E\pi^2}{(L/r)^2}$$

(16-1)

The Euler equation is graphically represented by the dashed curve in Fig. 16-7. Notice that P/A is a parabolic function of L/r and becomes ever greater as L/r lowers in value. If there were no limit on the strength of the steel, then the curve would extend and approach the P/A axis asymptotically. Ideally, Euler's equation should be valid only down to the value of L/r that corresponds to a stress equal to the proportional limit because above this stress, the modulus of elasticity E becomes nonlinear. This point is designated B in Fig. 16-7. At this point and only at this point is the critical load expressed by the Euler equation synonymous with the actual stress in an ideal column.

The value of L/r at point B may be calculated by substituting into Eq. (16-1) the stress at the proportional limit that for A7 structural steel is 30,000 psi and the modulus of elasticity E taken as 29×10^6 psi.

$$\frac{L}{r} = \sqrt{\frac{E\pi^2}{P/A}} = \sqrt{\frac{(29 \times 10^6)\pi^2}{30 \times 10^3}} \approx 100$$

The critical load P/A given by Eq. (16-1) is expressed in pounds per square inch and is not to be confused with the actual stress in the column for values of $L/r > 100$. It is the load that if exceeded, causes failure of the column.

However, for practical steel columns, the Euler equation is useful to describe column action only for long, slender columns where the values of slenderness ratio are greater than about 150. This is shown in Fig. 16-7 where for values of L/r lower than 150, the Euler curve and the experimentally determined column curve diverge rapidly.

It will be seen in Sec. 16-4 that the AISC specifies the use of Euler's equation for values of slenderness ratio somewhat lower than 150. The Euler equation so specified incorporates a factor of safety adequate to cover any divergence between the experimental and analytical curves.

Although structural steels have different specified yield points, all have the same modulus of elasticity E. In the range of its practical application, the critical load given by Euler's equation is not a function of the strength of the material; rather, it is a function of E and L/r. Since E is independent of the strength of structural steel, a long, slender column made of low-cost A7 structural steel will support the same load as, say, high-cost, high-strength silicon structural steel.

16-3   EFFECTIVE COLUMN LENGTH

The column curve demonstrates the very profound effect that increasing slenderness ratio has on the load-carrying capability of a column. Also affecting a column's load-carrying capability is the degree to which rotation of the column ends is restrained. In the Euler equation considered in the preceding section, and in the parabolic equation that is discussed in Sec. 16-4, the slenderness ratio is really the effective slenderness ratio KL/r wherein the actual unbraced length L is modified by the effective length factor K to give the effective column length KL. In Secs. 16-1 and 16-2, it was assumed that every column was hinged at its ends in a way that imposed no restraint on rotation and for this condition K = 1. Zero moment exists at such end connections and the effective length then is the distance between points of zero moment.

It will be recalled from Sec. 12-3, that points of inflection are points on the elastic curve at which the curve changes concavity and at which the bending moment passes through zero. A column having both ends ideally fixed is shown in Fig. 16-9; this column changes concavity at the points indicated and the effective length KL is 0.5L. The effective length factor K for centrally loaded columns with various idealized end conditions is given in Fig. 16-10. The recommended values of K take cognizance of the fact that in practice true fixed ends are not realizable.

The recommended values of K in cases (A), (B), (C), (E), and (F) of Fig. 16-10 are not to be used unless it is made clear that the end connection approaches a true fixed end. If this latter condition is not clearly established, then it must be assumed that the column is hinged to end connections that impose no rotational restraint. Indeed, because of the indeterminate nature of column fabrication imperfections and the likelihood that the axial load will be somewhat eccentric, it is customary to assume rotation-free hinged-end connections for which, as case (D) indicates, K = 1.

16-4 AISC COLUMN FORMULA

The column curve of Fig. 16-7 is typical of test results obtained for compression members that are tested to failure. The curve gives the critical load expressed in pounds per square inch at which ultimate failure occurs for any given slenderness ratio. For design purposes, it is desirable to have an equation that establishes a relation between the safe or *allowable* load and the slenderness ratio; the equation when plotted should approximate the shape of the experimental column curve. These qualifications are provided by the AISC Column Formula.

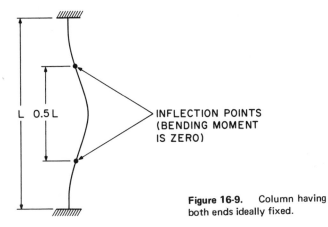

L   0.5 L

INFLECTION POINTS
(BENDING MOMENT
IS ZERO)

Figure 16-9. Column having both ends ideally fixed.

	(A)	(B)	(C)	(D)	(E)	(F)
BUCKLED SHAPE OF COLUMN IS SHOWN BY SOLID LINE	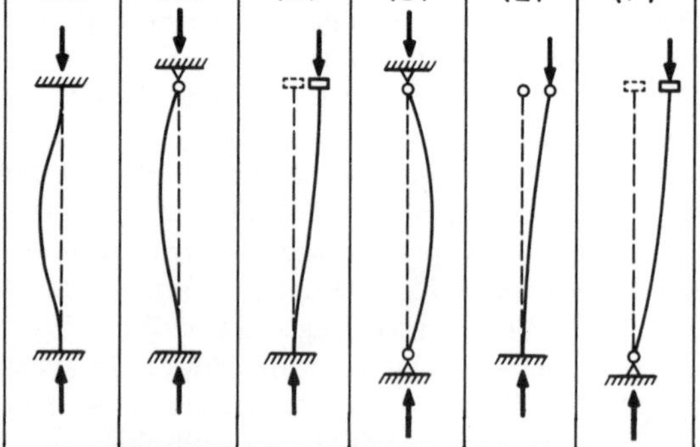					
THEORETICAL K VALUE	0.5	0.7	1.0	1.0	2.0	2.0
RECOMMENDED K VALUE WHEN IDEAL CONDITION IS APPROXIMATED	0.65	0.80	1.2	1.0	2.10	2.0
END CONDITION CODE	ROTATION FIXED		TRANSLATION FIXED			
	ROTATION FREE		TRANSLATION FIXED			
	ROTATION FIXED		TRANSLATION FREE			
	ROTATION FREE		TRANSLATION FREE			

Figure 16-10.   Effective length factor K for centrally loaded columns. (*Guide to Design Criteria for Metal Compression Members,* Column Research Counsel, Second Edition, Chapter 2.)

For axially loaded compression members, the AISC Specification provides: "On the gross section of axially loaded compression members when KL/r, the *largest* effective slenderness ratio of any *unbraced* segment, is less than C_c,"

$$f_a = P/A = \frac{\left[1 - \frac{(KL/r)^2}{2C_c^2}\right] f_y}{F.S.}$$ (16-2)

where

$$F.S. = \text{factor of safety} = \frac{5}{3} + \frac{3(KL/r)}{8C_c} - \frac{(KL/r)^3}{8C_c^3}$$ (16-3)

and

$$C_c = \sqrt{\frac{2\pi^2 E}{f_y}}$$ (16-4)

Recall that in Sec. 16-3 it was observed that the recommended values of K in cases (A), (B), (C), (E), and (F) of Fig. 16-10 are not to be used unless it is made clear that the end connection approaches a true fixed end. If this latter condition is not clearly established, then it must be assumed that the column is hinged to end connections that impose no rotational restraint for which, as case (D), Fig. 16-10, indicates, $K = 1$.

An illustration of the kind of language that would establish the existence of end connections approaching a true fixed end is: "A 12WF50 beam used as a column *with flat ends.*" This column would be covered by case (A) of Fig. 16-10 and the *recommended* value of 0.65 for K would be used.

f_a in the AISC column formula, Eq. (16-2), is the *allowable* axial load P/A expressed in pounds per square inch rather than a critical load because the formula incorporates the proper factor of safety. Equation (16-2) enables the determination of the allowable load for both compression blocks and intermediate columns, and incorporates the steel strength as evidenced by the specified yield point stress f_y. This is an important factor influencing the load-carrying capability of compression blocks and intermediate columns, the former failing in whole, and the latter failing in part, as a consequence of direct axial stress.

The range of effective slenderness ratio values over which Eq. (16-2) is applicable extends from zero at the lower limit to an upper-limit value of KL/r equal to C_c, i.e.,

$$KL/r = C_c = \sqrt{2\pi^2 E/f_y} \tag{16-4}$$

where the modulus of elasticity E for steel is taken as 29×10^6 psi and f_y is the specified yield point stress of the particular steel used.

Just as the allowable load is expressed in terms of effective slenderness ratio KL/r, so is the factor of safety. This causes the factor of safety to increase with increasing KL/r, thereby taking cognizance of the greater propensity for bending of the intermediate columns as the upper limit C_c is approached. The variable factor of safety recognizes that the increased susceptibility to bending and the associated flexural stresses will permit ever lower allowable loads to be carried as the slenderness ratio increases.

Equation (16-2) is applicable to compression blocks and all columns whose effective slenderness ratio KL/r is less than C_c, the latter being intermediate columns. For long slender columns, i.e., for columns having an effective slenderness ratio KL/r greater than C_c, the AISC Specification provides that the allowable load f_a shall be determined from the Euler equation. The Euler equation so specified incorporates a factor of safety of 1.92.

$$f_a = \frac{P}{A} = \frac{E\pi^2}{(F.S.)(KL/r)^2} = \frac{(29 \times 10^6)(\pi^2)}{(1.92)(KL/r)^2} = \frac{149 \times 10^6}{(KL/r)^2} \tag{16-5}$$

This equation does not incorporate the specified yield point stress f_y of the particular steel employed and can be used as it stands for all grades of steel. It will be recalled that this characteristic is axiomatic of long slender columns where failure is caused by excessive bending that bears no relation to steel strength.

Figure 16-11 shows a graphical representation of the column design Eqs. (16-2) and (16-5) for A7 steel. The parabolic design Eq. (16-2) extends with complete continuity into the Euler design Eq. (16-5) at $KL/r = C_c$. This composite curve very closely approximates the shape of the column

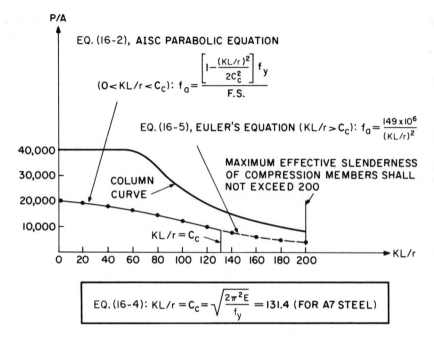

Figure 16-11.   Column curve and curve representing the AISC analytical column design equation. This curve is drawn here for A7 steel (f_y = 33,000 psi).

curve drawn some distance above. The displacement of the composite curve beneath the column curve reflects the incorporation into the design equations of the requisite factors of safety.

The AISC Specification requires that the effective slenderness ratio KL/r of compression members shall not exceed 200; this too is indicated in Fig. 16-11.

Equations (16-2) and (16-5) may also be used in the design of axially loaded bracing and secondary members having a slenderness ratio L/r of up to 120. For bracing and secondary members having a value of L/r exceeding 120, the AISC specification requires that the allowable load calculated by either Eq. (16-2) or (16-5) be divided by (1.6 − L/200r), i.e., the allowable load for bracing and secondary members having a slenderness ratio greater than 120 is

$$f_a = \frac{P}{A} = \frac{f_a[\text{by Eq. (16-2) or (16-5)}]}{(1.6 - L/200r)} \tag{16-6}$$

For bracing and secondary members, the value of K is always taken as unity.

To eliminate the burdensome calculations associated with Eqs. (16-2), (16-5), and (16-6), the AISC publishes a set of tables for each of the important steels as designated by their specified yield point stress f_y. These tables list the allowable load f_a calculated for each value of effective slenderness ratio

KL/r. For example, what is the allowable load that a steel column, having a KL/r value of 90, may carry? The steel used has a 33,000 psi specified yield point stress. Turn to the Manual and in the appropriate table read the value of f_a: 13.43 ksi. Therefore, the allowable load f_a which the column may carry expressed in pounds per square inch is 13,430 psi.

The tables also list the allowable load f_{as} for bracing and secondary members having a slenderness ratio L/r greater than 120 but not exceeding 200.

Problem 16-3 Allowable load that a laterally unsupported column may carry

A steel H-column is made up of a 12-in. X 3/8-in. web plate and four 6-in. X 4-in. X 3/8-in. angles with the long legs outstanding. What axial load may be placed on this column if its length is 20 ft?

Solution:

The problem makes no reference to the nature of the end connections. Therefore, it is assumed that the column is hinged at both ends in a way that imposes no restraint on bending in any direction. Also, there is no lateral support applied to any point along its entire length. A column fulfilling these conditions will tend to bend about the axis of the transverse cross-sectional area with respect to which the radius of gyration is a minimum. And for this column, the minimum value of r establishes the maximum value of effective slenderness ratio KL/r. It is the maximum value of KL/r that is used in the appropriate column formula. Recall from Sec. 16-1 that this is not necessarily true if there is lateral bracing of the axis of minimum r at a point or points along the length of the column.

Since the column has hinged end connections and is free to rotate about these ends, the effective length factor K is unity, K = 1, and the effective length KL is equal to the actual length of 20 ft.

The least radius of gyration for a column having the same section was found in Problem 16-2 to be 2.51 in. with respect to the OY-axis. The column section is shown in Fig. 16-5.

The effective slenderness ratio can now be calculated.

$$\frac{KL}{r} = \frac{(1)(20)(12)}{2.51} = 95.6$$

With Eq. (16-4), calculate C_c and compare with KL/r = 95.6 to ascertain which column equation is applicable. No steel type is specified, so assume that A7 steel is used. This steel has a specified yield point stress f_y of 33,000 psi.

$$C_c = \sqrt{\frac{2\pi^2 E}{f_y}} = \sqrt{\frac{2\pi^2(29 \times 10^6)}{33 \times 10^3}} = 131.4$$

The column has an effective slenderness ratio of 95.6, which is less than C_c. Therefore, the appropriate column formula is Eq. (16-2). If KL/r had been greater than C_c, then of course, the Euler formula, Eq. (16-5), would be applicable.

Calculate the factor of safety with Eq. (16-3):

$$F.S. = \frac{5}{3} + \frac{3(KL/r)}{8C_c} - \frac{(KL/r)^3}{8C_c^3} = \frac{5}{3} + \frac{3(95.6)}{8(131.4)} - \frac{(95.6)^3}{8(131.4)^3} = 1.893$$

Calculate the allowable load f_a with Eq. (16-2),

$$f_a = \frac{\left[1 - \frac{(KL/r)^2}{2C_c^2}\right]f_y}{F.S.} = \frac{\left[1 - \frac{(95.6)^2}{2(131.4)^2}\right]33 \times 10^3}{1.893} = 12,810 \text{ psi}$$

Calculate the axial load that may be placed on this column:

$P/A = f_a$

$A = 4(\text{area of } 6 \times 4 \times \frac{3}{8} \text{ angle}) + 12(\frac{3}{8}) = 4(3.61) + 12(\frac{3}{8}) = 18.94 \text{ in.}$

$P = f_a A = (12,810)(18.94)$

   $= 242,000 \text{ lb} \qquad Answer$

The preceding burdensome calculations are eliminated by using the set of tables included in the Appendix to the Specification of the Manual that list KL/r and f_a. Once the value of KL/r is established, it is a simple matter to find the value of f_a. Turn to the table in the AISC Manual, which lists KL/r and f_a for steel having $f_y = 33,000$ psi.

Enter the appropriate column at the KL/r value of 96, read the value of f_a: 12.81 ksi. The axial load that may be placed on this column is calculated as before:

$P = f_a A = (12.81)(1000)(18.94)$

   $= 242,000 \text{ lb} \qquad Answer$

If KL/r is less than C_c, always be certain that the table used corresponds to the strength of the steel employed. This is true because the parabolic Eq. (16-2), as emphasized in Sec. 16-4, contains as a factor the steel strength f_y.

Problem 16-4 Minimum column length for a given section for which Euler's formula is applicable

A rectangular steel bar 2 in. by 3 in. is used as a column with fixed ends. (a) Determine the minimum length at which Euler's formula can be used if the steel has a specified yield point stress of 36,000 psi. (b) What axial load may the column safely carry?

Solution:

(a) The AISC Specification states that Euler's equation shall be used for columns having an effective slenderness ratio KL/r equal to or greater than C_c.

$$KL/r = C_c = \sqrt{\frac{2\pi^2 E}{f_y}} \qquad (16-4)$$

In this equation the modulus of elasticity E for steel is taken as 29×10^6 psi and f_y is given as 36,000 psi.

$$C_c = KL/r = \sqrt{\frac{2\pi^2 E}{f_y}} = \sqrt{\frac{2\pi^2 (29 \times 10^6)}{36 \times 10^3}} = 126$$

The value of L that will just make KL/r equal to C_c is the lowest value for which Euler's formula is applicable. For columns having a length less than this minimum value, the AISC Specification requires that the parabolic Eq. (16-2) be used.

The column will tend to bend about the principal axis of the cross section with respect to which the radius of gyration is a minimum, there being no lateral support applied to the weak axis (axis of minimum r) at any point along the column length that could cause the effective slenderness ratio to be a maximum with respect to the strong axis (axis of maximum r). The existence of a maximum effective slenderness ratio with respect to the strong axis would cause the column to bend about the strong axis.

Refer to Fig. 16-12 and calculate the radius of gyration with respect to both principal axes and compare.

$$I_{OX} = (1/12)(b)(h)^3 = (1/12)(3)(2)^3 = 2 \text{ in.}^4$$

$$r_{OX} = \sqrt{I_{OX}/A} = \sqrt{2/6} = 0.578 \text{ in.}$$

$$I_{OY} = (1/12)(b)(h)^3 = (1/12)(2)(3)^3 = 4.5 \text{ in.}^4$$

$$r_{OY} = \sqrt{I_{OY}/A} = \sqrt{4.5/6} = 0.866 \text{ in.}$$

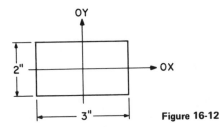

Figure 16-12

Therefore, the minimum radius of gyration of the column is with respect to the OX-axis, $r_{OX} = 0.578$ in.

The problem stipulates that the column has fixed-end connections. These end connections are assumed to impose an equivalent restraint on rotation in all directions. It is further assumed that the fixed ends approximate ideal conditions. This corresponds to case (A) of Fig. 16-10 and the recommended value of the effective length factor K is 0.65

Now the minimum length at which Euler's formula can be used may be calculated.

$$KL/r = 126$$

$$L = \frac{126(r)}{K} = \frac{(126)(0.578)}{0.65} = 112.1 \text{ in.}$$

$$= 9.34 \text{ ft} \qquad Answer$$

(b) The 10-ft column has a $KL/r > C_c$ and the Euler formula is applicable.

$$\frac{KL}{r} = \frac{(0.65)(10)(12)}{0.578} = 135.1 \text{ in.}$$

Substitute into Euler's formula, Eq. (16-5), and calculate the safe axial load.

$$f_a = P/A = \frac{149 \times 10^6}{(KL/r)^2} = \frac{149 \times 10^6}{(135.1)^2}$$

$$P = \frac{149 \times 10^6}{(135.1)^2}(A) = \frac{149 \times 10^6}{(135.1)^2}(6)$$

$$= 49,200 \text{ lb} \qquad Answer$$

Or turn to the tables in the AISC Manual. Enter the table at $KL/r = 135$ and read the value of f_a: 8.19 ksi. Solve for the safe axial load P:

$$P/A = f_a$$
$$P = (8.19)(1000)(6)$$
$$= 49,200 \text{ lb} \qquad Answer$$

The table for $f_y = 36,000$ psi was used. However, the table for any other steel strength could be used because $KL/r > C_c$. The Euler equation is applicable and, as emphasized in Sec. 16-4, it is independent of steel strength f_y.

chapter 17

REINFORCED TIMBER
AND CONCRETE STRUCTURES

Timber beams are sometimes reinforced by securing steel plates or channels to one or more longitudinal faces. In a somewhat similar manner concrete beams are reinforced with imbedded steel rods. Because materials of different modular elasticity are used, these beams are not homogeneous and the flexure formula is not applicable without some modification. The required modification is made by transforming the section into an equivalent homogeneous beam.

17-1 REINFORCED TIMBER BEAMS

The timber beam of Fig. 17-1(A) is reinforced by securely bolting a steel plate to its lower surface. Before the flexure formula can be used in an analysis of the beam, the section shown in Fig. 17-1(B) must be transformed into an equivalent homogeneous section of the same material, for example, by imagining the steel to be replaced with wood having a cross section adequate to carry the same load as the steel.

The composite beam acts as a unit, which means that the longitudinal deformation of each fiber, including the steel fibers, is directly proportional to its distance from the neutral axis. Since strain ϵ is merely the per unit deformation, the strain in a fiber also is directly proportional to this distance. Therefore, at the interface of the steel and wood, the strains of both materials are equal: $\epsilon_s = \epsilon_w$. Using the stress-strain relation $f = \epsilon E$, this condition can be expressed in terms of stress and modular elasticity.

$$\frac{f_s}{E_s} = \frac{f_w}{E_w} \qquad f_s = \frac{E_s}{E_w} f_w$$

Because the modular elasticity E_s of steel is much greater than the modular elasticity E_w of wood, the stress f_s in the steel is also much greater than the stress f_w in the wood; this is expressed algebraically by $f_s = n(f_w)$, where n is the ratio of the moduli of elasticity.

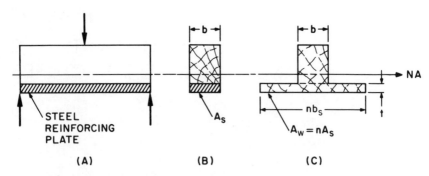

Figure 17-1.   Reinforced timber beam. (A) Steel reinforced timber beam. (B) Composite section. (C) Equivalent homogeneous section.

With the beam subjected to a downward load as shown in Fig. 17-2(A), the steel fibers are in tension and carry an internal load T_s; this load is equal to the product of the stress developed in the steel f_s and the area A_s of the steel: $T_s = f_s A_s$. The equivalent area of wood adequate to carry the same load as the steel plate is given by

$$A_w = \frac{T_s}{f_w} = \frac{A_s f_s}{f_w} = \frac{A_s}{f_w}\left(f_w \frac{E_s}{E_w}\right) = A_s n$$
$$= nA_s \tag{17-1}$$

For steel and wood the ratio n is about 20 and so the equivalent area of wood is 20 times that of the steel. The equivalent homogeneous section is shown in Fig. 17-1(C) where the equivalent wood area A_w is distributed horizontally and occupies a position at the same distance from the neutral axis as did the steel it replaces. The area A_w has the same vertical dimension t as the steel. Its width is given by

$$A_w = nA_s$$
$$b_w t = nb_s t$$
$$b_w = nb_s \tag{17-2}$$

This configuration is required because the internal load carried by the steel must be carried by wood having the equivalent wood area A_w.

If desired, the flexure formula may now be applied to the equivalent homogeneous section.

Problem 17-1 Bending stress in a steel-reinforced timber beam

A beam having a 10-ft span is made up of a 4-in. × 8-in. piece of wood and a $\frac{1}{2}$-in. × 4-in. piece of steel. The steel is attached to the bottom of the wood so as to create composite action when the beam is bent. If the modulus of elasticity of the wood is 1.5×10^6 psi and of the steel is 30×10^6 psi, what applied uniform load will cause a stress in the wood of 1500 psi? At this load, what is the stress in the steel?

Solution:

Before the flexure formula can be applied, the composite section must be transformed into an equivalent homogeneous section of the same material.

The steel-plate section is replaced by an equivalent wood area A_w having the same vertical dimension and located at the same distance from the neutral axis. The area A_w is found from Eq. (17-1).

$$A_w = nA_s = \frac{E_s}{E_w}A_s = \frac{30 \times 10^6}{1.5 \times 10^6}(A_s) = (20)(4)(\tfrac{1}{2}) = 40 \text{ in.}^2$$

Its width b_w is determined from Eq. (17-2): $b_w = nb_s = (20)(4) = 80$ in. The composite and transformed sections are shown in Fig. 17-2.

The uniform load is assumed to act in the longitudinal plane of symmetry and, for a homogeneous beam so loaded, the neutral axis passes through the centroid of the cross section. The transformed section is homogeneous and the neutral axis coincides with the horizontal centroidal axis; this axis is a distance y_c above the reference X-axis as shown in Fig. 17-2(B).

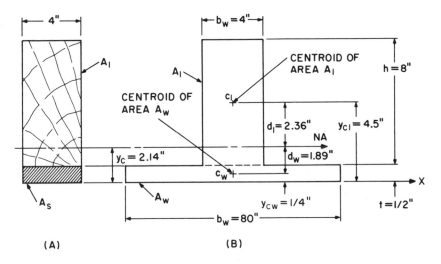

Figure 17-2. (A) Composite section. (B) Transformed section.

Determine the value of y_c:

$$[A_1 + A_w]y_c = A_1y_{c1} + A_wy_{cw}$$
$$[(4)(8) + (80)(\tfrac{1}{2})]y_c = (4)(8)(4.5) + (80)(\tfrac{1}{2})(\tfrac{1}{4})$$
$$y_c = 2.14 \text{ in.}$$

The application of the flexure formula requires that the moment of inertia I_{NA} with respect to the neutral axis be known. Calculate I_{NA} using the method of Sec. 2-6

$$I_{NA} = \sum_{n=1}^{n=p} I_{OYn} + \sum_{n=1}^{n=p} a_ny_{cn}^2$$

$$I_{NA} = (1/12)b_1h_1^3 + (1/2)b_wt^3 + A_1d_1^2 + A_wd_w^2$$
$$= (1/12)(4)(8)^3 + (1/12)(80)(\tfrac{1}{2})^3 + (4)(8)(2.36)^2 + (80)(\tfrac{1}{2})(1.89)^2$$
$$= 495 \text{ in.}^4$$

The beam is loaded with a uniform load and is simply supported as shown in Fig. 17-3. Consequently, the maximum bending moment occurs at midspan and is given by

$$M = wL^2/8 = w(120)^2/8 = 1800w$$

Notice that the length of the beam is expressed in terms of inches. This is done to accommodate the other quantities such as I_{NA}.

The external bending moment M is expressed in terms of the bending stress developed in the beam fibers with the flexure formula, Eq. (13-2), as follows:

$$(f_b)_y = My/I_{NA} \qquad M = (f_b)_y I_{NA}/y$$

where y is the distance from the neutral axis to the fiber at which the stress $(f_b)_y$ is developed.

The maximum stress develops in the fibers outermost from the neutral axis. This stress must not exceed the allowable 1500 psi for wood. Applying the flexure formula to the transformed section,

$$M = \frac{(f_b)_{y=6.36 \text{ in.}} (I_{NA})}{y}$$

$$1800w = \frac{(1500)(495)}{6.36}$$

$$w = 64.8 \text{ lb/in.} = 778 \text{ lb/ft} \qquad Answer$$

Therefore, it requires a uniform load of 778 lb/ft to cause a stress of 1500 psi in the wood.

In the outermost fibers of the *equivalent wood area* A_w, this load causes a bending stress to develop given by

$$(f_b)_{y=2.14 \text{ in.}} = f_w = \frac{My}{I_{NA}} = \frac{(1800)(64.8)(2.14)}{495}$$

$$f_w = 504 \text{ psi}$$

This corresponds to a stress f_s in the steel:

$$f_s = nf_w = (20)(504) = 10,080 \text{ psi}$$
$$= 10,080 \text{ psi} \qquad Answer$$

Problem 17-2 Allowable load for a steel-reinforced timber beam

A 4-in X 12-in. timber beam 16 ft long is positioned with its 12-in. face vertical. A steel plate, $\tfrac{1}{4}$ in. X 12 in. X 16 ft, is properly secured to each of the 12-in. faces. Based on a concentrated load at midspan, what is the load that this beam can carry? For steel: allowable stress, $f_s = 20,000$ psi; $E_s = 29 \times 10^6$ psi. For wood: allowable stress, $f_w = 1600$ psi; $E_w = 1.6 \times 10^6$ psi.

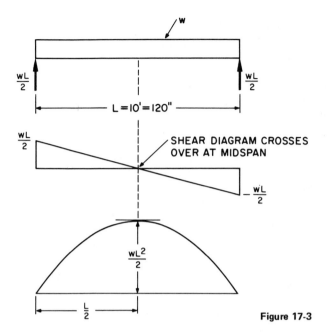

Figure 17-3

Solution:

When a beam is subjected to positive bending, its fibers above the neutral axis are in compression and those below are in tension and so carry compressive and tensile loads, respectively. The equivalent wood areas that replace the steel plates in the transformed section must be adequate to carry the load that was carried by the steel. Consequently, its fibers must occupy corresponding positions with respect to the neutral axis. This requires that the equivalent wood areas have the same height as the steel. Their widths are given by Eq. (17-2): $b_w = nb_s$.

The composite and transformed sections are shown in Fig. 17-4. The width of the equivalent wood areas is calculated

$$b_w = nb_s = \frac{E_s}{E_w}b_s = \frac{29 \times 10^6}{1.6 \times 10^6}\left(\frac{1}{4}\right) = 4.5 \text{ in.}$$

Since the transformed section is symmetrical, the position of the horizontal centroidal axis, and hence the neutral axis, is evident from inspection. Referring to Fig. 17-4(B), calculate I_{NA}

$$I_{NA} = (1/12)bh^3 = (1/12)(2b_w + b_1)h^3 = (1/12)(13)(12)^3 = 1872 \text{ in.}^4$$

A simple beam with a concentrated load P at midspan develops a maximum moment equal to PL/4 at midspan. This external bending moment, and hence P, is expressed in terms of the bending stress developed in the beam fibers by the flexure formula, Eq. (13-2), as follows:

$$(f_b)_y = My/I_{NA} \qquad M = PL/4 = (f_b)_y I_{NA}/y$$

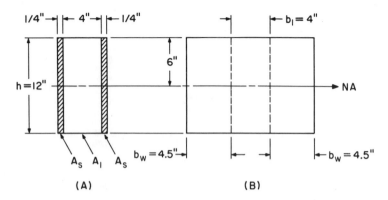

Figure 17-4.   (A) Composite section. (B) Transformed section.

The maximum stress develops in the fibers outermost from the neutral axis. The outermost fibers of both the equivalent wood area and the actual wood area are 6 in. distant from the neutral axis. Although the stress in the actual wood may go as high as 1600 psi, the stress in the fibers of the equivalent wood area may not be greater than the value of f_w given by

$$f_w = \frac{f_s}{n} = \frac{f_s}{E_s E_w} = \frac{20,000}{29 \times 10^6 / 1.6 \times 10^6} = 1104 \text{ psi}$$

if the allowable stress in the steel is not to be exceeded. The stress of $f_w = 1104$ psi therefore controls. Applying the flexure formula to the transformed section,

$$PL/4 = (f_b)_y I_{NA}/y = (1104)(1872)/6 = 0.345 \times 10^6$$

Solving for P,

$$P = \frac{4}{L}(345 \times 10^3) = \frac{4}{(16)(12)}(345 \times 10^3) = 7190 \text{ lb}$$
$$= 7190 \text{ lb} \qquad Answer$$

Therefore, a concentrated load of 7190 lb at midspan is the maximum load that may be carried by the beam and not exceed the allowable stress of either the steel or wood.

17-2 REINFORCED CONCRETE BEAMS

Most beams are subjected to positive bending and this places the beam fibers below the neutral axis in tension and those above in compression. Concrete is strong in compression but is very weak in tension. To adapt the useful compressive qualities of concrete to beams, steel bars are positioned in the concrete on the tension side near the lower surface. These bars carry virtually the entire tensile load and come in a variety of sizes, as indicated in Table 17-1. The bars are usually fabricated with closely spaced projections called deformations which serve to minimize longitudinal slippage between the steel and concrete.

Table 17-1　Steel Bars for Concrete Reinforcement

Bar designation number	Nominal dimensions			
	Diameter, in.	Cross-sectional area, in.^{2}	Perimeter, in.	Perimeter per in.^{2} of area, in.
3	0.375	0.11	1.178	10.7
4	0.500	0.20	1.571	8.0
5	0.625	0.31	1.963	6.4
6	0.750	0.44	2.36	5.4
7	0.875	0.60	2.75	4.6
8	1.000	0.79	3.14	4.0
9	1.128	1.00	3.54	3.54
10	1.270	1.27	3.99	3.14
11	1.410	1.56	4.43	2.84

The analysis of a reinforced concrete beam is begun by transforming the given composite section into an equivalent homogeneous section. The steel is replaced with an area n times as great as its area A_s, where n is the ratio of the modulus of elasticity of steel to the modulus of elasticity of concrete E_s/E_c. As before, the equivalent area nA_s is distributed horizontally so that it will occupy a position at the same distance from the neutral axis as did the steel it replaces. The area nA_s then, is the effective area over which the tensile stress f_s^*/n in the transformed beam is distributed. The stress acting over the equivalent area nA_s is $1/n$ as great as the stress f_s^* in the steel bars of the composite section. The asterisk (*) indicates that f_s^* is the stress for any given applied bending moment and so is distinguished from the allowable steel stress f_s.

ACI Building Code Section 1102 provides that the modular ratio $n = E_s/E_c$ may be taken as the nearest whole number but not less than 6. The modulus of elasticity E_c for concrete may be taken as $w^{1.5}(33)\sqrt{f_c'}$, in psi, for value of w between 90 and 155 lb/ft^3. For normal weight concrete, w may be considered as 145 lb/ft^3. The value E_s for reinforcing steel is usually taken as 29×10^6 psi, so that n is given by

$$n = \frac{29{,}000{,}000}{w^{1.5}(33)\sqrt{f_c'}} \tag{17-3}$$

The quantity f_c' is the ultimate compressive stress of concrete. Concrete is able to develop this stress 28 days after it is placed and it is related to the allowable compressive stress f_c by the equation

$$f_c = 0.45 f_c' \tag{17-4}$$

Values of n and f_c are listed in Table 17-2 for several strengths of concrete. Table 17-2 also lists values of shear stress v_c that are of importance in design for shear. This aspect of beam design is treated in Secs. 17-4 and 17-5.

Table 17-2   Allowable Stresses in Concrete*

Description	Parameter	For any strength of concrete[†]	Allowable stresses Parameter values for strength of concrete shown below			
			$f'_c =$ 2500 psi	$f'_c =$ 3000 psi	$f'_c =$ 4000 psi	$f'_c =$ 5000 psi
Modulus of elasticity ratio: n (for concrete weighing 145 lb/ft^3)	n	$\dfrac{29{,}000{,}000}{w^{1 \cdot 5}(33)\sqrt{f'_c}}$	10	9	8	7
Flexure: f_c (extreme fiber stress in compression)	f_c	$(0.45)f'_c$	1125	1350	1800	2250
Shear: v (as a measure of diagonal tension at a distance d from the face of the support)						
Beams with no web reinforcement	v_c	$(1.1)\sqrt{f'_c}$	55	60	70	78
Members with vertical or inclined web reinforcement or properly combined bent bars and vertical stirrups	v	$(5)\sqrt{f'_c}$	250	274	316	354

*From Table 1002(a) of the 1966 ACI Standard Building Code.
[†]Provided concrete is prepared in accordance with Code Section 502.

Refer now to Fig. 17-5(A), which shows a composite section, and to Fig. 17-5(B), which depicts the transformed section. The distance from the outermost fibers in compression to the horizontal centerline of area nA_s is the effective beam depth and is designated as d.

Figure 17-5(C) shows a linear compressive stress distribution for the concrete section above the neutral axis. The distance from the neutral axis to the outermost fibers in compression is kd where k is less than unity. Figure 17-5(B) and (C) indicates that the area over which the compressive stress acts is equal to the product of kd and b.

In a homogeneous beam, the horizontal centroidal axis of the transverse section is coincident with the neutral axis. The neutral axis is therefore located by equating the moment of area above the neutral axis to the moment of area below the neutral axis, the moments being taken about the neutral axis.

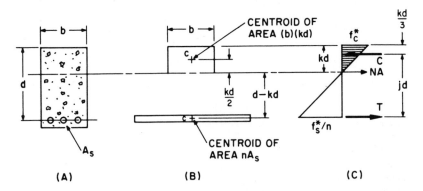

Figure 17-5. Reinforced concrete beam. (A) Composite section. (B) Transformed section. (C) Stress distribution diagram.

$$b(kd)\frac{(kd)}{2} = nA_s(d - kd) \tag{17-5}$$

This quadratic equation is solved for kd.

$$kd = -\frac{nA_s}{b} \pm \sqrt{\left(\frac{nA_s}{b}\right)^2 + 2\left(\frac{nA_s}{b}\right)d} \tag{17-6}$$

The total compressive force C acts at the centroid of the compressive stress distribution diagram, i.e., at a distance $\frac{1}{3}kd$ from the outermost compression fibers. The force C is equal to the average stress $\frac{1}{2}f_c^*$ and the area b(kd) over which the compressive stress acts.

$$C = \frac{1}{2}f_c^* b(kd) \tag{17-7}$$

where f_c^* is the stress in the outermost compression fibers and therefore is also the maximum compressive stress developed by the concrete for a given applied bending moment.

The tensile stress f_s^*/n acting across the equivalent area nA_s is assumed to be uniformly distributed since this area is very narrow. Consequently, the tensile force T acts at the centroid of the area and is equal to the product of f_s^*/n and nA_s.

$$T = \left(\frac{f_s^*}{n}\right)(nA_s) = f_s^* A_s \tag{17-8}$$

The analysis could be continued along the lines established for the reinforced timber beam by applying the flexure formula. However, it is more convenient to use a method based on equating the external and internal moments.

The forces C and T constitute an internal couple having a moment arm equal to jd which from Fig. 17-5 is given by

$$jd = d - \frac{(kd)}{3} \tag{17-9}$$

The beam develops the internal couple to resist the externally applied bending moment M at the section in question. The quantity M can be expressed in terms of the resisting moment offered by the concrete in compression and the steel in tension.

$$M = C(jd) = \tfrac{1}{2}f_c^* b(kd)(jd)$$
$$M = T(jd) = f_s^* A_s(jd)$$

By solving these equations for f_c^* and f_s^*, respectively, these stress values may be calculated for a given applied bending moment M.

$$f_c^* = \frac{2M}{(b)(kd)(jd)} \tag{17-10}$$

$$f_s^* = \frac{M}{A_s(jd)} \tag{17-11}$$

Often it is required to determine the applied bending moment a given beam can sustain without exceeding either the allowable stress for concrete f_c or the allowable stress for steel f_s. In this event, the resisting moments $(M_r)_c$ and $(M_r)_s$ for concrete and steel, respectively, are calculated based on the allowable values f_c and f_s.

$$(M_r)_c = \tfrac{1}{2}f_c b(kd)(jd) \tag{17-12}$$
$$(M_r)_s = f_s A_s(jd) \tag{17-13}$$

The lower value of $(M_r)_c$ and $(M_r)_s$ controls and is the maximum bending moment that may be safely applied to the beam at the section in question.

Problem 17-3 Allowable bending moment for a reinforced concrete beam

Given a rectangular concrete beam 12 in. wide, with an effective depth of 18 in., reinforced with an area of steel equal to 4.00 sq in., find the permissible bending moment that the section may carry. Allowable stress: $f_s = 20,000$ psi, $f_c = 1350$ psi; n = 10.

Solution:

From the statement of the problem, the transformed section may be drawn directly as shown in Fig. 17-6(A). Figure 17-6(B) shows the corresponding stress distribution diagram.

First, locate the neutral axis by equating the moment of area above the neutral axis to the moment of the area below the neutral axis, the moments being taken about the neutral axis. Applying Eq. (17-5),

$$b(kd)\frac{(kd)}{2} = nA_s(d - kd)$$

The solution to this quadratic is given by Eq. (17-6):

$$kd = -\frac{(nA_s)}{b} \pm \sqrt{\left(\frac{nA_s}{b}\right)^2 + 2\left(\frac{nA_s}{b}\right)d}$$

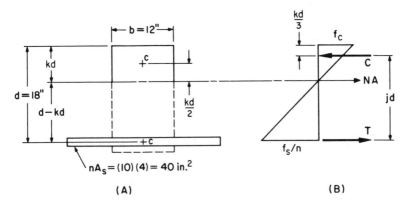

Figure 17-6. (A) Transformed section. (B) Stress distribution.

$nA_s/b = (10)(4)/12 = 3.33$

$kd = -(3.33) \pm \sqrt{(3.33)^2 + 2(3.33)(18)} = 8.12, -14.78$

The negative root is meaningless; therefore, $kd = 8.12$ in. The moment arm jd of the C-T couple is given by Eq. (17-9):

$jd = d - kd/3 = 18 - 8.12/3 = 15.30$ in.

The resisting moment developed by the concrete when the outermost compression fibers are impressed with the allowable stress f_c can be calculated using Eq. (17-12), $(M_r)_c = \frac{1}{2}f_c b(kd)(jd) = \frac{1}{2}(1350)(12)(8.12)(15.30) = 1006 \times 10^3$ in.-lb.

Similarly, the resisting moment developed by the steel when its fibers are impressed with the allowable stress f_s can be calculated using Eq. (17-13), $(M_r)_s = f_s A_s(jd) = (20,000)(4)(15.30) = 1225 \times 10^3$ in.-lb.

The bending moment of

$(M_r)_c = 1006 \times 10^3$ in.-lb   *Answer*

for concrete controls and indicates that the beam contains more steel than is necessary for adequate reinforcement. The steel is understressed and the beam is said to be overreinforced. The value of 1006×10^3 in.-lb is the highest bending moment that the section may carry. A larger bending moment would cause the compressive stress in the concrete to exceed its allowable value.

17-3 DESIGN OF RECTANGULAR REINFORCED CONCRETE BEAMS

The design of a reinforced concrete beam to resist an externally applied bending moment M is usually made so that the concrete and steel reach their allowable stress f_c and f_s simultaneously—a balanced design. A design relation incorporating this requirement is established by equating the appropriate proportions of the similar triangles formed by the flexural stress distribution diagram. Refer to Fig. 17-7, and by similar triangles,

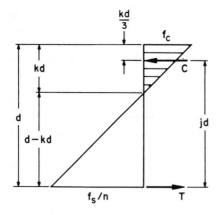

Figure 17-7. Stress distribution of internal C-7 couple.

$$\frac{f_c}{kd} = \frac{f_s/n}{d - kd}$$

This relation is solved for the design factor k,

$$k = \frac{f_c}{f_c + f_s/n} \tag{17-14}$$

Having determined k, j is easily found from Eq. (17-9) after canceling out d.

$$j = 1 - k/3 \tag{17-15}$$

A relation incorporating the effective depth d and width b of the beam is needed. Shown in Fig. 17-7 is the internal C-T couple that the beam develops to resist the bending moment M applied to the supported load. The quantity M can be equated to the internal couple expressed in terms of the resisting moment developed by the concrete,

$$M = C(jd) = \tfrac{1}{2}f_c(b)(kd)(jd)$$
$$= \tfrac{1}{2}f_c(bd^2)(jk)$$

Solving for bd^2,

$$bd^2 \doteq 2M/f_c kj \tag{17-16}$$

Every conceivable combination of b and d would satisfy Eq. (17-16). However, it is reasonable to assume that the effective depth of the section will be about 1.5 times its width b,

$$d = 1.5b \tag{17-17}$$

Equations (17-16) and (17-17) are solved simultaneously for b and d.

It is now possible to determine the tension steel area A_s required for the balanced design. The bending moment M is equated to the internal couple expressed in terms of the resisting moment developed by the reinforcing steel, $M = T(jd) = f_s A_s(jd)$. Solving for A_s,

$$A_s = \frac{M}{f_s jd} \tag{17-18}$$

Before proceeding with an illustrative example, certain beam construction details covered by the Code should be considered. Figure 17-8 shows that the steel reinforcement has a covering of concrete. This cover provides protection for the steel against corrosion and fire. Code Section 808(b) provides that for beams not exposed directly to the ground or weather, the concrete protective covering shall not be less than $1\frac{1}{2}$ in.

Code Section 804(a) provides that the clear spacing between parallel bars in a single plane shall be not less than the nominal diameter of the bars, $1\frac{1}{3}$ times the maximum size of the coarse aggregate, nor 1 in. Figure 17-8 schematically defines the clear spacing dimension.

The lateral placement of the bars should be made so that a clear space of $1\frac{1}{2}$ in. be left between the outside bars and the side walls of the beam.

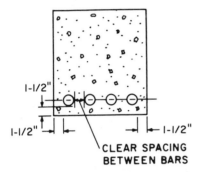

CLEAR SPACING
BETWEEN BARS   **Figure 17-8**

Problem 17-4 Design of a reinforced concrete beam for bending

Design a reinforced concrete beam on a simple span of 20 ft to carry a uniform live load of 3000 lb/linear ft, taking proper consideration of dead load. $f'_c = 3000$ psi, $f_s = 20,000$ psi, $E_s = 29,000,000$ psi.

Solution:

The weight of the beam is the dead load. Since the dimensions of the beam section are not yet known, a per foot weight for the beam must be assumed and included as part of the load that the beam is to carry. The normal weight of concrete is 145 lb/ft³. Assume that the beam weighs 450 lb/ft.

Since the live load and dead load are both uniformly distributed, they may be summed together and treated as one uniform distributed load of 3000 + 450 = 3450 lb/linear ft. For a simply supported beam carrying a uniform load, the maximum bending moment occurs at midspan and is given by

$$M = wL^2/8 = (3450)(20)^2/8 = 172.5 \times 10^3 \text{ ft-lb} = 2070 \times 10^3 \text{ in.-lb}$$

The design of the section, including the determination of the tension steel area, is based on the maximum bending moment that the beam must resist.

The concrete is specified as having a strength f'_c of 3000 psi. From Eq. (17-3), or Table 17-2, the allowable stress f_c is 1350 psi. The allowable steel stress f_s is 20,000 psi. The modular ratio n can be calculated from Eq. (17-3) or it can be taken directly from Table 17-2. Referring to the table, n = 9.

It is assumed that the most economical design is wanted. In such a design both materials reach their allowable stresses simultaneously—a balanced design.

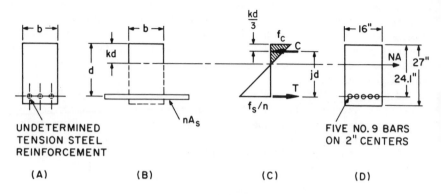

Figure 17-9

Equations (17-14) and (17-15) were formulated on this supposition. Use these equations to determine, respectively, the design factors k and j:

$$k = \frac{f_c}{f_c + f_s/n} = \frac{1350}{1350 + 20,000/9} = 0.378$$

$$j = 1 - k/3 = 1 - 0.378/3 = 0.874$$

Figure 17-9(A) shows the composite section for which the dimensions b and d and the reinforcing steel are to be determined. The transformed section is shown in Fig. 17-9(B). The stress distribution diagram and C-T couple are shown in Fig. 17-9(C).

Equating the applied bending moment M to the resisting moment developed by the concrete provides an expression incorporating b and d; thus,

$$M = C(jd) = \tfrac{1}{2}f_c(b)(kd)(jd)$$

$$bd^2 = \frac{2M}{f_c kj} = \frac{(2)(2070 \times 10^3)}{(1350)(0.378)(0.874)} = 9310$$

Assume that d = 1.5b, and solve simultaneously for b and d.

d = 24 in.   and   b = 16 in.

Determine the required area of tension reinforcing steel by equating the applied bending moment M to the resisting moment developed by the steel.

$$M = T(jd) = A_s f_s(jd)$$

$$A_s = \frac{M}{f_s(jd)} = \frac{2070 \times 10^3}{(20,000)(0.874)(24)} = 4.91 \text{ in.}^2$$

= 4.91 in.² tension steel area   *Answer*

Refer to Table 17-1, and determine the bar size and quantity to provide the required steel area of 4.91 in.² Five No. 9 bars provide a total steel area of 5 in.², just a fraction more than required.

Use 5 No. 9 bars   *Answer*

Since the beam is to be 16 in. wide, the bars may be conveniently positioned on 2.75-in. centers as shown in Fig. 17-8(D). The bars have a diameter of 1.128 in., which leaves a clear spacing of 1.622 in. between adjacent bars. This is more than adequate to satisfy the spacing requirements of Code Section 804(a). The maximum size of coarse aggregate is not given and so is not considered.

The bars must be protected against fire and corrosion. Code Section 808(b) requires that a protective covering of concrete not less than 1.5 in. be provided. Therefore the total depth d_t of the beam is

Total depth of beam: d_t = d + ½(bar diameter) + (thickness of protective covering)

$$= 24.0 + ½(1.128) + 1.5 = 26.06 \text{ in., say } 27 \text{ in.}$$

Width of beam: b = 16 in.　　*Answer*
Total depth of beam: d = 27 in.

Adequate protection is also provided for the bars adjacent to the sidewalls of the beam. The 2.75-in. bar spacing leaves a clear space of more than 1½ in. between the outside bars and the sidewalls.

Check to determine the accuracy of the assumed dead load of 450 lb/ft,

$$\text{Dead load} = \frac{bd_t}{144}(145 \text{ lb/ft}^3) = \frac{(16)(27)}{144}(145) = 435 \text{ lb/ft}$$

The dead load of the designed beam is only 15 lb/ft less than the assumed value indicating a safe design. Had the assumed value differed substantially, then a new design based on a more appropriate assumed value of dead load would have been required. An actual dead load much greater than an assumed dead load indicates an unsafe design.

The design of a reinforced concrete beam is not complete until there has been an evaluation of shear and of bond strength between concrete and steel. The next section will consider these aspects of beam design.

17-4　SHEAR AND BOND

Although a concrete beam has been designed for flexure by reinforcing the beam with steel bars longitudinally placed in its tension fibers, the beam may still fail in shear. Also, if the bond between the longitudinal steel bars and the concrete is not adequate, slippage between bars and concrete can occur.

In Sec. 13-2 it was pointed out that for a loaded beam, a horizontal shearing stress develops to prevent the beam fibers from sliding past each other. This shearing stress is attended by a shearing stress of equal value acting across an orthogonal surface. The total action on a typical element is shown in Fig. 17-10. As shown, these shearing stresses tend to pull the element apart across its diagonal. Shearing action therefore produces a diagonal tensile stress.

If the allowable shearing stress is exceeded, the beam can fail in diagonal tension. Such a failure is characterized by diagonal cracks, as shown in Fig. 17-11. The presence of longitudinal reinforcement does not preclude shear failure because it resists only the horizontal component of shear and not the attendant orthogonal acting shear.

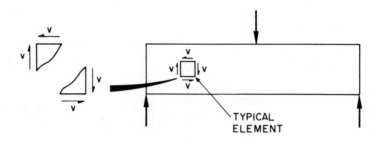

Figure 17-10.   Shear failure.

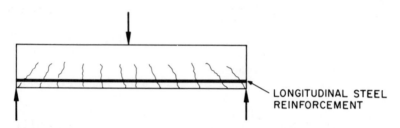

Figure 17-11.   Shear failure characterized by diagonal tensile cracks.

The ACI Standard Building Code provision relating to shear* states in part that the nominal shear stress, as a measure of diagonal tension, in reinforced concrete members shall be computed by

$$v = V/bd \qquad\qquad (17\text{-}19)$$

where d is the effective depth of the beam.

For design, the maximum shear shall be considered as that at the section a distance d from the face of the support.[†] The shear stress v_c, permitted on an unreinforced web, shall not exceed $1.1\sqrt{f'_c}$ at a distance d from the face of the support. The shear stresses at sections between the face of the support and the section a distance d therefrom shall not be considered critical.[†] Values of $1.1\sqrt{f'_c}$ for different strengths of concrete are given in Table 17-2.

It will be shown in Sec. 17-5 that the shear strength of a concrete beam can be increased by reinforcing the web with U-shaped steel reinforcing elements known as stirrups.

The ability of the longitudinally placed steel reinforcement bars and the concrete not to slip with respect to each other is measured in terms of flexural bond stress and is expressed in pounds per square inch.

The ACI Standard Building Code provides in part** that in flexural members in which the tension reinforcement is parallel to the compression face, the flexural bond stress at any cross section will be computed by

---

*ACI Standard Building Code, Section 1201.
[†]This provision does not apply to brackets and other short cantilevers.
**ACI Standard Building Code, Section 1301.

$$u = \frac{V}{(jd)\Sigma o} \tag{17-20}$$

where V is the shear and Σo is the sum of the perimeters of the reinforcing bars. Critical sections occur at the face of the support, at each point where tension bars terminate within a span, and at the point of inflection.

The bond stress u shall not exceed the limits given below:

1. For tension bars with sizes and deformations conforming to ASTM A 305:

   Top bars: $3.4\sqrt{f_c'}/D$ nor 350 psi

   Bars other than top bars: $4.8\sqrt{f_c'}/D$ nor 500 psi

   where D is the nominal bar diameter.

2. For tension bars with sizes and deformations conforming to ASTM A 408:

   Top bars*: $2.1\sqrt{f_c'}$

   Bars other than top bars: $3\sqrt{f_c'}$

3. For all deformed compression bars: $6.5\sqrt{f_c'}$ nor 400 psi.

4. For plain bars the allowable bond stresses shall be one-half of those permitted for bars conforming to ASTM A 305 but not more than 160 psi.

Problem 17-5 Evaluation of a reinforced beam for shear and bond

Determine if the beam designed in Problem 17-4 is adequate in shear and bond.

Solution:

The nominal shear stress is computed with Eq. (17-19), $v = V/bd$. For design, the maximum shear shall be considered as that at the section a distance d from the face of the support. (See Fig. 17-12.) If the beam is not symmetrically loaded, then the distance d would be measured from the face of the support at which the shear is greater. Calculating the nominal shear stress,

$$v = \frac{V}{bd} = \frac{\dfrac{wL}{2} - wd}{bd} = \frac{\dfrac{(286)(240)}{2} - (286)(24)}{(16)(24)} = 71.1 \text{ psi}$$

where w = 3435 lb/ft $\times$ ft/12 in. = 286 lb/in.

The shear stress v_c permitted on the unreinforced web is given by $1.1\sqrt{f_c'}$. The concrete was specified in Problem 17-4 as having a strength $f_c' = 3000$ psi. The value of v_c may be calculated or obtained directly from Table 17-2. From Table 17-2, $v_c = 60$ psi.

The actual shear stress exceeds the allowable v_c and the designed member will fail in shear.   *Answer*

Section 17-5 will show that shear failure is prevented by the suitable placement of steel web reinforcement elements.

It will next be determined if the beam is adequate in bond. The actual flexural bond stress u that develops at the longitudinal interface of the tension reinforcement bars and the concrete is calculated using Eq. (17-20),

---

*Top bars, in reference to bond, are horizontal bars so placed that more than 12 in. of the concrete is cast in the member below the bars.

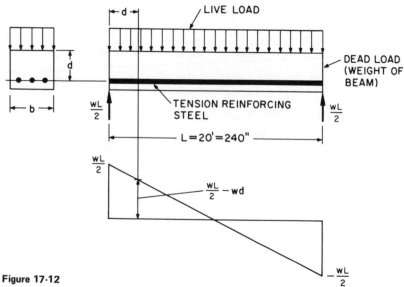

$$w = \text{LIVE LOAD} + \text{DEAD LOAD} = 3000 + 435 = 3435 \text{ lb/ft} = 286 \text{ lb/in.}$$

Figure 17-12

$$u = \frac{V}{(jd)\Sigma o}$$

The steel bars are assumed to extend the entire length of the beam. The critical section occurs at the support. It is here where the shear is a maximum. The shear at the support is $wL/2$ and the perimeter of the No. 9 bar is given in Table 17-1 as 3.54 in. In Problem 17-4 it was determined that five such bars are required, hence, $\Sigma o = (5)(3.54) = 17.7$ in.

Calculating the actual bond stress u,

$$u = \frac{V}{(jd)\Sigma o} = \frac{wL/2}{(jd)\Sigma o} = \frac{(286)(240)/2}{(0.874)(24)(17.7)} = 92 \text{ psi}$$

Assume that the tension reinforcing bars conform to ASTM A 408. Then the allowable bond stress is given by $3\sqrt{f'_c} = 3\sqrt{3000} = 164.5$ psi.

The actual bond stress is less than the allowable and the designed member is adequate in bond.   *Answer*

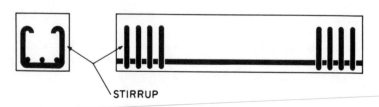

Figure 17-13.   Web reinforcement: stirrups.

If the actual bond stress exceeds the allowable, it may be reduced by increasing Σo; this can be done by selecting a greater number of bars of smaller diameter and having a cross-sectional area equal to or greater than that necessary to meet the requirements of tension reinforcement.

17-5   WEB REINFORCEMENT STIRRUPS

In Sec. 17-4 it was pointed out that the shearing action in a longitudinally reinforced concrete beam is accompanied by tension stress that is characterized by diagonal tensile cracks. The tension stress is produced by orthogonally acting shear forces of which only the horizontal is resisted by the longitudinal reinforcing bars. The vertical shear is resisted exclusively by the concrete in the absence of web reinforcement.

The ACI Standard Building Code, Section 1202(a), relating to web reinforcement, states in part that wherever the value of shear stress v_1 computed by Eq. (17-19), plus the effects of torsion,* exceed the shear stress v_c permitted for the concrete of an unreinforced web, reinforcement shall be provided to carry the excess. Such web reinforcement shall also be provided for a distance equal to the depth d of the member beyond the point theoretically required. Web reinforcement between the face of the support and the section at a distance d therefrom shall be the same as required at that section.

Code Section 1202(b) lists several web reinforcement configurations. Of these, stirrups perpendicular to the longitudinal reinforcement are the most commonly used and are treated in this book.

Section 1203 of the Code provides that the area of steel required for these stirrups shall be computed by

$$A_v = V's/f_v d \tag{17-21}$$

where V' = shear carried by web reinforcement

s = spacing of stirrups in direction parallel to longitudinal reinforcement

f_v = tensile stress in web reinforcement

d = distance from extreme compression fiber to centroid of tension reinforcement

The stirrup is the most common form of web reinforcement used to increase beam shear strength. The stirrups are placed in the beam as shown in Fig. 17-13. The upper hooks of the stirrups are anchored in the compression concrete. The longitudinal spacing of the stirrups is a function of the amount by which the actual shear stress exceeds the allowable shear stress v_c. Equation (17-21) may be solved for the spacing s between stirrups at any point,

$$s = A_v f_v d/V' \tag{17-22}$$

where A_v is the total area of web reinforcement in tension within a distance s measured in a direction parallel to the longitudinal reinforcement. The area A_v includes the area of both stirrup legs because both transmit tensile stress.

---

*The beams in this chapter are assumed not to be affected by torsion.

The ACI Standard Building Code imposes certain restrictions on web reinforcement, namely:

Section 1205–Stress Restrictions
(a) The tensile stress in web reinforcement f_v shall not exceed the values given in Section 1003, e.g., billet-steel or axle-steel concrete reinforcing bars of structural grade: $f_v = 18,000$ psi.
(b) The shear stress v_c shall not exceed $5\sqrt{f_c'}$ in section with web reinforcement.

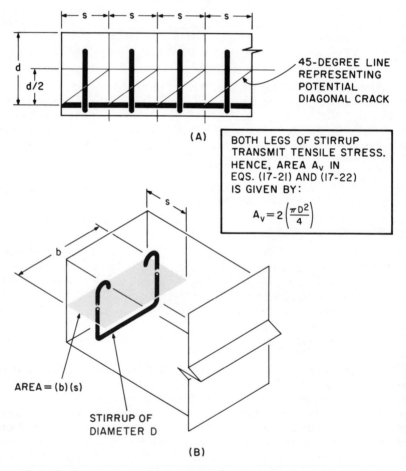

45-DEGREE LINE
REPRESENTING
POTENTIAL
DIAGONAL CRACK

(A)

BOTH LEGS OF STIRRUP
TRANSMIT TENSILE STRESS.
HENCE, AREA A_v IN
EQS. (17-21) AND (17-22)
IS GIVEN BY:

$$A_v = 2\left(\frac{\pi D^2}{4}\right)$$

AREA $= (b)(s)$

STIRRUP OF
DIAMETER D

(B)

Figure 17-14.   Diagrams illustrating provisions of Code Sections 1206 (a) and (b). (A) The stirrup spacing may not be exceeded provided that the stress in the concrete is not greater than $3\sqrt{f_c'}$. Each 45-degree line is crossed by at least one line of web reinforcement. (B) The total cross-sectional area A_v of the reinforcement within the area $(b)(s)$. A_2 must not be less than $0.0015(b)(s)$.

Section 1206—Web Reinforcement Restriction

(a) Where web reinforcement is required, it shall be spaced so that every 45-degree line, representing a potential diagonal crack and extending from middepth d/2 of the member to the longitudinal tension bars, shall be crossed by at least one line of web reinforcement. [See Fig. 17-14(A).] When the shear stress exceeds $3\sqrt{f_c'}$, every such 45-degree line shall be crossed by at least two lines of web reinforcement.

(b) Where web reinforcement is required, its area shall not be less than 0.15 *percent* of the area bs, computed as the product of the width of the web and the spacing of the web reinforcement along the longitudinal axis of the member. [See Fig. 17-14(B).]

The design of web reinforcement must be made with these Code sections in mind. With respect to Section 1206, the stirrup spacing computed by Eq. (17-22) must occasionally be reduced so that its provisions are not violated.

Problem 17-6 Design of a reinforced beam for shear

A reinforced concrete beam 12 in. wide and having an effective depth of 18 in. carries a uniform total load (live load plus dead load) of 2000 lb/ft on a span of 30 ft. What spacing will be required for 3/8-in. U-stirrups. The beam is of 3000-lb concrete. Allowable tensile stress for stirrups is 18,000 psi.

Solution:

First determine if web reinforcement is indeed permissible. Code Section 1205(b) requires that the stress v_1 not exceed $5\sqrt{f_c'}$ in sections with web reinforcement: $v = 5\sqrt{f_c'} = 5\sqrt{3000} = 274$ psi. This corresponds to an allowable shear V_{all} given by $V_{all} = bdv = (12)(18)(274) = 59,300$ lb.

Section 1201(a) of the Code states that for design, the maximum value of shear shall be that at a distance d from the face of the support. The load and shear diagrams are drawn in Fig. 17-15. The shear V_d at a distance d from the support face is determined from $V_d = \Sigma(F_Y)_L = 30,000 - wd = 30,000 - (2000) \times (1.5) = 27,000$ lb. The maximum design value of shear is less than the allowable and stirrup reinforcement is permitted.

The allowable shear stress v_c permitted on the unreinforced web is given by $v_c = 1.1\sqrt{f_c'} = 1.1\sqrt{3000} = 60$ psi.

And the shear V_c that the concrete alone without web reinforcement can resist is determined by solving Eq. (17-19), $V_c = bdv_c = (12)(18)(60) = 13,000$ lb.

A horizontal line is drawn on the shear diagram at values of shear V_c and $-V_c$. The ordinate V' of the shaded area is the shear that the web reinforcement must carry. Stirrups are placed at positions along the beam length ϕ corresponding to the shaded areas and extending to a distance d beyond the point theoretically required. The extension, a distance d beyond the point where V' becomes zero, is stipulated by Section 1202(a) of the Code.

Thus, stirrups are required in the distance $(\phi + d)$. (See Fig. 17-15.)

The beam length ϕ corresponding to the shaded area of the shear diagram is calculated. V' becomes zero at the point where the shear V equals V_c. Referring to Fig. 17-15,

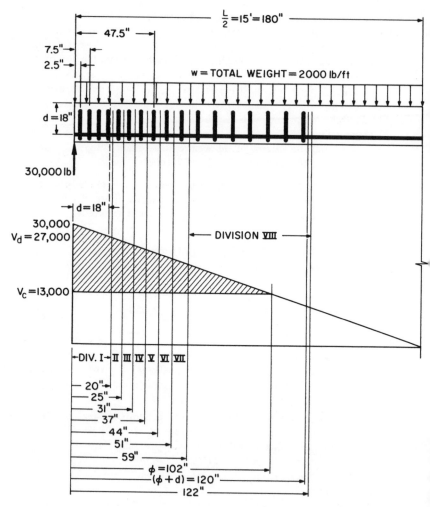

Figure 17-15.   The beam and its loading are symmetrical. For convenience in presentation, only half the member is shown.

$$30,000 - w\phi = V$$
$$30,000 - (2000)\phi = 13,000$$
$$\phi = 102 \text{ in.}$$

Reinforcing stirrups must be placed over the beam length $(\phi + d)$ at each end of the beam, $\phi + d = 102 + 18 = 120$ in.

Section 1202(a) also requires that the web reinforcement between the face of the support and the section at a distance d therefrom be the same as required at that section. In other words, the value of V' at a distance d from the face of the support is to be used to calculate the stirrup spacing s in the entire distance d measured from the face of the support.

At a distance d from the support face, the value of V' is $V' = V_d - V_c = 27,000 - 13,000 = 14,000$ lb.

The spacing s between stirrups is determined from Eq. (17-22), $s = A_v f_v d/V'$. Both legs of the stirrup transmit tensile stress and A_v is given by

$$A_v = 2\left[\frac{\pi(\text{bar dia.})^2}{4}\right] = 2\left[\frac{\pi(3/8)^2}{4}\right] = 0.22 \text{ in.}$$

Substituting,

$$s = \frac{A_v f_v d}{V'} = \frac{(0.22)(18,000)(18)}{14,000} = 5.09 \text{ in., say 5 in.}$$

This is the stirrup spacing required in the distance d measured from the face of the support. At 5-in. intervals, this set of spacings ends 20 in. from the support face and covers the entire distance d of 18 in. The 20-in. length is designated as Division I in Fig. 17-15.

The stirrup spacing should be checked against the web reinforcement restrictions of Code Section 1206(a). It is therein specified that the web reinforcement be placed so that every 45-degree line, representing a potential diagonal crack and extending from middepth d/2 of the member to the longitudinal tension bars, shall be crossed by at least one line of web reinforcement.

Since the effective depth d is 18 in., the stirrup spacing must not be greater than 9 in. The computed 5-in. spacing is less than d/2 and is therefore used.

Another provision of Code Section 1206(a) requires that when shear stress exceeds $3\sqrt{f_c'}$, every such 45-degree line shall be crossed by at least two lines of web reinforcement, i.e., the spacing between stirrups must not be greater than d/4. For 3000-psi strength concrete the shear stress is 164.3 psi; this corresponds to a shear bdv = $(12)(18)(164.3) = 35,500$ lb, which is more than the design value for maximum shear V_d of 27,000 lb. Thus, the more stringent spacing restriction is not applicable in this example.

The stirrup spacing over the remaining part of $(\phi + d)$ is now calculated. The shear $V'_{20 \text{ in.}}$ at the end of Division I is used to calculate the stirrup spacing for Division II.

Table 17-3

Division	Stirrup spacing s, in.	Distance from support face at which division ends, in.
I	5	20
II	5	25
III	6	31
IV	6	37
V	7	44
VI	7	51
VII	8	59
VIII	9	122

$$V'_{20 \text{ in.}} = V_{20 \text{ in.}} - V_c = \left[30,000 - (2000)\left(\frac{20}{12}\right) \right] - 13,000 = 13,700 \text{ lb}$$

$$s = \frac{A_v f_v d}{V'_{20 \text{ in.}}} = \frac{(0.22)(18,000)(18)}{13,700} = 5.2, \text{ say } s = 5 \text{ in.}$$

For Division III:

$$V'_{25 \text{ in.}} = V_{25 \text{ in.}} - V_c = \left[30,000 - (2000)\left(\frac{25}{12}\right) \right] - 13,000 = 12,800 \text{ lb}$$

$$s = \frac{A_v f_v d}{V'_{25 \text{ in.}}} = \frac{(0.22)(18,000)(18)}{12,800} = 5.57, \text{ say } s = 6 \text{ in.}$$

Similar calculations for the remaining stirrup spacings will yield the results listed in Table 17-3. The calculated values of s are all rounded off to the nearest whole inch.

Since V' decreases with increasing distance from the support face, the stirrup spacing increases accordingly. In Division VIII, the spacing calculated using Eq. (17-22) yields higher values than 9 in. However, because of Code Section 1206(a), the spacing can not exceed d/2 or 9 in.; this insures that every 45-degree line representing a potential diagonal crack is crossed by at least one line of web reinforcement.

Divisions I through VIII extend consecutively for a distance of 122 in. from the support face and covers the entire distance $(\phi + d)$ of 120 in. over which web reinforcement is required. A stirrup is placed at the midpoint of each spacing interval, e.g., the first stirrup is at a distance of 2.5 in. from the support face; the second, 7.5 in. from the support face; the eighth, 47.5 in. from the support face; etc.

The stirrup spacing must still be checked with respect to Code Section 1206(b), which establishes the minimum cross-sectional web reinforcement area permitted per horizontal spacing area bs. The area of the web reinforcement within the area bs shall not be less than 0.15% of the before mentioned area bs. Considering the area for the longest spacing, 0.0015(bs) = 0.0015(12)(9) = 0.162 in.[2] That is, the area of web reinforcement within area bs = 0.22 in.[2]

The web reinforcement restrictions of Code Section 1206(a) and (b) are not violated and the stirrup spacings listed in Table 17-3 and shown in Fig. 17-15 may be used. The simply supported beam is symmetrically loaded and the same stirrup configuration is at each end.

Problem 17-7 Stirrup spacing at a given section of a reinforced concrete beam

A concrete beam, 10 in. wide × 12 in. net depth (14 in. total depth) and 20 ft long, is loaded with a total load (live load plus dead load) decreasing uniformly from 6400 lb/ft at each end to 400 lb/ft at the center. Assuming a 3000-psi concrete, 3/8-in. U-stirrups and American Concrete Institute stresses, compute the stirrup spacing at a section 2 ft from the end of the beam.

Solution:

The effective depth d is 12 in. and the width b is 10 in. Assume that the stirrups are made of billet steel and the allowable tensile stress is: $f_v = 18,000$ psi.

First determine if web reinforcement is indeed permissible. In accordance with Code Section 1205(b), the maximum allowable stress is

$$v = 5\sqrt{f_c'} = 5\sqrt{3000} = 274 \text{ psi}$$

This corresponds to an allowable shear $V_{all} = bdv = (10)(12)(274) = 32,900$ lb.

Section 1201(a) of the Code states that for design, the maximum value of shear shall be that at a distance d from the face of the support. The beam and its loading is drawn in Fig. 17-16. Referring to this figure, the shear V_d at distance d (d = 12 in.) from the face of the support is determined using the relation $V = \Sigma(F_Y)_L$.

$$V_d = \Sigma(F_Y)_d = 34,400 - [\tfrac{1}{2}(600)(1) + (5800)(1)] = 28,300 \text{ lb}$$

The maximum value of shear is less than the allowable and stirrup reinforcement is permitted.

Next determine the shear V_c that the concrete alone without web reinforcement can resist. Use Eq. (17-19).

$$V_c = bdv_c = bd(1.1\sqrt{f_c'}) = (10)(12)(1.1\sqrt{3000}) = 7200 \text{ lb}$$

At a distance 2 ft from the end of the beam, the shear $V_{2 \text{ ft}}$ is

$$V_{2 \text{ ft}} = \Sigma(F_Y)_{2 \text{ ft}} = 34,400 - [\tfrac{1}{2}(1200)(2) + (5200)(2)] = 22,400 \text{ lb}$$

The shear V' that the web reinforcement must carry at a distance 2 ft from the end of the beam is $V' = V_{2 \text{ ft}} - V_c = 22,400 - 7200 = 15,200$ lb.

The stirrup spacing s is determined from Eq. (17-22), $s = A_v f_v d/V'$. Both legs of the stirrup transmit tensile stress and A_v is given by

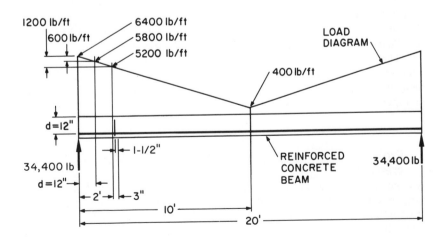

Figure 17-16

$$A_v = 2\left[\frac{\pi(\text{bar dia.})^2}{4}\right] = 2\left[\frac{\pi(3/8)^2}{4}\right] = 0.22 \text{ in.}^2$$

And the stirrup spacing 2 ft from the end of the beam

$$s = \frac{A_v f_v d}{V'} = \frac{(0.22)(18,000)(12)}{15,200} = 3.13 \text{ in., say 3 in.}$$

However, before it can be said that this is the spacing that may be used, it is necessary to be certain that the web reinforcement restrictions of Code Section 1206 are not violated.

With respect to Section 1206(a): A stirrup spacing of 3 in. causes every 45-degree line representing a potential diagonal crack to be crossed by two lines of web reinforcement. Thus, it turns out that the most stringent provision of Code Section 1206(a) is satisfied. This is indeed necessary because at 2 ft from the end of the beam, the shear stress v is

$$v = \frac{V}{bd} = \frac{22,400}{(10)(12)} = 187 \text{ psi}$$

which exceeds $3\sqrt{f'_c}$ or 164.5 psi.

With respect to Section 1206(b): The area of web reinforcement is not less than 0.15 percent of the area bs:

Area of web reinforcement within area bs = 0.22 in.^{2}

0.0015 bs = 0.0015(10)(3) = 0.045 in.^{2}

The web reinforcement restrictions of Section 1206 are not violated and a stirrup spacing of 3 in. may be used at a distance 2 ft from the end of the beam.   *Answer*

17-6   REINFORCED CONCRETE COLUMNS

The application of an axial load to a reinforced concrete column causes the concrete to compress vertically and expand laterally. The axial load carrying capacity of the column is greatly increased by steel reinforcement in the form of vertical bars that are placed at equal or near equal intervals around the column periphery. The vertical reinforcement bars receive lateral support from the enveloping concrete. Column failure occurs when the concrete crumbles and causes the vertical rods to lose their lateral support. When it fails, the column buckles as a unit.

The strength of the column can be further increased by providing reinforcement that applies additional lateral support to the vertical bars and restrains the lateral expansion of the concrete. This is achieved by either a continuous spiral or individual closely spaced lateral ties, as shown in Fig. 17-17. And it is the type of lateral reinforcement that classifies the column, namely: spiral columns and tied columns.

Code Sections 1402 and 1403 specify the equations to be used in determining the maximum allowable axial load P.

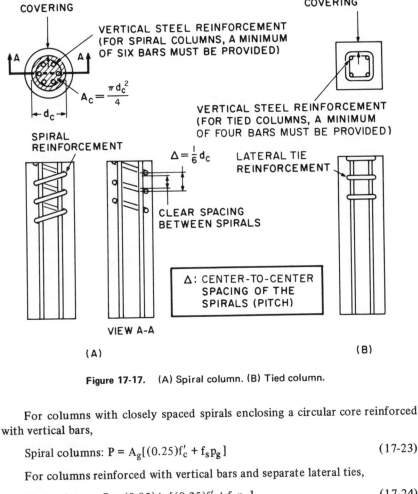

Figure 17-17. (A) Spiral column. (B) Tied column.

For columns with closely spaced spirals enclosing a circular core reinforced with vertical bars,

Spiral columns: $P = A_g[(0.25)f'_c + f_s p_g]$ (17-23)

For columns reinforced with vertical bars and separate lateral ties,

Tied columns: $P = (0.85)A_g[(0.25)f'_c + f_s p_g]$ (17-24)

where A_g = gross area of spirally reinforced or tied column

f'_c = specified compressive strength of concrete

f_s = allowable stress in column vertical reinforcement

p_g = ratio of area of vertical reinforcement A_{st} to gross area A_g

$p_g = A_{st}/A_g$ (17-25)

The equations show that the spiral column is stronger than the tied column. The spiral reinforcement, because of its continuity and compactness, is more effective in laterally supporting the vertical bars and restraining the lateral expansion of the concrete than are the individual lateral ties.

Equations (17-23) and (17-24) apply provided the requirements of Code Sections 915 and 916 are not applicable. These Code Sections deal with the effect of slenderness on column strength. Insofar as reinforced concrete columns are concerned, the effect of slenderness has not been within the scope of the EIT Examination and is not treated in this book.

The design of a reinforced concrete column is really a matter of understanding and carefully following the applicable sections of the ACI Building Code. The Code sections and parts of sections believed to be pertinent to design problems encountered in EIT examinations are listed below. Explanatory notes to help the reader understand the quoted parts of the Code are provided where it is deemed necessary.

Section 804—Spacing of bars

(d) In spirally reinforced and in tied columns, the clear distance between longitudinal bars shall be not less than $1\frac{1}{2}$ times the bar diameter, $1\frac{1}{2}$ times the maximum size of the coarse aggregate, nor $1\frac{1}{2}$ in.

Section 806—Lateral reinforcement

(a) . . . The material used in spirals shall have a minimum diameter of $\frac{1}{4}$ in. for rolled bars or No. 4 AS&W gage for drawn wire. . . . The center to center spacing of the spirals shall not exceed one-sixth of the core diameter. The clear spacing between spirals shall not exceed 3 in. nor be less than $1\frac{3}{8}$ in. or $1\frac{1}{2}$ times the maximum size of the coarse aggregate used.

The center to center spacing is the spiral pitch Δ shown in view A-A of Fig. 17-17(A). The column core is the part of the column that is contained within the cylindrical surface defined by the outer periphery of the lateral reinforcement. The core diameter d_c is measured to the outside diameter of the spiral and the core area A_c is shown by the cross hatched lines. [See Fig. 17-17(A).] The clear spacing between spirals is shown in view A-A of Fig. 17-17(A).

(b) All bars for tied columns shall be enclosed by lateral ties at least $\frac{1}{4}$ in. in diameter spaced apart not over 16 bar diameters, 48 tie diameters, or the least dimension of the column. The ties shall be so arranged that every corner and alternate longitudinal bar shall have lateral support provided by the corner of a tie having an included angle of not more than 135 degrees and no bar shall be farther than 6 in. from such a laterally supported bar. Where the bars are located around the periphery of a circle, a complete circular tie may be used.

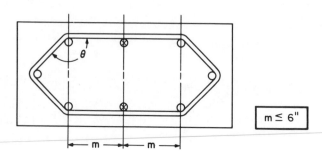

$m \le 6"$

Figure 17-18

A transverse section of a tied column is shown in Fig. 17-18. The angle θ may not be more than 135 degrees. All vertical bars must be enclosed within ties. However, those vertical bars that are within 6 in. on each side of adequately tied bars are exempt from the requirement that lateral support be provided by the corner of a tie, e.g., as in the case of the bar designated $\otimes$ in Fig. 17-18.

Section 808—Concrete protection of reinforcement
(c) Column spirals or ties shall be protected everywhere by a covering of concrete cast monolithically with the core, for which the thickness shall be not less than $1\frac{1}{2}$ in. ...

Section 912—Limiting dimensions of columns
(a) Minimum size—Columns constituting principal supports of a floor or roof shall have a diameter of at least 10 in., or in the case of rectangular columns, a thickness of at least 8 in., and a gross area not less than 96 sq. in. ...

Section 913—Limits for reinforcement of columns
(a) The vertical reinforcement for columns shall be not less than 0.01 nor more than 0.08 times the gross cross-sectional area. The minimum size of a bar shall be No. 5. The minimum number of bars shall be six for spiral columns and four for tied columns. [0.01 and 0.08 are the limits within which the value of p_g used in Eqs. (17-23) and (17-24) may fall.]
(b) The ratio of spiral reinforcement p_s shall be not less than the value given by

$$p_s = 0.45(A_g/A_c - 1)f'_c/f_y \tag{17-26}$$

where f_y is yield strength of spiral reinforcement $\not> 60,000$ psi.

The product of p_s and the core volume establishes the lower limit of volume that the spiral reinforcing steel is to occupy within the total core volume. Problem 17-8 will show how this volume of spiral reinforcement is used to determine the required center to center spiral spacing or pitch Δ.

Section 1003—Allowable stresses in reinforcement
(b) In compression, vertical column reinforcement.
   Spiral columns, 40 percent of the minimum yield strength, but not to exceed .... 30,000 psi
   Tied columns, 85 percent of the value for spiral columns, but not to exceed .... 25,500 psi
(d) Spirals [yield strength for use in Eq. (17-26)]
   Hot rolled rods, intermediate grade .... 40,000 psi
   Hot rolled rods, hard grade .... 50,000 psi
   Hot rolled rods, ASTM A 432 grade, cold-drawn wire ... 60,000 psi

The Code will now be applied to the design of a spiral column and a tied column. In designing the vertical reinforcement, it is customary to select an even number of bars.

Problem 17-8 Design of a reinforced concrete column of circular section

Determine the diameter and proper steel for a reinforced concrete column 18 ft high to carry a concentric load of 700,000 lb using 2500-lb concrete and 18,000-lb steel, if the spirals are cold drawn steel with $1\frac{1}{2}$-in. cover.

Solution:

Since the steel content is not given, the column will be designed on the supposition that maximum economy is desired. On a volume basis and on a load-carrying basis, steel is more costly than concrete. Therefore, the minimum amount of steel that the ACI Building Code allows will be used. This according to Code Section 913(a) is 0.01 times the gross cross-sectional area A_g. From this it may be stated using Eq. (17-25), $p_g = 0.01 = A_{st}/A_g$. From the statement of the problem:

Maximum allowable load P = 700,000 lb

Specified compressive strength of concrete $f_c' = 2500$ psi

Allowable stress in column vertical reinforcement $f_s = 18,000$ psi

The required gross cross-sectional area A_g may now be calculated using the spiral column Eq. (17-23),

$$P = A_g[(0.25)f_c' + f_s p_g]$$

$$A_g = \frac{P}{(0.25)f_c' + f_s p_g} = \frac{700,000}{(0.25)(2500) + (18,000)(0.01)} = 869 \text{ in.}^2$$

Determine the required outside diameter d_g of the column.

$$A_g = \pi d_g^2/4$$
$$d_g = \sqrt{(4)A_g/\pi} = 33.3 \text{ in., say 34 in.}$$

This is more than adequate to meet the minimum size requirements of Code Section 912(a).

Calculate the vertical reinforcing steel required: $A_{st} = p_g A_g = (0.01)(869) = 8.69 \text{ in.}^2$

According to Code Section 913(a), the minimum bar size that may be used is No. 5 and for a spiral column at least six bars must be used. Using Table 17-1, six No. 5 bars have a total cross-sectional area of $6(0.31) = 1.86 \text{ in.}^2$ Clearly, the minimum vertical reinforcement permitted by the Code is inadequate.

List the possible bar configurations to determine the quantity of which bar number offers the greatest economy. Keep in mind that the quantity of bars selected should be an even number.

Description	A_{st}, in.^{2}
30 No. 5 bars	9.30
20 No. 6 bars	8.80
16 No. 7 bars	9.60
12 No. 8 bars	9.48
10 No. 9 bars	10.00
8 No. 10 bars	10.16
6 No. 11 bars	9.36

Twenty No. 6 bars provide the least area which is still greater than the required 8.69 in.^{2}

Because of the space required for the protective covering and spiral reinforcement, the bars will be placed in a circle having a diameter of approximately 30 in. (approximate because the spiral steel has not been selected); this corresponds to a circumference of 94.2 in. A preliminary check of the spacing requirements of Code Section 804(d) shows that the clear distance between bars is more than adequate.

Use 20 No. 6 bars.

Code Section 808(c) requires that all reinforcement receive a $1\frac{1}{2}$ in. protective covering of concrete. The core diameter d_c is assumed to be 31 in. The core diameter is measured to the outside diameter of the spiral reinforcement. (See Fig. 17-19).

Determination of spiral reinforcement: The spirals are cold drawn steel. Code Section 1003(d) states that yield strength f_y for this steel is $f_y = 60,000$ psi.

Code Section 913(b) is used to determine the lower limit of the ratio p_s of spiral reinforcement.

$$p_s = 0.45 \left[\frac{A_g}{A_c} - 1 \right] \frac{f'_c}{f_y} = 0.45 \left[\frac{\pi d_g^2/4}{\pi d_c^2/4} - 1 \right] \frac{f'_c}{f_y}$$

$$= 0.45 \left[\left(\frac{34}{31} \right)^2 - 1 \right] \frac{2500}{60,000}$$

$$= 0.00375$$

The core volume contained in 1 in. of column height is

$$\frac{\pi d_c^2}{4}(1) = \frac{\pi (31)^2}{4} = 755 \text{ in.}^3$$

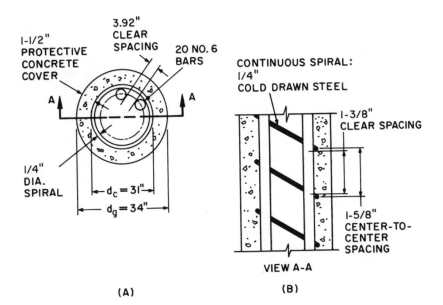

Figure 17-19.   (A) Transverse cross section. (B) View A-A: part of vertical section.

The minimum amount by volume of cold drawn spiral reinforcing steel in 1 in. of column height is $p_s(755) = (0.00375)(755) = 2.83$ in.^{3}

Code Section 806(a) states that the material used in spirals shall have a minimum diameter of $\frac{1}{4}$ in. Spiral reinforcement also comes in larger diameter sizes, e.g., $\frac{3}{8}$ in., $\frac{1}{2}$ in., and $\frac{5}{8}$ in.

Try a $\frac{1}{4}$-in. round bar. The length of one spiral L_s is $L_s = \pi(31 - \frac{1}{4}) = 96.6$ in.

The volume of spiral material contained in this length is

$$\frac{\pi(\frac{1}{4})^2}{4}(L_s) = \frac{\pi(\frac{1}{4})^2}{4}(96.6) = 4.74 \text{ in.}^3$$

Since 1 in. of column height must contain at least 2.83 in.^{3} of spiral material, one complete spiral having a volume of 4.74 in.^{3} will satisfy the spiral volume requirements for Δ inches of column height.

$$\frac{\Delta}{1 \text{ in.}} = \frac{4.74 \text{ in.}^3}{2.83 \text{ in.}^3}$$

$$\Delta = 1.675 \text{ in.}$$

The quantity Δ is the pitch or center spacing of the spirals. Tentative spiral selection: $\frac{1}{4}$-in. diameter rod with center to center spacing of $1\frac{5}{8}$ in.; See Fig. 17-19 (B).

Code Section 806(a) requires that the center-to-center spacing of the spirals not exceed one-sixth of the *core* diameter d_c.

$$\Delta \leqslant d_c/6 = 31/6 = 5\frac{1}{6} \text{ in.}$$

Code Section 806(a)* also requires that the clear spacing between spirals shall not exceed 3 in. nor be less than $1\frac{3}{8}$ in.

For a $\frac{1}{4}$-in. diameter spiral wound at a pitch of $1\frac{5}{8}$ in., the *clear* spacing is $1\frac{5}{8} - \frac{1}{4} = 1\frac{3}{8}$ in.

The center-to-center spacing is less than one-sixth of the core diameter and the clear spacing is not less than $1\frac{3}{8}$ in. nor greater than 3 in. The provisions of Code Section 806(a)* are not violated; therefore use

Spiral reinforcement: $\frac{1}{4}$-in. diameter rod with center-to-center spacing of $1\frac{5}{8}$ in.   *Answer*

Now that the spiral reinforcement has been selected, the circle on which the vertical bars will be placed can be precisely determined. The core diameter is measured out to out of the spiral steel. Since the spiral reinforcement rod has a diameter of $\frac{1}{4}$ in. and the No. 6 vertical steel bars have a diameter of 0.750 in., the vertical steel is placed in a circle having a diameter of $29\frac{3}{4}$ in. as shown in Fig. 17-19(A).

Placing the 20 bars on this circle at equal intervals leaves a clear distance of

$$\pi(29.75)/20 - 0.750 = 3.92 \text{ in.}$$

between adjacent bars.

---

*Aggregate size is not given and so is not considered.

The clear spacing of 3.92 in. is not less than $1\frac{1}{2}$ times the bar diameter nor is it less than $1\frac{1}{2}$ in. Therefore, the spacing requirement of Code Section 804(d)* is satisfied.

Use 20 No. 6 bars for vertical reinforcement.   *Answer*

Problem 17-9 Design of a reinforced concrete column of square section

Design a square, short, reinforced concrete column to support a central load of 493,000 lb using 4 percent reinforcement. Give the gross area of concrete and area of main reinforcing steel. Show the ties and determine their required vertical spacing. Yield point for vertical steel f_y = 42,000 psi. Use 3000-lb concrete.

Solution:

Determine allowable stress in vertical reinforcement. From Code Section 1003(b),

For spiral columns: allowable stress = $0.40f_y$ = $(0.4)(42,000)$ = 16,800 psi

For tied columns: f_s = $(0.85)(16,800)$ = 14,280 psi, but not to exceed 25,500 psi

From the statement of the problem,

Maximum allowable load P = 493,000 lb

Specified compressive strength of concrete f_c' = 3000 psi

Ratio p_g of area of vertical reinforcement A_{st} to gross area A_g: p_g = 4% = 0.04

The required gross cross-sectional area A_g may now be calculated using the tied column Eq. (17-24),

$$A_g = \frac{P}{(0.83)[(0.25)f_c' + f_s p_g]} = \frac{493,000}{(0.85)[(0.25)(3000) + (14,280)(0.04)]}$$
$$= 438 \text{ in.}^2$$

The column is to be square or 20.9 in. on a side, say 21 in. This is more than adequate to meet the minimum size requirements of Code Section 912(a).

Calculate the vertical reinforcing steel required: $A_{st} = p_g A_g = 0.04(21)^2 = 17.6$ in.^{2}

Code Section 913(a) states that the minimum bar size that may be used is No. 5 and that a tied column shall have at least four bars. Using Table 17-1, four No. 5 bars have a total cross-sectional area of $4(0.31) = 1.24$ in.^{2} Clearly, the minimum vertical reinforcement permitted by the Code is inadequate.

Determine a suitable bar configuration for the vertical reinforcement. Since the column is square, the number of bars should be a multiple of four. This will permit the bars to be placed around the column periphery at equal intervals.

Twelve No. 11 bars provide an area of 18.72 in.^{2}, which is not too much greater than the required 17.6 in.^{2} The bars are positioned as shown in Fig. 17-20. The configuration assumes that $\frac{1}{2}$-in. diameter lateral ties are used and makes provision for the $1\frac{1}{2}$-in. concrete protection for the reinforcement required by Code Section 808(c).

---

*Aggregate size is not given and so is not considered.

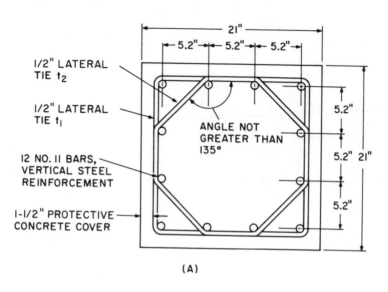

(A)

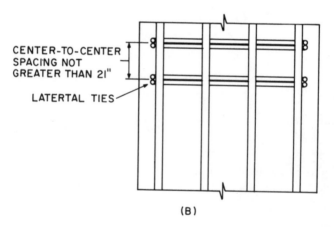

(B)

Figure 17-20.   (A) Transverse cross section. (B) Part of vertical section.

With the vertical bars positioned as shown in Fig. 17-20, there is a clear distance of 5.2 − (diameter of No. 11 bar) = 5.2 − 1.41 = 3.79 in. between adjacent bars.

The clear spacing of 3.79 in. is not less than $1\frac{1}{2}$ times the bar diameter nor is it less than $1\frac{1}{2}$ in. Therefore, the spacing requirement of Code Section 804(d)* is satisfied.

Use 12 No. 11 bars for vertical reinforcement.   *Answer*

---

*Aggregate size is not given and so is not considered.

Lateral tie reinforcement: The placement of the lateral ties is governed by Code Section 806(b). The Code requires that:

1. All ties shall be enclosed by lateral ties at least $\frac{1}{4}$ in. in diameter.
2. Lateral ties shall not be placed further apart than
    (a) 16 bar diameters: $(16)(1.41) = 22.6$ in.
    (b) 48 tie diameters: $(48)(0.5) = 24$ in.
    (c) least dimension of column: 21 in.
3. The ties shall be so arranged that every corner and alternate longi-tudinal bar shall have lateral support provided by the corner of a tie having an included angle of not more than 135 degrees.

The requirements of the above three provisions are met by the two lateral ties t_1 and t_2 shown in Fig. 17-20(A). The ties are assumed to be $\frac{1}{2}$-in. diameter and are spaced apart center to center no more than 21 in. as shown in Fig. 17-20 (B).

BIBLIOGRAPHY

Albertson, M. L., Barton, J., and Simons, D. *Fluid Mechanics for Engineers.* Englewood Cliffs, N.J.: Prentice-Hall, 1960.

Allendoerfer, C. B. and Oakley, C. O. *Fundamentals of Freshman Mathematics,* 2nd ed. New York: McGraw-Hill, 1965.

Angus, R. B. *Electrical Engineering Fundamentals,* 2nd ed. Reading, Mass.: Addison-Wesley, 1968.

Baumeister, T. and Marks, L. *Standard Handbook for Mechanical Engineers,* 7th ed. New York: McGraw-Hill, 1967.

Beer, F. P. and Johnston, Jr., E. R. *Mechanics for Engineers.* New York: McGraw-Hill, 1962.

Beiser, A. *Essential Math for the Sciences.* New York: McGraw-Hill, 1969.

Binder, R. C. *Fluid Mechanics,* 4th ed. Englewood Cliffs, N.J.: Prentice-Hall, 1962.

Brescia, F. *et al. Fundamentals of Chemistry: A Modern Introduction.* New York: Academic Press, 1966.

Brown, T. L. *General Chemistry,* 2nd ed. Columbus, Ohio: Charles Merrill, 1968.

Cernica, J. N. *Fundamentals of Reinforced Concrete.* Reading, Mass.: Addison-Wesley, 1964.

Daugherty, R. L. and Franzini, J. B. *Fluid Mechanics with Engineering Applications,* 6th ed. New York: McGraw-Hill, 1966.

de Garmo, E. P. *Engineering Economy,* 4th ed. New York: Macmillan, 1967.

Eblin, L. P. *The Elements of Chemistry.* New York: Harcourt, 1965.

Elliot, W. W. and Miles, E. R. *College Mathematics: A First Course,* 2nd ed. Englewood Cliffs, N.J.: Prentice-Hall, 1951.

Eshbach, O. W. *Handbook of Engineering Fundamentals,* 2nd ed. New York: Wiley, 1952.

Faires, V. M. *Thermodynamics,* 4th ed. New York: Macmillan, 1962.

Fitzgerald, A. E. and Higginbotham, D. E. *Basic Electrical Engineering,* 3rd ed. New York: McGraw-Hill, 1967.

Gerstle, K. H. *Basic Structural Design.* New York: McGraw-Hill, 1967.

Gregg, D. C. *Principles of Chemistry,* 3rd ed. Boston, Mass.: Allyn and Bacon, 1968.

Hagerty, W. W. and Plass, Jr., H. J. *Engineering Mechanics.* Princeton, N.J.: Van Nostrand, 1967.

Hawkins, G. A. *Thermodynamics,* 2nd ed. New York: Wiley, 1951.

Hein, M. *Foundations of College Chemistry.* Belmont, Calif.: Dickenson, 1967.

Henney, K. *Radio Engineering Handbook,* 5th ed. New York: McGraw-Hill, 1959.

Higdon, A. *et al. Mechanics of Materials,* 2nd ed. New York: Wiley, 1967.

Horner, D. R. *A Survey of College Mathematics.* New York: Holt, Rinehart, and Winston, 1967.

Jakob, M. and Hawkins, G. A. *Elements of Heat Transfer,* 3rd ed. New York: Wiley, 1957.

Keenan, J. H. *Thermodynamics.* New York: Wiley, 1941.

McAdams, W. H. *Heat Transmission,* 3rd ed. New York: McGraw-Hill, 1954.

Nevill, G. E. *Programmed Principles of Statics.* New York: Wiley, 1969.

Obert, E. F. and Gaggioli, R. A. *Thermodynamics,* 2nd ed. New York: McGraw-Hill, 1963.

Pender, H. and Del Mar, W. A. *Engineer's Relay Handbook,* 4th ed., vol. 1. New York: Wiley, 1949.

Pender, H. and McIlwain, K. *Engineer's Relay Handbook,* 4th ed., vol. 2. New York: Wiley, 1950.

Physical Science Study Committee. *College Physics.* Boston, Mass.: Raytheon, 1968.

Schenck, H. V. *Heat Transfer Engineering.* Englewood Cliffs, N.J.: Prentice-Hall, 1959.

Schure, A. *A Programmed Course in Basic Transistors.* New York: McGraw-Hill, 1964.

Scott, R. E. *Linear Circuits.* Reading, Mass.: Addison-Wesley, 1960.

Sears, F. W. and Zemansky, M. W. *College Physics,* 3rd ed. Reading, Mass.: Addison-Wesley, 1960.

Semat, H. and Blumenthal, R. H. *College Physics: A Programmed Aid.* New York: Holt, Rinehart, and Winston, 1967.

Shanley, F. R. *Mechanics of Materials,* New York: McGraw-Hill, 1967.

Siskind, C. S. *Electrical Machines: Direct and Alternating Currents,* 2nd ed. New York: McGraw-Hill, 1959.

—— *Electricity: Direct and Alternating Currents,* 2nd ed. New York: McGraw-Hill, 1955.

Souders, M. *The Engineer's Companion.* New York: Wiley, 1966.

Thueson, H. G. and Fabrycky, W. *Engineering Economy,* 3rd ed. Englewood Cliffs, N.J.: Prentice-Hall, 1964.

INDEX